ROGET'S THESAURUS

1989 Edition

P.S.I. & Associates, Inc.
13322 S.W. 128th Street
Miami, Florida 33186

DEFINITIONS

SYNONYMS —   Words that have the same meaning
Example: big, large

ANTONYMS —   Words that have opposite meanings
Example: large, small
Note: Antonyms appear in parentheses ( )
following the synonyms.

HOMONYMS —   Words that sound alike, but are spelled dif-
ferently and have different meanings
Example: one, won
Note: Homonyms begin on page 238.

A

abandon—v. abdicate, leave, jilt, desert, vacate, cease, resign, drop, waive, discontinue, yield, surrender, forsake, retire, quit, relinquish, let go, repudiate, part with. *(cherish, keep, retain, adopt, pursue, uphold, occupy, support, favor, depend, maintain, vindicate, assert, advocate, claim, seek, embrace.)*

abandoned—adj. cast aside, bad, forsaken, deserted, wicked, vacated, vicious, rejected, sinful, depraved, unprincipled, corrupt, left, discarded, dropped, demoralized, forlorn. *(good, honest, righteous, steady, pure, virtuous, cherished, correct, upright, loved, respectable.)*

abase—v. disgrace, debase, mock, scorn, belittle, mortify, reduce, degrade, dishonour, despise, shame, lower, expose, humble, confuse, humiliate. *(elevate, uplift, exalt, honour, cherish, respect, praise, dignify, glorify, lift, laud, extol.)*

abate—v. alleviate, terminate, wane, reduce, diminish, ebb, decrease, restrain, lessen, allay, lower, decline, subside, slacken, slow down, ease. *(increase, prolong, extend, intensify, enlarge, magnify, amplify, enhance, aggravate, grow, accelerate, speed.)*

abbreviate—v. curtail, shorten, clip, reduce, lessen, condense, prune, abridge, cut short, cut down, trim, diminish, compress. *(lengthen, increase, expand, distend, dilate, prolong, swell, amplify, enlarge, augment, add to, supplement.)*

abdicate—v. cede, renounce, yield, resign, abandon, give up, relinquish, quit, forego, surrender, waive. *(claim, retain, hold, assume, maintain, challenge, defy, seize, possess.)*

abet—v. help, encourage, assist, aid, condone, uphold, stimulate, sustain, support, promote, incite, subsidize, sanction. *(hinder, impede, thwart, obstruct, discourage, frustrate, deter, oppose, resist, counteract, dampen, baffle.)*

abeyance—n. inactivity, recess, suspension, expectation, rest, reservation, pause, adjournment, latency. *(continuation, operation, exercise, enjoyment, force, possession, revival, enforcement, renewal, action.)*

abhor—v. loathe, detest, avoid, abominate, shun,

scorn, distain, hate, dislike, recoil from. (cherish, adore, prize, love, desire, enjoy, treasure, admire, value, approve, covet.)

abide—v. stay, dwell, sojourn, rest, remain, lodge, anchor, exist, live, settle, tarry, confront, sit, bide, endure, await. (move, proceed, go, leave, migrate, despise, journey, avoid, deport, mistake.)

ability—n. aptitude, capability, power, energy, skill, talent, knack, cleverness, strength, qualification, flair, know-how, vigor. (inability, weakness, helplessness, incompetence, ineffectiveness, unreadiness, inadequacy.)

abject—adj. base, mean, degrade, low, vile, worthless, contemptible, dishonourable, sordid, miserable, hangdog, outcast, hopeless, wretched, fawning, servile. (noble, haughty, proud, dignified, honorable, magnificent, lofty, bold, arrogant, worthy, aristocratic, vain, respected, exalted, hopeful, staunch, manly.)

abjure—v. disclaim, deny, assert, demand, repudiate, reject, discard, disown, abrogate, revoke, unsay, renege, disavow, forswear. (attest, profess, demand, affirm, maintain, hug, certify, justify, praise, cherish, vindicate, approve, command, laud.)

able—adj. skillful, adroit, competent, strong, accomplished, gifted, clever, capable, expert, proficient, adept, powerful, apt, talented, highly qualified. (incapable, weak, incompetent, inept, unqualified, inefficient, mediocre, indifferent, useless, stupid, delicate, fair.)

ablution—n. purification, bathing, cleansing, washing, lavation, ceremonial washing. (soil, soiling, tainting, pollution, contaminating, taint, defiling.)

abnegation—n. abstinence, refusal, relinquishment, denial, rejection, surrender, abandonment, temperance, giving up. (abandon, self-indulgence, indulgence, concession, intemperance, affirmation.)

abnormal—adj. eccentric, weird, exceptional, irregular, unnatural, peculiar, atypical, bizarre, strange, devious, monstrous, queer, odd, unconventional. (natural, customary, common, routine, normal, ordinary, familiar, usual, conventional, typical.)

abode—n. residence, home, nest, pad, lodgings,

berth, habitat, domicile, house, address, quarters. *(halt, tent, pilgrimage, ramble, perch, bivouac, peregrenation.)*

abolish—*v.* eliminate, efface, annihilate, destroy, cancel, repeal, annul, erase, revoke, repudiate, nullify, end, suppress, obliterate, quash, extinguish, overturn. *(introduce, enforce, restore, support, sustain, establish, continue, create, renew, enact, repair, promote, reinstate, legalize.)*

abominable—*adj.* vile, detestable, despicable, contemptible, hateful, horrid, revolting, repugnant, wretched, offensive, nauseous, infamous, foul, atrocious. *(choice, select, delightful, attractive, pure, charming, typical, routine, conventional, admirable, familiar, enjoyable.)*

aboriginal—*adj.* original, native, earliest, indigenous, ancient, primary, first, prime, primitive. *(foreign, immigrant, alien, late, imported, exotic, recent, modern.)*

abortion—*n.* disaster, failure, miscarriage, unsuccessful attempt, fiasco, blunder, termination, ending, mishap, misproduction. *(achievement, delivery, success, childbirth, perfection, development, realization, feat, parturition, completion.)*

abound—*v.* swarm, increase, flow, multiply, teem, overflow, be numerous, swell, luxuriate, flourish, be rich in, revel, be well supplied, stream, superabound. *(lack, have too few, fall, want, waste, decay, be scant, dry, die, lessen, vanish, wane, fail, need, be destitute of.)*

about—*adj.* around, nearly, regarding, relative to, concerning, approximately, connected with, over, surrounding, generally, almost, round, touching, respecting. *(unlike, afar, precisely, exactly, remote, distant, separated.)*

above—*adv.* over, aloft, overhead, beyond, higher, on top of, exceeding. *(within, beneath, below, under.)*

abridge—*v.* condense, compress, curtail, abbreviate, lessen, reduce, diminish, digest, epitomize, recap, summarize, telescope, shorten. *(amplify, expand, extend, spread out, enlarge, lengthen, detail.)*

abrogate—*v.* cancel, abolish, annul, nullify, quash, repeal, revoke, recind, set aside, invalidate, override, reverse. *(enforce, maintain, ratify, create, institute,* establish, found, uphold, sanction, revive, continue, confirm.)

abrupt—adj. rude, curt, harsh, sudden, craggy, zigzag, jagged, sharp, brusque, uneven, violent, broken, blunt. (civil, easy, blending, gliding, gracious, polite, polished, smooth.)

absent—v. depart, not appear, play truant, withdraw. (attend, appear at, stay, remain.)

absent—adj. missing, listless, gone away, truant, pre-occupied, oblivious, inattentive, elsewhere, dreamy, out, heedless. (present, aware.)

absolute—adj. unrestricted, pure, perfect, dogmatic, full, supreme, irrespective, complete, unqualified, despotic, certain, arbitrary, unconditional, entire. (mild, conditional, gentle, dubious, meek, relative, imperfect, incomplete, dependent, accountable, docile, qualified.)

absolve—v. pardon, acquit, clear, excuse, exonerate, forgive, release, deliver, condone, liberate. (accuse, bind, blame, censure, condemn, hold to, convict, compel.)

absorb—v. sponge up, suck up, swallow, devour, monopolize, drink in, drown, engulf, consume, engross, exhaust, merge. (impart, cast off, emit, belch, dissipate, distil, eject, disperse, distract, disgorge, eliminate, weary.)

abstain—v. avoid, eschew, withhold, forgo, scruple, decline, forbear, refrain, discontinue, refuse, desist, avoid, demur. (yield to, wanton, overdue, reveal, indulge, exceed.)

abstemious—adj. teetotal, sober, temperate, non-indulgent, self-denying, sparing, abstinent, frugal, moderate. (greedy, intemperate, self-indulgent, sensual, excessive, gluttonous, uncontrolled.)

abstract—v. discriminate, subtle, abridge, purloin, outline, separate, appropriate, detach, take away, eliminate, steal, withdraw. (mend, add, unite, concrete, return, specific, restore, impose, conjoin, adduce, surrender.)

absurd—adj. ludicrous, silly, stupid, comical, ridiculous, funny, unreasonable, asinine, monstrous, senseless, foolish, listless. (smart, judicious, wise, sensical, prudent, sensible, reflective, sound, rational, consistent, logical, sagacious, reasonable.)

accessory—*n.* retainer, associate, colleague, complement, aide, additional, assistant, crutch, auxiliary, accomplice, henchman, helper. *(opponent, spy, adversary, rival, enemy, foe, antagonist, irrelevant, immanent, superfluous, cumbersome.)*

accident—*n.* hazard, collision, chance, wreck, fortuity, crash, calamity, misadventure, incident, mishap, adventure, misfortune. *(intent, design, purpose, plan, decree, appointment, law, ordainment, provision.)*

accommodate—*v.* oblige, provide, aid, suit, help, supply, fit, adapt, serve, harmonize, reconcile, lodge. *(disturb, impede, deprive, censure, aggravate, inconvenience, hinder, hissing, block.)*

accommodating—*adj.* courteous, gracious, neighborly, polite, kind, yielding, obliging, unselfish, considerate. *(churlish, exacting, rude, disobliging, selfish, imperious, dictatorial, hostile.)*

accomplice—*n.* cohort, coworker, assistant, aide, supporter, ally, colleague, henchman, partner, accessory, associate, helper. *(objector, rival, foe, denouncer, opponent, betrayer, enemy, antagonist.)*

accomplish—*v.* conclude, do, discharge, effect, perform, carryout, fulfil, perfect, realize, attain, execute, achieve, associate, manage, finish. *(give up, leave undone, fall short, defeat, baffle, fail, destroy, spoil.)*

accord—*v.* give, admit, cede, allow, tally, render, agree, answer, consist, consent, grant, bequeath. *(deny, disagree, clash, collide, differ, refuse, misfit, withhold, discord.)*

accordingly—*adv.* whence, whereupon, thence, suitably, conformably, hence, agreeably, conversely. *(conversely.)*

accost—*v.* solicit, confront, stop, waylay, greet, salute. *(avoid, shun, overlook, slight.)*

abundant—*adj.* enough, copious, replete, overflowing, profuse, large, liberal, lavish, rich, plentiful, teeming, luxuriant. *(meager, poor, scant, skimpy, uncommon, rare, drained, deficient, scarce, short, sparing, dry, exhausted.)*

abuse—*v.* harm, hurt, injure, misuse, desecrate, disparage, damage, ill-use, revile, malign, pervert, maltreat, upbraid, prostitute, defame, asperse, vilify.

(eulogize, shield, care for, extol, laud, cherish, flatter, tend, regard, consider, respect, protect, sustain.)

abuse—*n.* unfair use, ill treatment, imposition, invective, improper use, ribaldry, reproach, insolence, ill usage, disgrace, blame, censure. *(praise, laudation, commendation, approval, sanction, deference, respect, kindness, good treatment.)*

academic—*adj.* learned, lettered, classical, bookish, scholarly, collegiate, pedantic. *(non-scholarly, untaught, unschooled, illiterate, ordinary, plain.)*

accelerate—*v.* quicken, rush, spur, urge, hasten, further, speed, hurry, promote, expedite, forward, precipitate. *(slow, hinder, resist, embarrass, impede, clog, delay, retard, obstruct, drag.)*

accent—*n.* stress, force, cadence, modulation, beat, pulsation, emphasis, rhythm. *(flow, smoothness, babble, monotony, inaccentuation, equableness.)*

accept—*v.* receive, concur, hail, allow, recognize, take, avow, admit, accede to, believe, agree. *(yield, spurn, disown, disacknowledge, deny, decline, refuse, ignore.)*

acceptable—*adj.* fitting, suitable, worthy, good, gratifying, agreeable, grateful, welcome, pleasant. *(repugnant, unfitting, annoying, poor, below par, disagreeable, unpleasant, unsuitable, ungrateful.)*

account—*n.* narrative, reckoning, value, charge, bill, recital, motive, description. *(riddle, silence, puzzle, unknown quantity, mystery, project.)*

account—*v.* think, judge, view as, rate, calculate, estimate, deem, value, hold, explain, reckon. *(leave unexplained, leave unsolved, mystify, perplex.)*

accountable—*adj.* answerable, censurable, responsible, beholden, liable, delegated, guilty, subordinate, blameworthy. *(innocent, despotic, autocratic, guiltless, absolute, supreme, unreliable.)*

accredit—*v.* delegate, commission, license, entrust, authorize, endorse, believe, sanction. *(distrust, discard, recall, supersede, disbelieve, suspect, dismiss.)*

accumulate—*v.* gather, pile up, amass, hoard, collect, add to, garner, augment, assemble, accrue. *(waste, scatter,* disperse, distribute, dissipate, get rid of, throw out.)

accumulation—n. store, amassing, agglomeration, gathering, heap, hoard, pile, mass, bulk, lot. (division, separation, scattering, unit, individual, segregation, dispersal.)

accurate—adj. minute, careful, nice, unerring, true, scrupulous, just, correct, close, strict, exact, faithful, truthful. (false, wrong, deceptive, careless, faulty, loose, inexact, defective, sloppy.)

accuse—v. indict, summon, impeach, against, incriminate, tax, blame, censure, taunt. (plea, pardon, blame, vindicate, acquit, condone, exonerate, deny, rebut.)

accustom—v. form, ingrain, train, discipline, harden, incure, reconcile, familiarize. (disaccustom, estrange, alienate, dishabituate, wean.)

achieve—v. accomplish, dispatch, attain, fulfill, realize, win, procure, finish. (be deprived of, lose, fail, miss.)

achievement—n. realization, fulfillment, exploit, performance, accomplishment.

(frustration, defeat, failure, loss, waste.)

acknowledge—v. recognize, admit, confess, accept, profess, concede, yield, own, grant. (disclaim, slight, reject, repudiate, ignore, deny, abandon.)

acme—n. height, peak, apex, summit, zenith, pinnacle, crown. (bottom, depth, base, nadir, low point, foundation.)

acquaint—v. familiarize, inform, reveal, advertise, enlighten, divulage, notify, tell, apprise. (hide, misinform, withhold, reserve, deceive, conceal, delude.)

acquaintance—n. relationship, experience, dealings, association, knowledge, intimacy. (stranger, ignore, inexperience, ignorance.)

acquiesce—v. allow, yield, concur, assent, comply, submit, bow to, grant. (contest, demur, protest, veto, resist.)

acquire—v. get, obtain, attain, gain, secure, achieve. (lose, relinquish, give up, forgo, be deprived of.)

acquit—v. clear, excuse, release, discharge, exonerate, vindicate, deliver, pardon.

(convict, declare, charge, constrain, compel, bind, condemn, damn, indict, accuse.)

acquittance—*n.* discharge, voucher, release, receipt. *(obligation, bond, charge, claim.)*

across—*prep.* & *adv.* against, transversely, athwart, crosswise, thwart. *(lengthwise, parallel, along, concurrently.)*

act—*n.* statute, movement, play, degree, bill, performance, operation, measure, pose, deed, *(inactivity, quiet, repose, inertia, rest, stop, procrastinate, suspension, immobility, sluggishness.)*

activate—*v.* turn on, drive, stimulate, impel, energize, nudge. *(stop, halt, paralyze, weaken, turn off, check.)*

active—*adj.* energetic, vigorous, brisk, supple, nimble, busy, vibrant, agile, prompt, dexterous, ambitious, forceful, bubbling. *(quiet, dormant, sluggish, heavy, inactive, inert.)*

actual—*adj.* concrete, positive, authentic, tangible, sure, certain, unquestionable, prevailing. *(fictional, hypothetical, probable, possible, potential, fabulous, unreal, made-up.)*

acumen—*n.* insight, keenness, sharpness, cleverness, wisdom, intelligence. *(dullness, ignorance, apathy, slowness, stupor, bad judgment.)*

acute—*adj.* clever, ingenious, severe, sharp, shrewd, violent, astute, sagacious, smart, fierce. *(stupid, obtuse, dense, mild, dull, stolid, blunt, heavy.)*

adamant—*adj.* determined, unbending, stubborn, firm, set, insistent, immovable. *(lax, yielding, flexible, indifferent, easy-going, undemanding.)*

adapt—*v.* adjust, temper, qualify, fit, attune, harmonize, comply, assimilate. *(confuse, jumble, misapply, misfit, disturb, displace.)*

add—*v.* enlarge, extend, increase, affix, append, adduce, sum up, count up, amplify. *(deduct, subtract, remove, withdraw, reduce, exclude.)*

addicted—*adj.* attached, prone, devoted, given, accustomed, disposed, dedicated. *(unaddicted, averse, free, contrary, opposed, indisposed, reluctant.)*

addition—*n.* totaling, appendage, enlargement, increase, adjunct, summation, enumeration, extension. *(sub-*

traction, loss, deterioration, deduction, decrease, shrinkage.)

address—*n.* speech, discourse, tact, oration, ability. *(awkwardness, rudeness, folly, stupidity.)*

address—*v.* approach, implore, solicit, greet, salute, appeal, invoke, hail, memorialize. *(pass, shun, elude, avoid, ignore.)*

adept—*n.* soothsayer, wizard, expert, master, peer, artist, performer, magician. *(faker, blunderer, novice, hypocrite, pretender, awkward, clumsy.)*

adequate—*adj.* suitable, fit, equal, capable, ample, able, enough, satisfactory, competent. *(unsuited, imperfect, inadequate, incompetent, unfit, inferior, worthless.)*

adherence—*n.* loyalty, attachment, endearment, fidelity, allegiance, devotion, constancy, adhesion. *(slickness, disunion, infidelity, unfaithfulness, desertion, disloyalty, breaking.)*

adherent—*n.* accessory, ally, follower, devotee, fan, disciple, backer, pupil, admirer. *(detractor, betrayer, opponent, renegade, opposer, adversary.)*

adhesive—*adj.* glutinous, gummy, waxy, sticky, adherent. *(attachment, free, apart, unattachable, oily, open, loose.)*

adieu—*n.* farewell, departure, parting, leave, good-bye, leave-taking, setting out. *(salutation, greeting, recognition, welcome.)*

adipose—*adj.* fat, greasy, obese, oily, corpulent, sebaceous, oleoginous. *(thin, bony, leathery, mummified.)*

adjacent—*adj.* next to, beside, neighboring, close, bordering, attached, adjoining, near. *(beyond, afar, remote, distant, detached, apart.)*

adjoin—*v.* border upon, near to, annex, adjacent to, connect, unite, add, touch, affix, join on, approximate, abut. *(dismember, part, remote, disunite, detach, disconnect, removed, distant, recede.)*

adjourn—*v.* suspend, recess, close, postpone, defer, delay, procrastinate, put off, dismiss. *(convene, stimulate, conclude, hasten, gather, convoke, expedite, consummate, protract, impel.)*

adjunct—*n.* accessory, auxiliary, addition, complement, attachment, aid, acquisition, dependency. *(lessening, removal, hindrance, essence, clog, separation, impediment, drawback, detriment.)*

adjust—*v.* arrange, regulate, harmonize, localize, organize, acclimate, callocate, set in order, compose, classify, prepare. *(scatter, disorder, dislocate, jumble, dismember, derange, disturb, involve, confuse.)*

ad-lib—*n.* wisecrack, extemporaneous, improvisation, speak off the cuff, speak impromptu. *(follow the script, speak from notes.)*

administer—*v.* supply, direct, accord, dole, furnish, govern, award, discharge, afford, execute, superintend, distribute, dispense. *(foil, resign, withhold, frustrate, refuse, resume, deny, nullify, betray, forego.)*

admirable—*adj.* worthy, excellent, captivating, pleasing, praiseworthy, astonishing, enticing, good. *(repelling, ridiculous, displeasing, unworthy, hateful, mediocre, repulsive.)*

admissible—*adj.* worthy, permissible, probable, proper, fair, just, likely, reasonable, qualified. *(intolerable, wrong, irrelevant, absurd, preposterous, unfair, excluded, inadmissible.)*

admit—*v.* invest, pass, accept, own, avow, welcome, acknowledge, receive, grant, tell. *(deny, shut, debar, repel, reject, dismiss, eject, repudiate, disavow, confute.)*

admonish—*v.* counsel, advise, rebuke, remind, censure, scold, criticize, forewarn, reprove, warn. *(laud, urge, extol, instigate, applaud, chide, abet, praise.)*

adolescent—*n.* teenager, lad, lass, youth, schoolboy, schoolgirl, young man or woman. *(adult, grown-up, child, mature.)*

adopt—*v.* acknowledge, select, affiliate, elect, endorse, espouse, avow, choose, accept, conform to, assume. *(annul, reject, discard, disinherit, repudiate, abrogate, decline, disclaim, disown.)*

adoration—*n.* worship, exaltation, glorification, veneration, honor, magnification, devotion. *(denunciation, blasphemy, reviling, execration, belittling.)*

adore—*v.* exalt, revere, praise, admire, idolize, glorify, hallow, reverence. *(loathe, dislike, revile, exercrate, abhor, blaspheme, abominate.)*

adorn—v. beautify, gild, garnish, embellish, bejewel, illustrate, ornament. *(mock, despise, curse, condemn, strip, bare, simplify, mar, spoil.)*

adulation—n. compliment, praise, fawning, flattering, courtship, cringing, fulsome, incense. *(loathing, dislike, hatred, defamation, obloquy, satire, sarcasm, detraction, abuse, censure.)*

advance—v. prosper, rise, go, proceed, promote, elevate, lend, increase, exalt, allege. *(stop, withhold, depress, hesitate, halt, withdraw, degrade, retreat, oppose, yield.)*

advantage—n. boon, success, interest, blessing, comfort, gain, help, superiority, utility, profit, victory, avail. *(hindrance, curse, loss, frustration, obstacle, disadvantage, dilemma, disservice, burden, barrier.)*

adventurous—adj. challenging, brave, risky, gallant, bold, fearless, rash, audacious, valiant. *(cautious, nervous, hesitant, dull, routine, boring, hesitating, cowardly, unenterprising.)*

adversary—n. opponent, rival, enemy, competitor, foe, antagonist. *(colleague, aider, friend, teammate, accessory, ally, accomplice, help, cooperation.)*

adverse—adj. contrary, negative, hostile, harmful, antagonistic, unfriendly, detremental, injurious. *(favorable, helpful, supporting, agreeable, auspicious, beneficial.)*

adversity—n. trial, calamity, woe, misfortune, misery, disaster, bad luck, affliction, ruin, unsuccess. *(blessings, prosperity, help, aid, happiness, approval.)*

advertise—v. call attention to, publicize, show, circulate, inform, advise, notify, proclaim, tout, display. *(hide, warn, deliberate, conceal, ignore, proclaim, hush, misinform, hoodwink.)*

advise—v. counsel, direct, acquaint, warn, deliberate, prompt, inform, admonish, show, apprise. *(fool, deter, curb, mislead, dissuade, inhibit, remonstrate, delude, misinform.)*

advocate—n. counsellor, propagator, champion, defender. *(opponent, impugner, accuser, enemy, antagonist.)*

aerial—adj. dreamy, ethereal, fanciful, airy, airborne, air, by air, windcreated, atmospheric. *(land, on the ground, by land, real, practical, pragmatic.)*

affable—*adj.* kindly, genial, courteous, condescending, polite, easy, civil, pleasant, mild, gracious. *(haughty, exclusive, sour, arrogant, surly, distant, unapproachable, contemptuous.)*

affect—*v.* soften, favor, assume, thrill, agitate, influence, like, overcome, interest, subdue, modify. *(repudiate, dislike, scorn, repel, shed, shun, feign.)*

affectation—*n.* airs, artifice, mannerism, pretext, frills, simulation, hypocrisy, pretense, sham. *(sincerity, naturalness, simplicity, artlessness, genuineness, unaffectedness.)*

affection—*n.* friendship, state love, desire, fondness, solicitude, mood, warmth, attachment, tenderness. *(hate, repugnance, indifference, insensibility, antipathy, loathing, coldness.)*

affinity—*n.* relation, harmony, attraction, alliance, connection, sympathy, compatibility, likeness, homology, interdependence. *(aversion, antipathy, disconnection, repugnance, repulsion, discordance, dissimilarity.)*

affirm—*v.* swear, tell, ratify, validate, declare, endorse, warrant, approve, state, aver, maintain. *(refute, deny, rescind, dispute, demur, impugn, oppose, veto, nullify, disallow.)*

affix—*v.* attach, fasten, fix, add on, set to, seal, glue, paste, stick. *(detach, unfasten, take off, unglue.)*

affliction—*n.* calamity, distress, trial, pain, curse, misery, woe, torment, misfortune. *(relief, blessing, pleasure, joy, solace, comfort, consolation, boon.)*

affluent—*adj.* rich, wealthy, prosperous, moneyed, well-off, well-fixed. *(poor, indigent, impoverished, impecunious, destitute.)*

afford—*v.* supply, offer, produce, yield, furnish, impart, grant, give, extend, bestow. *(grudge, retain, stint, withhold, deny, withdraw.)*

affront—*v.* insult, outrage, wrong, vex, provoke, abuse, annoy, displease, shame. *(compliment, placate, soothe, mollify, please.)*

afloat—*adj.* loose, distracted, dazed, adrift, wrong. *(snug, tight, close, fast, collected, ashore, concentrated.)*

afoot—*adj.* instituted, started, established, afloat, launched, working, agoing. *(contemplated, designed, pro-*

jected, incomplete, uncommenced, proposed.)

afraid—*adj.* panicky, alarmed, terrified, faint-hearted, apprehensive, uneasy, aghast, cautious, fearful. *(unafraid, bold, hopeful, fearless, inapprehensive, unsolicitous, secure, reckless, eager, audacious, confident.)*

afresh—*adv.* over again, anew, repeatedly, again, intermittently, frequently. *(unintermittently, connectedly, uniformly, continuously, uninterruptedly.)*

after—*prep.* afterwards, following, latter, behind, subsequent. *(introducing, preceeding, afore, before.)*

again—*adv.* another, frequently, over, afresh, once more, anew. *(uninterruptedly, uniformly, continuously, once, unintermittently.)*

against—*prep.* abreast of, close to, over, despite, counter, opposing, fronting, resisting. *(aiding, promoting, with, accompanying, suiting, for.)*

age—*n.* generation, date, forever, millennium, era, century, senility, duration, period, epoch. *(infancy, moment, instant, childhood, adolescence, second.)*

agent—*n.* executor, performer, force, mechanic, deputy, doer, operator, cause, envoy, delegate. *(opponent, neutralizer, counteragent, counteraction, counteractor.)*

aggravate—*v.* annoy, provoke, vex, intensify, nettle, affront, irritate, exasperate, enhance, embitter, inflame, worsen. *(soften, soothe, mitigate, diminish, assuage, neutralize, lessen, alleviate.)*

agile—*adj.* limber, active, brisk, quick, dexterous, lithe, fleet, nimble, supple, swift, rapid, lively, graceful. *(sluggish, inert, awkward, bulky, clumsy, lethargic, ponderous, slow.)*

agitate—*v.* trouble, ruffle, shake, excite, oscillate, fluster, convulse. *(soothe, compose, quiet, pacify, smooth, still.)*

agog—*adj.* thrilled, astir, awestruck, enthralled, excited. *(bored, uninterested, indifferent.)*

agony—*n.* torture, distress, affliction, anxiety, pain, anguish, torment, woe, suffering. *(pleasure, enjoyment, ease, consolation, ecstacy, comfort, joy, relief, gratification.)*

agree—*v.* match, tally, harmonize, concur, chime, suit, consent, consort, coincide, dovetail, square. *(dispute, op-*

pose, protest, demur, refute, contradict, revolt, disagree.)

agreeable—*adj.* concurring, pleasant, enticing, suitable, acceptable, amenable, ready, willing, accommodating, loving. *(unfitting, harsh, unpleasant, ungrateful, offensive, unacceptable, disobliging, repugnant, revolting, odious.)*

agreement—*n.* compact, unison, mutuality, welcome, harmony, contract, bond, undertaking, concord, bargain, compliance. *(disagreement; difference, discrepancy, discord.)*

aid—*v.* assist, support, minister to, favor, help, sustain, serve, protect, encourage, befriend, foster, promote, instigate, encourage. *(harm, oppose, resist, hurt, obstruct, thwart, discourage, baffle, deter, impede, hinder.)*

ailment—*n.* malady, sickness, disease, infection; complaint, affliction, weakness. *(health, fitness, sanity, robusiness, vigor, convalescence.)*

aim—*n.* goal, design, aspiration, purpose, endeavor, wish, tendency, scope. *(oversight, neglect, carelessness.)*

airy—*adj.* light, sprightly, frolicsome, jaunty, animated, joyous, fairylike. *(heavy, gloomy, dark, doleful, stony, ponderous, cheerless.)*

akin—*adj.* homogeneous, allied, related, analogous, similar, sympathetic, agnate, cognate. *(unrelated, dissimilar, unconnected, alien, unsympathetic, hostile, antagonistic.)*

alacrity—*n.* agility, briskness, animation, compliance, speed, promptitude, eagerness, zeal, alertness. *(repugnance, apathy, dislike, slowness, lethargy, dullness, laziness.)*

alarm—*n.* terror, fright, distress, fear, misgiving, dread, panic, apprehension, agitation. *(quiet, security, calmness, coolness, tranquillity, peace, repose.)*

alarming—*adj.* imminent, formidable, perilous, terrible, frightful, ominous, fearful. *(assuring, hopeful, attractive, soothing, inviting, alluring.)*

alert—*adj.* diligent, brisk, lively, vigilant, watchful, sprightly, hustling, prompt, nimble, wary. *(lazy, oblivious, heavy, stupid, lethargic, languid, dilatory, slow, absent, lackadaisical.)*

alien—*adj.* foreign, strange, remote, undomesicated, hostile, estranged, irrelevant. *(germane, akin, alike, congenial, pertinent, proper, naturalized, native.)*

alike—*adj.* identical, uniform, similar, equal, same, kindred, parallel, homogeneous, resembling. *(apart, unlike, distinct, different, heterogeneous.)*

alive—*adj.* together, animate, breathing, equal, vivacious, alert, brisk, agile, resembling, safe. *(departed, lifeless, inanimate, cold, dull, dead, apathetic, morose, drowsy.)*

allay—*v.* ease, soften, soothe, pacify, diminish, appease, quiet, calm, tranquilize. *(agitate, aggravate, provoke, stimulate, stir, arouse, intensify, magnify.)*

allege—*v.* profess, affirm, assert, contend, accuse, cite, plead, maintain, state, aver. *(neutralize, repel, retract, deny, refute, disclaim, contradict, quash.)*

allegiance—*n.* homage, devotion, loyalty, fealty, faithfulness, deference, fidelity, duty. *(treason, rebellion, treachery, sedition, alienation, deceit, ressistance, disloyalty.)*

alleviate—*v.* soften, lessen, mitigate, diminish, subdue, mollify, remove. *(enhance, embitter, intensify, increase, multiply, augment.)*

alliance—*n.* treaty, union, junction, coalition, partnership, friendship, confederation, association, syndicate. *(secession, enmity, discord, disunion, rebellion, separation, divorce, revolution.)*

allot—*v.* destine, award, tabulate, grant, mete out, catalogue, classify, distribute, parcel, yield. *(resume, repudiate, grasp, resist, withstand, guard, shuffle, refuse, protest, retain.)*

allow—*v.* acknowledge, confess, apportion, recognize, authorize, warrant, approve, avow, grant, tolerate, concede, admit. *(withdraw, forbid, prohibit, withstand, reject, deny, resume, protest, disallow.)*

alloy—*n.* deterioration, lower impairment, debasement, adulteration, admixture, abatement, degradation. *(enhancement, integrity, purity, genuineness.)*

allude—*v.* mention, glance, hint, point, refer, insinuate, cite, quote, imply, remark. *(keep secret, state, declare,* be closemouthed about, specify.)

ally—*n.* supporter, helper, confederate, league, affiliate, accomplice, colleague. *(rival, competitor, foe, opponent, antagonist, adversary, enemy.)*

aloft—*adv.* overhead, heavenward, high up, in the clouds, above. *(down, below, beneath, lower, earthward, low.)*

aloud—*adv.* plainly, clearly, audibly, sonorously, clamorously, loudly. *(silently, suppressedly, softly, inaudibly.)*

alter—*v.* transform, substitute, vary, convert, modify, diversify, recast, regulate, twist. *(keep, retain, stay, arrest, refrain, continue, stereotype, solidify, preserve.)*

altercation—*n.* disagreement, controversy, wrangle, spat, fracas, dissension, dispute. *(union, accord, agreement, unity, peace, harmony, consonance.)*

alternative—*n.* option, choice, preference, pick, election. *(necessity, fix, quandry, urgency, obligation, coercion.)*

altogether—*adv.* thoroughly, collectively, totally, quite, fully, perfectly, completely, on the whole. *(incompletely,* partially, separately, partly, somewhat, individually.)

altruistic—*adj.* humane, kind, charitable, philanthropic, generous. *(selfish, self-centered, malevolent, mean.)*

amass—*v.* assemble, heap, aggregate, muster, pile up, gather, collect, hoard. *(squander, dispense, scatter, portion, divide, waste, parcel, distribute.)*

amazement—*n.* admiration, wonder, awe, shock, astonishment, confusion, perplexity, surprise. *(indifference, coolness, calmness, anticipation, preparation, composure, steadiness.)*

ambiguous—*adj.* indefinite, puzzling, vague, equivocal, uncertain, perplexing, dubious, doubtful, misleading, cryptic. *(explicit, clear, obvious, necessary, frank, uncertain, perplexing, plain, lucid, unequivocal.)*

ambition—*n.* goal, aim, hope, longing, intent, yearning, dream, desire, enterprise. *(indolence, sloth, indifference, laziness, modesty, simplicity.)*

ameliorate—*v.* correct, raise, amend, reform, rectify, elevate, advance, promote.

(impair, injure, depress, debase, vitiate, mar, spoil.)

amend—*v.* better, rectify, mend, repair, meliorate, promote, cleanse, mitigate, correct. *(harm, corrupt, spoil, vitiate, blemish, tarnish, mar, impair, hurt.)*

amiable—*adj.* gentle, engaging, benevolent, cordial, pleasing, gracious, lovable, fascinating, charming, polite, genial. *(hostile, hateful, churlish, sullen, surly, offensive, abminable, repellent.)*

amiss—*adj.* untrue, bad, faulty, mistaken, defective, wrong, incorrect, false, inappropriate, erroneous. *(good, proper, suitable, right, complete, successful, opportune, expedient.)*

amnesty—*n.* absolution, pardon, truce, reprieve, condonation, dispensation, remission. *(penalty, retribution, requital, trial, retaliation, account, punishment.)*

ample—*adj.* abundant, liberal, copious, generous, enough, bountiful, adequate. *(sparse, narrow, scant, mean, insufficient, meager, scrimpy, bare, stint.)*

amplify—*v.* increase, augment, widen, dilate, expand, stretch, magnify, develop, swell, unfold, deepen. *(gather, epitomize, curtail, reduce, amputate, condense, collect, lessen, compress, abbreviate, shorten.)*

amuse—*v.* divert, occupy, charm, cheer, entertain, please, engross. *(bore, sadden, tire, wear, annoy, vex.)*

analogy—*n.* resemblance, metaphor, relation, affinity, parallelism, simile, comparison, likeness. *(difference, dissimilarity, incongruity, inaffinity, heterogeneousness, disharmony.)*

analysis—*n.* judgement, separation, partition, reduction, segregation, investigation, inquiry. *(synthesis, combination, union, aggregation, coalition, uniting.)*

anarchy—*n.* chaos, tumult, riot, misrule, rebellion, insubordination, disorder. *(control, law, order, organization, government, subjection.)*

anatomy—*n.* structure, framework, dissection, segregation, resolution, division. *(structure, union, organization, synthesis, body, form, collocation.)*

ancestry—*n.* family, parentage, genealogy, progenitors, pedigree, line, stock. *(posterity, descendants, issue, progeny.)*

ancient—*adj.* aged, old-time, antiquated, obsolete, archaic, primeval, olden, remote. *(modern, new, recent, fresh, young, newfangled, modish, juvenile.)*

anger—*n.* outrage, vexation, gall, bile, exasperation, petulance, fury, irritation, grudge, hostility, hatred, ire, choler. *(patience, peace, contentment, mildness, goodwill, peacefulness, gratitude.)*

anger—*v.* ruffle, vex, fret, provoke, embitter, annoy, irritate, wound. *(compose, calm, please, delight, soothe, conciliate, heal, gratify.)*

animosity—*n.* rancor, anger, hatred, feud, acrimony, enmity, malice, resentment, bitterness, virulence, strife, dislike. *(love, friendship, harmony, sympathy, congeniality, companionship, alliance, kindliness.)*

annex—*v.* attach, incorporate, acquire, subjoin, unite, add, expropriate, seize, appendage. *(detachment, detach, disconnect, remove, separate, disengage.)*

annihilate—*v.* nullify, destory, exterminate, eradicate, abolish, extirpate, liquidate, demolish, efface, erase, uproot, end. *(create, keep, cherish, build, make, develop, augment, cultivate,* construct, foster, perpetuate, let live.)

announce—*v.* speak, enunciate, circulate, herald, trumpet, broadcast, declare, publish, report, divulge, reveal. *(refrain, hush, suppress, withhold, silence, hide, stifle, smother, reserve, bury.)*

annoy—*v.* bore, badger, irritate, tease, plague, nag, exasperate, provoke, pester, incommode, harass, chafe, inconvenience, molest. *(appease, calm, foster, mollify, console, conciliate, cherish, solace, calm, please.)*

anomaly—*n.* rarity, abnormality, eccentricity, exception, aberration, oddity, peculiarity. *(the norm, the rule, conformity, specimen, illustration, regularity, exemplification.)*

anonymous—*adj.* nameless, unsigned, unacknowledged, unattested, authorless, unauthenticated, unnamed. *(acknowledged, signed, identified, known, attested, verified, named, authorized.)*

answer—*n.* plea, reply, defense, solution, vindication, apology, retort, counterpart, acknowledgment, confutation, response. *(question, inquiry, call, summons, interrogation, challenge, ask.)*

antecedent—*adj.* anterior, earlier, prior, previous, preliminary, former. *(later, posterior, consequent, succeeding, following.)*

anticipate—*v.* await, expect, prevent, count upon, hope for, prepare, forecast, forsee, apprehend, forestall. *(despair of, fear, remember, cure, doubt, dread, misapprehend, remedy, recollect.)*

anticipation—*n.* prospect, awaiting, foresight, prevention, preclusion, preconception, prelibation, provision, antepast. *(non-expectation, realization, unprepardness, surprise, consummation, enjoyment.)*

antipathy—*n.* dislike, hatred, aversion, enmity, rancor, bitterness, repugnance, ill-will, digust, abhorrence. *(affinity, respect, regard, sympathy, love, approval, esteem, reverence, affection.)*

antique—*adj.* ancient, quaint, relic, curio, objet d'art. trinket, antiquated, pristene, immemorial. *(new, modern, recent, modish, fashionable, current, up-to-date, stylish.)*

anxiety—*n.* unease, worry, trouble, solicitude, misgiving, anguish, concern, apprehension, fear. *(contentment, relief, apathy, ease, aplomb,* nonchalance, tranquility, composure.)

anxious—*adj.* uneasy, keen, watchful, solicitous, ardent, concerned, careful, intent, restless. *(careless, cool, inert, certain, confident, ease, unruffled, nonchalent.)*

apathy—*n.* insensibility, unconcern, passiveness, indifference, coolness, lack of interest. *(concern, interest, care, sensibility, eagerness, fervor, zeal, irritability.)*

ape—*v.* simulate, copy, mimic, echo, mock, follow, imitate, emulate. *(vary, change, modify, not to imitate, originate.)*

apiece—*adv.* analytically, each, respectively, severally, individually. *(together, en masse, synthetically, collectively, overall, as a group.)*

apology—*n.* explanation, plea, defense, confession, pretext, evasion, vindication, excuse, acknowledgment of error. *(wrong, censure, offense, impeachment, insult, charge, complaint, accusation, injury.)*

appal—*v.* daunt, dismay, shock, alarm, horrify, revolt, discourage, abash, sicken, frighten, cow, nauseate. *(rally, calm, reassure, please, at-*

tract, console, comfort, encourage.)

apparel—n. garments, robes, attire, vesture, habit, togs, costume, dress, clothing, gear. (rags, nudity, divestiture, dishabille, tatters.)

apparent—adj. understandable, evident, obvious, visible, likely, overt, presumable, ostensible, conspicious, certain, distinct, open. (hidden, real, veiled, disguised, obscure, uncertain, improbable, inapparent, dubious.)

appeal—v. invoke, beseech, urge, request, apply, plea, petition, solicit, address, invite, apostrophize. (deny, disclaim, recall, refuse, repudiate, protest, reject, disavow.)

appearance—n. advent, arrival, appearing, aspect, manner, look, pretense, manifestation, emergence, coming. (vanishing, passing, concealment, departure, unlikelihood, presumption.)

append—v. add, attach, join, supplement, fasten, affix, hang. (remove, omit, separate, disconnect, subtract, detach, take away.)

appetite—n. passion, yearning, craving, tendency, gusto, thirst, proclivity, zest, impulse, want, propension. (apathy, dislike, surfeit, loathing, repugnance, aversion, fill, revulsion, hatred.)

applause—n. plaudits, eulogy, cheers, acclamation, ovation, fanfare, praise, commendation, homage, compliments, encoring, approval. (disapproval, blame, condemnation, criticism, contempt, ridicule, hissing, obloquy, vituperation.)

applicable—adj. germane, useful, apropos, pertinent, appropriate, apt, suitable. (unfit, wrong, irrelevant, inconducive, useless, unsuitable.)

appoint—v. establish, arrange, allot, apportion, nominate, select, employ, choose, fix, prescribe, elect, invest, institute, ordain. (fire, cancel, dismiss, discharge, reverse, withdraw, suspend, disappoint, strip, dismantle, divest, recall.)

apportion—v. allocate, ration, distribute, administer, dole out, dispense, share, deal, consign, prorate, adjust. (resume, reappoint, collect, give all, divert, assemble, retain, receive, reserve, withhold, gather.)

appreciate—v. cherish, recognize, regard, value, relish, admire, savor, acknowledge, respect, treasure. *(disparage, depreciate, misconceive, ignore, misjudge, deflate, underrate, belittle.)*

apprehend—*v.* seize, detect, arrest, dread, comprehend, fear, discern, anticipate, catch, capture, understand, perceive. *(lose, liberate, ignore, misconjecture, misapprehend, release, free, discharge, let go.)*

apprentice—*n.* pupil, novice, neophyte, beginner, student, indentured assistant. *(master, expert, professional.)*

approach—*v.* advance, gain upon, near. *(leave, retreat, diverge, exist, retire.)*

appropriate—*v.* take, confiscate, expropriate, allocate, allot, set apart, assign, earmark. *(donate, relinquish, cede.)*

approve—*v.* praise, sanction, respect, authorize, second, prize, cherish, value. *(repudiate, censure, dislike, criticize, reject, refute, disown.)*

approximate—*adj.* resemble, near, border, nearly equal, abut, closely resemble, suggest, verge on. *(precise, vary, exact, accurate, correct, recede, deviate, differ.)*

apt—*adj.* clever, suitable, proper, liable, relevant, pertinent, ready, seemly, apropos, appropriate. *(awkward, averse, slow, inapt, illtimed, dull, improper.)*

arbitrary—*adj.* despotic, harsh, willful, capricious, fanciful, tyrannical, selfish, irresponsible, domineering, whimsical. *(lenient, impersonal, modest, objective, limited, constitutional, lawful.)*

arbitrate—*v.* adjust, compose, mediate, adjudicate, settle, umpire, judge, referee, decide. *(claim, negotiate, dispute, litigate, misjudge, appeal.)*

ardent—*adj.* fervent, eager, warm, passionate, vehement, fierce, emotional, lusty, keen, feverish, zealous, burning, earnest. *(cold, nonchalant, apathetic, unloving, frigid, phlegmatic, passionless, detached, indifferent.)*

argue—*v.* dispute, battle, wrangle, reason, question, imply, demonstrate, bicker, quibble, denote. *(propound, agree, concur, assert, doubt, conceal, command, assent.)*

argument—*n.* controversy, quarrel, dispute, reasoning, debate, embroilment, altercation, clash. *(assumption,* agreement, harmony, assertion, rebuttal, response, accord.)

arid—*adj.* barren, sterile, dry, unproductive, lifeless, dreary, dull. (damp, fertile, lush, pithy, luxuriant, moist, productive, lively, verdant.)

aright—*adv.* well, truly, correctly, justly, properly, appropriately, suitably, without error. (wrongly, awry, incorrectly, erroneously, properly, defectively.)

aromatic—*adj.* sweet smelling, scented, fragrant, spicy, pungent, odoriferous. (unscented, rank, putrid, acrid, bad smelling, malodorous.)

arouse—*v.* stimulate, animate, spur, kindle, stir, incite, provoke, foster, quicken, whet, goad, excite. (mollify, pacify, still, alleviate, calm, quell, allay, mitigate, dampen.)

arraign—*v.* impute, cite, accuse, indict, impeach, denounce, prosecute. (condone, pardon, discharge, acquit, vindicate, absolve, exonerate.)

arrange—*v.* array, classify, marshall, rank, adjust, pose, systematize, sort, harmonize, prepare, order, parcel. (scatter, disarray, strip, jumble, confuse, disperse, derange, divest, disturb.)

array—*v.* deploy, don, garnish, place, dispose, arrange, attire, decorate. (confuse, jumble, strip, mess up, disarray, denude.)

arrest—*v.* capture, hold, halt, retain, apprehend, catch, detain, hinder, obstruct, suspend, incarcerate. (free, release, let go, discharge, liberate, dismiss.)

arrive—*v.* approach, near, enter, attain, land, come, reach, succeed, make good. (start, leave, depart, retire, embark, withdraw.)

arrogance—*n.* contemptuousness, hauteur, assurance, loftiness, vanity, conceit, egoism, self-importance, discourtesy, swagger, contempt. (shyness, modesty, meekness, bashfulness, humility, simplicity, deference, courtesy, politeness, self-effacement.)

artful—*adj.* maneuvering, subtle, shrewd, diplomatic, scheming, contriving, deceitful, underhand. (innocent, open, natural, candid, unsophisticated, frank, naive, simple.)

artificial—*adj.* false, invented, manmade, imitation, fake, simulated, concocted, unnatural, phony, synthetic. *(genuine, real, natural, spontaneous, artless, unaffected, sincere, candid, actual, frank.)*

ascertain—v. establish, verify, confirm, prove, learn, detect, settle, ferret out. *(surmise, suppose, conjecture, presume, guess.)*

ascribe—v. credit, refer, render, trace to, charge, arrogate, impute, assign. *(discount, refuse, dissociate, deny, disconnect.)*

askew—adv., adj. crooked, awry, lopsided, aslant, crookedly. *(line, aligned, plumb, straight as an arrow.)*

aspiration—n. ambition, hope, yearning, endeavor, daydream, purpose, desire, effort, craving. *(dullness, inertia, aversion, aimlessness, callousness, repudiation.)*

assembly—n. throng, council, conclave, meeting, conference, collection, pack, gathering, body, flock, congregation. *(disunion, dismissal, disruption, dissipation.)*

assent—v. accede, acquiesce, agree, approve, allow, comply, concur, yield, permit, acknowledge. *(differ, dissent, deny, repudiate, disclaim, reject, negate, refuse, veto.)*

assign—v. name, apportion, refer, allot to, convey, specify, stipulate, determine, prescribe. *(retain, disconnect, withhold, discharge, keep, open, divest, hold in abeyance.)*

assist—v. collaborate, reinforce, succor, support, cooperate, aid, boost, help, second, uphold, abet, serve. *(hamper, impede, obstruct, antagonize, clog, counteract, oppose.)*

assistant—n. aider, attendant, ally, partner, adjutant, aide, auxiliary, colleague, accomplice, helper. *(rival, foe, opposer, hinderer, antagonist.)*

association—n. companionship, alliance, membership, society, fellowship, partnership, corporation, league, intimacy, friendship, community. *(solitude, avoidance, severance, disunion, disconnection, separation, alienation, independence.)*

assortment—n. quantity, stock, collection, variety, miscellany, lot, motley, store, conglomeration, diversity, array. *(misplacement, sameness, monotony, mixing, heaping together, displacement.)*

assume—v. arrogate, postulate, uphold, certify,

wear, fancy, infer, presume, judge, surmise, gather. *(allow, render, concede, know, prove, leave, relinquish, put aside.)*

assure—*v.* promise, rally, encourage, aid, uphold, guarantee, clinch, secure, confirm, ensure, advise, certify. *(deter, warn, age, unsettle, intimidate, deny, refute, lie, disavow, fib, doubt.)*

astonish—*v.* amaze, surprise, startle, stun, shock, alarm, stupefy, daze, stagger, dumb, perplex, confuse, bewilder. *(rally, embolden, encourage, assure, anticipate, foresee, bore, count upon.)*

astray—*adj., adv.* loose, missing, erring, wrong, amiss, afield, off, into error. *(close, safe, at home, right, on course.)*

athletic—*adj.* muscular, powerful, brawny, burly, strong, strapping, manly, vigorous, herculean, sinewy, hardy. *(puny, feeble, effeminate, fragile, weak, frail, strengthless.)*

atrocious—*adj.* diabolical, wicked, shameful, infamous, ruthless, savage, monstrous, cruel, flagrant, nefarious, brutal. *(humane, kind, admirable, benevolent, gentle, chivalrous, merciful, noble.)*

attach—*v.* conciliate, tie, adhere, couple, add, secure, bind, unite, fasten, append, annex, join. *(loosen, detach, estrange, untie, release, disconnect, alienate.)*

attack—*v.* censure, invade, besiege, storm, threaten, assault, aggress, criticize. *(vindicate, retreat, defend, support, sustain, excuse, uphold, resist, befriend, cover.)*

attack—*n.* assault, onset, pelt, invasion, stone, aggression, onslaught, trespass. *(protection, aid, withdrawal, support, flight, defense, resistance.)*

attain—*v.* grasp, acquire, procure, win, master, fulfill, execute, reach, accomplish, reap, score. *(forfeit, lose, miss, let go, fail at, abandon, fall short of.)*

attempt—*v.* strive, venture, force, experiment, undertake, effort, violate, aim, hazard. *(abandon, dismiss, neglect, shun, disregard, drop, pretermit.)*

attend—*v.* observe, escort, oversee, listen, mark, watch, superintend, mind, notice, guard, serve, note. *(disregard, forsake, miss, leave, skip, ignore, desert, disassociate, abandon, wander.)*

attention—*n.* alertness, care, consideration, study, respect, civility, concentration, thought, note, observation, concern. *(remission, carelessness, absence, neglect, rudeness, abstraction, negligence, unconcern.)*

attest—*v.* certify, corroborate, display, support, vouch, aver, show evidence, seal, testify, prove, authenticate, imply, ratify, warrant, demonstrate, suggest. *(contradict, exclude, refute, deny, belie, disprove, gainsay, negate, falsify, exclude.)*

attire—*v.* garb, costume, dress, outfit. *(strip, bare, undress, disrobe, unclothe.)*

attract—*v.* dispose, allure, pull, fascinate, enchant, evoke, influence, captivate, invite, precipitate. *(estrange, repel, alienate, disgust, offend, deter.)*

attractive—*adj.* magnetic, winning, alluring, enticing, handsome, fetching, chic, elegant, tasteful, charming, lovely, fair, captivating. *(repugnant, deformed, loathsome, ugly, repulsive, repellent, unattractive, unpleasant, deterrent.)*

attribute—*v.* assign, arrogate, refer, connect, credit, blame, associate. *(disconnect, divorce, dissever, dissociate.)*

attribute—*n.* characteristic, sign, indication, reduction, erosion, weakening, quality. *(essence, substance, its correlative, viz, etc. misnomer, mask, semblance.)*

attrition—*n.* repentance, erosion, remorse, friction, sorrow, self-reproach, grinding. *(callousness, buildup, relentlessness, strengthening, impenitence.)*

audacious—*adj.* adventurous, reckless, rash, hardy, brave, valiant, impudent, insolent, fearless, dauntless. *(cautious, timid, unenterprising, shy, humble, polite, cowardly, unventuresome.)*

audacity—*n.* temerity, boldness, daring, recklessness, spunk, nerve, effrontery, arrogance. *(self-preservation, prudence, forethought, calculation, caution, timidity, meekness, gentility.)*

augment—*v.* enlarge, swell, inflate, increase, add, acquire, supply, deepen, amplify, widen, magnify. *(withdrawal, lose, reduce, diminish, subside, curtail, detract, waste, abridge, narrow, shrink, lessen.)*

augury—*n.* omen, prediction, conjecture, forerunner,

indication, herald, forecasting. *(science, experience, observation.)*

august—*adj.* dignified, lofty, solemn, eminent, venerable, majestic, exalted, pompous, regal. *(common, paltry, mean, undignified, ridiculous, despicable, unstately, lowly, petty.)*

auspicious—*adj.* lucky, successful, hopeful, timely, felicitous, right, golden, fortunate, opportune, encouraging. *(unfavorable, abortive, hopeless, ill-fated, unpromising, doomed, pathetic, unlucky.)*

austere—*adj.* rigid, strict, spartan, grave, severe, stiff, rigorous, harsh, chaste, stark. *(affable, tender, cheerful, sunny, mild, lavish, indulgent, relaxed.)*

authentic—*adj.* real, true, accurate, genuine, actual, bona fide, legitimate, reliable, dependable, factual, accredited, trustworthy. *(false, fake, disputed, unauthorized, sham, unreliable, deceptive, corrupt, fraudulent, counterfeit, fictitious, untrue, phony.)*

authoritative—*adj.* conclusive, sure, potent, imperious, sanctioned, ruling, lordly, dogmatic, firm, arrogant, autocratic, tyrannical, commanding, peremptory.

(vague, vacillating, deceptive, weak, inconclusive, servile, meek, bland, indefinite, conciliatory, affable, frivolous, invalid.)

authority—*n.* authenticity, control, weight, supremacy, jurisdiction, sufferance, prestige, rule, esteem, force, command, direction, respect, administration, influence. *(indecision, weakness, groundlessness, servility, wrong, inconclusiveness, servitude, incompetency, inoperativeness.)*

autocratic—*adj.* arbitrary, absolute, tyrannical, depotic, czaristic, dictatorial, irresponsible. *(subordinate, limited, democratic, lenient, indulgent, constitutional, responsible.)*

auxiliary—*adj.* abetting, conducive, helping, secondary, backup, ancillary. *(superfluous, cumbersome, chief, primary, irrelevant, unassisting.)*

avail—*v.* hold, endure, service, aid, utilize, profit, answer, suffice, benefit, use. *(fail, betray, harm, ignore, hinder, disappoint.)*

available—*adj.* convertible, handy, on tap, obtainable, accessible, applicable, helpful, suitable. *(inappropriate, in-*

operative, inconducive, unobtainable, unserviceable.)

avarice—*n.* cupidity, stinginess, griping, venality, greed, covetousness, penury, miserliness, greediness, rapacity. (bountifulness, extravagance, waste, generosity, liberality, munificence.)

aver—*v.* oblige, protest, affirm, insist, profess, avow, maintain. (contradict, repudiate, disclaim, doubt, dispute, deny, be uncertain.)

avidity—*n.* eagerness, longing, varacity, hankering, greed, ravenousness, desire. (apathy, nausea, repugnance, loathing, coldness, unwillingness, disdain, aversion.)

avoid—*v.* abandon, forsake, eschew, shun, fly, elude, escape, dodge, shirk, evade. (approach, address, court, invite, pursue, find, solicit, accost.)

award—*v.* attribute, accord, divide, give, confer on, assign, decree, grant, determine. (withdraw, retain, withhold, refuse, deny, misappropriate.)

aware—*adj.* sensible, certified, knowledgeable, mindful, conversant, cognizant, informed, known. (insensible, unaware, ignorant, unmindful, oblivious, unconscious.)

awful—*adj.* appalling, ugly, dreadful, solemn, horrendous, deplorable, ghastly, hideous, portentous. (unalarming, alluring, terrific, pretty, unnoticeable, likeable, delightful, unimposing.)

awkward—*adj.* clownish, unhandy, unskillful, uncouth, boorish, stiff, gauche, ungainly. (agile, neat, dexterous, deft, adroit, supple, nimble.)

axiom—*n.* Truth, aphorism, postulate, maxim, principle, self-evidence. (absurdness, paradox, absurdity, nonsense, contradiction.)

B

babble—*n.* dribble, gabble, jabbering, twaddle, cackle, chatter, prattle, chitchat. (sense, wisdom, learning, knowledge, understanding, erudition.)

babel—*n.* clamor, din, clang, turmoil, confusion, bedlam, hubbub, discord, jargon. (articulation, calm, intonation, monotony, elocution, enunciation, tranquility, distinctness, consecutiveness.)

backing—*n.* help, assistance, sanction, endorsement, succor, aid, championing, cooperation. (opposition, *hindrance, resistance, subversion, repudiation.)*

bad—*adj.* defective, useless, imperfect, faulty, unfit, awful, inferior, below par, inadequate. *(excellent, fine, first rate, superior, exemplary, healthful, agreeable, pleasant.)*

baffle—*v.* disconcert, defeat, mystify, frustrate, elude, neutralize, amaze, counteract, perplex, dodge, foil, mar, restrain, balk, estop, counterfoil, upset, mock. *(aid, promote, transmit, point, assist, allow, encourage, advance, abet, enforce.)*

bait—*n.* decoy, allurement, hound, snare, inducement, badger, morsel, tease. *(intimidation, calm, deterrent, soothing, warning, prohibition, lull, dissuasion.)*

balance—*v.* estimate, weigh, pit, equalize, counteract, adjust, set, redress. *(tilt, subvert, overbalance, upset, cant, mispoise.)*

balderdash—*n.* flummery, fustian, drivel, froth, nonsense, bombast, twaddle, rhodomontade. *(wisdom, truth, sense, reason, fact, logic.)*

balk—*v.* thwart, nullify, defeat, impede, baffle, circumvent, hinder, prevent, bar, foil, estop, frustrate, stop, counteract. *(promote, aid, cooperate, encourage, instigate, progress, advance, abet.)*

balm—*n.* solve, emollient, sedative, narcotic, panacea, comfort, tranquilizer. *(stimulant, abrasive, irritant, nuisance.)*

balmy—*adj.* mild, pleasant, temperate, soft, gentle, refreshing, soothing. *(inclement, stormy, unpleasant, irritating, chafing, sensible, sound, normal.)*

banish—*v.* abandon, extrude, relegate, exile, repudiate, eject, eliminate, expel, expatriate, disclaim, eradicate. *(admit, cherish, protect, accept, foster, encourage, entertain, harbor, domiciliate, locate, retain.)*

banquet—*n.* festivity, carouse, dine, feast, treat, entertainment, cheer, repast. *(starvation, fast, snack, abstinence.)*

banter—*n.* mockery, irony, chaff, joshing, jesting, ridicule, badinage, ragging. *(discourse, kid, needle, argument, discussion, jolly, ride.)*

bar—*v.* obstruct, hinder, impede, thwart, restrain, exclude, forbid. *(allow, permit, let, accept, admit, welcome, receive, invite.)*

bargain—*n.* business, gain, agreement, speculation, pact, profit, treaty, transaction, hawking, haggling. *(misprofit, extravagance, swindle, loss.)*

barren—*adj.* depleted, useless, futile, ineffectual, dull, unfruitful, prosaic, uninformative, unrewarding, stale. *(productive, fertile, prolific, lush, rich, luxuriant, fruitful, interesting, instructive.)*

base—*adj.* vile, sordid, mean, pedestal, infamous, ignoble, source, cheap, corrupt, worthless, shameful, vulgar, dishonorable. *(exalted, noble, esteemed, correct, pure, precious, virtuous, shrill, honored, lofty, refined, valued.)*

bashful—*adj.* diffident, shy, timorous, modest, sheepish, retiring, reserved. *(impudent, forward, brazen, bold, impudent, arrogant, pert, unreserved, conceited.)*

basic—*adj.* fundamental, vital, essential, cardinal, key, necessary, care, prime, prerequisite. *(supporting, secondary, frill, trivial, accessory, superfluous, extra.)*

battle—*n.* skirmish, contest, engagement, fight, massacre, action, encounter, conflict, combat. *(harmony, truce, council, peace, reconcile, arbitrament, mediation.)*

bawl—*v.* roar, bellow, yell, clamor, vociferate, shout. *(babble, whisper, whimper, mumble, weep, wail.)*

beach—*n.* coast, seaboard, shore, seashore, rim, sands, water edge. *(deep, main, ocean, sea.)*

beaming—*adj.* radiant, bright, transparent, happy, gleaming, glowing, beautiful, translucid. *(opague, wan, gloomy, dingy, matt, sullen, morose.)*

bear—*v.* transport, maintain, brace, tolerate, sustain, lift, undergo, buttress, carry, admit, suffer, support, harbor, enact, endure, generate, produce. *(protest, eject, stroke, surrender, shed, resent, defend, relinquish, drop, reject, repel, decline.)*

beat—*v.* whack, conquer, pound, pommel, strike, batter, overcome, truncheon, surpass, vanquish, thrash, belabor. *(stroke, shield, defend, submit, relinquish, fall, surrender, protect, caress.)*

beauty—*n.* grace, exquisiteness, embellishment, radiance, picturesqueness, adornment, attractiveness, bloom, comeliness. *(ugliness, bareness, repulsiveness, foulness, hideousness, homeliness, unattractiveness.)*

because—*conj.* consequently, accordingly, owing, on account of. *(independently, inconsequently, unconnectedly, irrespectively.)*

beck—*n.* signal, instructions, control, mandate, authority, gesture, indication, command, summons, call, nod, influence, sign, subserviency. *(unsubservience, independence.)*

becoming—*adj.* neat, proper, seemly, enhancing, comely, graceful, befitting, pleasing, decorous, improving, beseeming, fit. *(unseemly, indecent, unattractive, uncomely, unbecoming, ungraceful, unsuitable, incongruous, derogatory.)*

befitting—*adj.* becoming, expedient, proper, relevant, desirable, appropriate, consistent, seemly, fitting, decent. *(unsuitable, improper, obligatory, unseemly, improper, inexpedient, compulsory, meaningless, incomptible, unbecoming.)*

before—*adv.* anteriorly, prior to, foremost, precedently, first. *(subsequently, later, afterwards, following, behind, after.)*

beg—*v.* request, supplicate, implore, plead, ask, petition, pray, crave, solicit.

(exact, require, demand, insist, give, bestow.)

beggarly—*adj.* miserable, scant, niggardly, despicable, poor, wretched, miserly, stingy, scant. *(princely, liberal, magnificent, noble, sumptuous, prodigal, stately, gorgeous.)*

begin—*v.* prepare, originate, inaugurate, initiate, start, arise, create, commence. *(complete, conclude, stop, finish, achieve, consummate, terminate, expire.)*

beginning—*n.* start, rise, outbreak, opening, source, foundation, precedent, prelude, inception, commencement, preface, threshold, outset, initiation, preparation. *(finale, close, conclusion, completion, end, termination, consummation.)*

behavior—*n.* comportment, manner, deportment, actions, conduct, demeanor, proceeding, attitude. *(misbehavior, misconduct, misdemeanor.)*

belief—*n.* credence, faith, opinion, acceptance, trust, confidence, creed, persuasion, admission, concession, avowal, reliance, permission. *(distrust, misgiving, skepticism, unbelief, denial, incredulity, disavowal, rejection.)*

belligerent—*adj.* hostile, pugnacious, quarrelsome, combative, defiant, argumentative, warlike, embattled, cantankerous. *(easygoing, cool, compromising, pacific, conciliatory, amicable.)*

belonging—*adj.* connected, obligatory, congenial, cognate, accompanying, related. *(alien, uninvolved, independant, optional, unrelated, discretional, irrelevant, unconnected, impertinent, unimplied, uncongenial.)*

bemuse—*v.* muddle, obscure, stupefy, confound, confuse, disorient, unsettle, daze. *(enlighten, clarify, illuminate, simplify, straighten out.)*

bend—*v.* incline, swerve, curve, bias, buckle, mold, influence, accompany, twist, deviate, lean. *(extend, advance, straighten, proceed, stiffen, crush, resist, continue.)*

benediction—*n.* commendation, blessing, thanksgiving, gratitude, boon, dedication, prayer. *(censure, curse, calumniation, obloquy, execration, malediction, disapproval.)*

benefactor—*n.* contributor, upholder, welldoer, backer, subscriber, friend, donor, subsidizer, well-wisher. *(antag-onist, foe, rival, backfriend, oppressor, disfavor, opponent.)*

beneficial—*adj.* salutory, wholesome, valuable, profitable, healthful, advantageous, good. *(noxious, detrimental, prejudicial, destructive, unprofitable, hurtful, baneful.)*

benefit—*n.* service, utility, good, profit, asset, advantage, blessing, reward, favor, avail, use. *(damage, injury, privation, detriment, handicap, calamity, bereavement, hinder.)*

benign—*adj.* kindly, warm, generous, amiable, benevolent, altruistic, affable. *(cold, hostile, violent, malign, nasty, mean, inclement.)*

bequeath—*v.* grant, devise, bestow, endow, give, impart, demise, leave, render, *(alienate, withhold.)*

bereavement—*n.* affliction, loss, destitution, adversity, tragedy, deprivation. *(donation, restoration, gift, substitution, consolation, blessing.)*

besotted—*adj.* steeped, drunk, gross, befuddled, intoxicated, prejudiced, dazed, stupefied. *(temperate, clear, steady, unbiased, enlight-*

ened, refined, self-possessed.)

bespeak—*v.* forestall, indicate, prearrange, suggest, betake, signify, provide. *(contradict, resign, negate, belie, countermand.)*

bestial—*adj.* animalistic, barbaric, wild, brutish, inhuman, disgusting. *(human, benevolent, compassionate, gentle, humane.)*

better—*adj.* superior, finer, preferable, choicer, worthier. *(poorer, worse, inferior, lesser, second-rate.)*

betimes—*adv.* early, prepared, readily, beforehand, soon, seasonably. *(slowly, sluggishly, belatedly, behindhand.)*

betray—*v.* delude, circumvent, abandon, deceive, dupe, defect, reveal, manifest, dishonor, ensnare. *(foster, dare, overlook, be faithful, support, protect, guard, cherish, adhere, preserve, cover.)*

beware—*v.* refrain, heed, take warning, care, fear, mind, consider, avoid. *(overlook, neglect, brave, dare, incur, ignore.)*

bewilder—*v.* confound, puzzle, muddle, astonish, nonplus, disconcert, daze, perplex, fluster, mystify,

mislead. *(inform, instruct, advise, guide, edify, lead, educate.)*

bewitch—*v.* fascinate, charm, entrance, beguile, enchant, enrapture, captivate. *(disgust, disillusionize, exorcise, disenchant, repulse.)*

bias—*n.* prejudice, bent, proclivity, feeling, idea, preconception, inclination, bigotry. *(fairness, impartiality, objectivity, tolerance, dispassionateness.)*

bid—*v.* request, direct, tell, charge, offer, summon, command, propose, enjoin, greet. *(deter, restrain, forbid, prohibit, ban, disallow.)*

bide—*v.* remain, stay, await, continue, tolerate, tarry, anticipate, suffer, stand, expect, abide. *(depart, move, resent, abominate, quit, move, repel, go, migrate, rebel, resist.)*

big—*adj.* wide, proud, fat, arrogant, mammoth, huge, pompous, enormous, massive, large, bulky. *(narrow, slight, easy, microscopic, lean, affable, petite, small, minute, little.)*

bilious—*adj.* irritable, peevish, angry, grumpy, cranky, grouchy, petulant, snappish, cantankerous. *(good, fine, attractive, amicable, gentle,* *mild, sympathetic, cordial, happy.)*

binding—*adj.* restraining, costive, mandatory, obligatory, styptic, compelling, astringent, restrictive. *(enlarging, flexible, loosening, elastic, opening, distending.)*

birth—*n.* nativity, origin, parentage, lineage, inception, source, race, nobility, beginning, rise, family, extraction. *(plebeianism, death, miscarriage, extinction, end.)*

bitter—*adj.* sharp, tart, severe, caustic, acrimonious, intense, afflictive, astringent, harsh, sarcastic, sad, stinging, pungent, cutting, acrid. *(pleasant, trivial, light, kindly, bland, mellow, genial, insipid, affable, mitigated, sweet.)*

blacken—*v.* befowl, defame, calumniate, asperse, discredit, malign, bespatter, slander, vilify, smear, dishonor, decry. *(eulogize, praise, vindicate, clear, exalt.)*

blackguard—*n.* rapscallion, villain, scamp, rogue, rascal, scoundrel. *(hero, gentleman.)*

blame—*v.* chide, reproach, dispraise, reprove, condemn, accuse, reprobate, reprehend, rebuke, censure, vituperate, disapprove, burden. *(exonerate, praise, approve, excuse, acquit, encourage, vindicate, exculpate.)*

bland—*adj.* gentle, courteous, gracious, monotonous, soft, complaisant, mild, tender, benign, prosaic, affable. *(abrupt, exciting, harsh, severe, rough.)*

blank—*adj.* vacant, clean, dull, empty, hollow, plain, futile, void. *(full, marked, busy, alert, sharp, valuable, significant, consequential.)*

blast—*v.* wither, shrivel, destroy, blight, ruin, wreck. *(swell, restore, expland, enlarge.)*

blast—*n.* explosion, burst, destruction, gale, tempest, tornado, squall, breeze, afflation, flurry, squall, frustration. *(neutralization, zephyr, gentle breeze, puff.)*

blatant—*adj.* gross, cheap, unpolished, harsh, noisy, crude, uncouth, tawdry, vulgar, tasteless. *(subtle, delicate, cultured, agreeable, unobtusive, acquiescent, genteel.)*

bleak—*adj.* bare, exposed, stormy, grim, open, dreary, nipping, blank, cold. *(verdant, halcyonic, balmy, warm, sheltered, lush, luxuriant, zephyrous, flourishing.)*

blemish—*n.* blot, speck, stain, obvious, blur, spot, tarnish, dishonor, gross, taint, disfigurement, disgrace, defect, daub, flow, discoloration. *(honor, purity, perfection, intactness, refinement, unsulliedness.)*

blend—*v.* harmonize, combine, merge, fuse, mingle, coalesce, amalgamate, unite, complement, assimilate. *(divide, separate, split, run, dissociate, confound, divide.)*

bless—*v.* gladden, endow, thank, consecrate, enrich, cheer, sanctify, felicitate, rejoice. *(ignore, sadden, condemn, deprive, curse, impoverish, harm, anathematize.)*

blind—eyeless, ignorant, visionless, unseeing, unaware, depraved, prejudiced, unperceptive, unconscious, undiscerning, irrational. *(penetrating, keen, clearsighted, aware, concerned, conscious, rational, farsighted, sensitive, discriminating.)*

blink—*v.* connive, ignore, wink, squint, overlook, peer. *(note, mark, visit, notice, be aware of.)*

bliss—*n.* joy, rapture, luxury, ectasy, blessedness, paradise. *(woe, suffering, agony, condemnation, misery, accursedness, grief, gloom.)*

blithe—*adj.* merry, happy, radiant, light, vivacious, gay, glee, blithesome, bonny, glad-

some, cheerful, lively, elastic. *(dejected, sad, dull, morose, heavy, sullen.)*

blockhead—*n.* dunce, dullard, booby, numskull, clod, dolt, ignoramus, ninny, chump, simpleton, dunderhead, loggerhead. *(luminary, adept, sage, savant, scholar, philosopher, schoolman.)*

bloom—*v.* blossom, height, perfection, prime, flourish, prosper, succeed, blush, florescence. *(decay, dwindle, wane, languish, waste away.)*

blooming—*adj.* flowering, young, flourishing, vigorous, beautiful, fair, blossoming, exuberant. *(blighted, old, fading, unsightly, withering, waning, paralysed, deformed, declining, blasted.)*

blot—*v.* tarnish, sully, discolor, obliterate, blur, blotch, smear, stain, erase, daub, obscure, pollute, smutch, spoil, stigma. *(clear, perpetuate, cleanse, honor, elucidate, conserve, credit.)*

blow—*n.* breath, knock, bang, puff, stroke, crack, shock, wound, calamity, disappointment, blast, affliction, misfortune, tragedy. *(consolation, comfort, sparing, calm, assuagement, relief, caress.)*

bluff—*adj.* bold, frank, rude, swaggering, blunt, gruff, surly, open, brusk, discourteous, rough, bullying, hectoring, coarse, blustering. *(courteous, polite, inclined, undulating, suave, inabrupt, reserved, polished.)*

blunder—*n.* mistake, fault, inaccuracy, indescretion, slip, oversight, delusion, fumble, error, omission. *(exactness, prevention, correction, success, foresight, accuracy, achievement, truthfulness, faultlessness, atonement, hit.)*

blush—*n.* flush, carnation, confusion, bloom, glow, color, shame, self-reproach, guiltiness, aspect, complexion. *(unconsciousness, purity, effrontery, paleness, innocence, ashen, boldness, quiltlessness.)*

boast—*v.* brag, swell, bluster, flaunt, truimph, vapor, glory, exhibit. *(be ashamed, disclaimer, cover up, deprecate, disavow.)*

body—*n.* mass, collection, organization, assemblage, association, whole, matter, substantiality, corporation, substance, denseness. *(soul, individual, intellect, spirit, mind.)*

boggle—*v.* blunder, halt, demur, blotch, spoil, vacillate, botch, hesitate, falter, dubitate. *(advance, face,*

beautify, clear, perfect, refine, encounter, advance, complete.)*

boisterous—*adj.* tumultuous, rowdy, obstreperous, shrill, clamorous, rambunctious, unruly, wild, loud. *(well-behaved, orderly, quiet, restrained, calm, tranquil, sedate, serene, disciplined.)*

bold—*adj.* fearless, brave, forward, dauntless, audacious, courageous, stout, daring, intrepid, brazen, lionhearted, adventurous. *(bashful, fearful, meek, timid, shy, weak, retiring.)*

bombast—*n.* braggadocio, bluster, pomposity, fustian, extravagance, tumidity, rhodomontade, gasconade, bravado. *(humility, truthfulness, refrain, modesty, veracity, reserve, shyness.)*

bond—*n.* association, compact, obligation, cement, link, tie, chain, security, fastening, manacle. *(honor, option, freedom, discretion, detachment.)*

bondsman—*n.* serf, captive, vassal, toiler, prisoner, slave. *(freeman, yeoman, master, lord, gentleman, aristocrat.)*

bonny—*adj.* pleasant, fair, cheerful, gay, pretty, shapely, merry, buxom, lively. *(dull,* *quiet, ill-favored, deformed, unseemly.)*

boost—v. lift, hoist, raise, elevate, pitch, shove, press, push, promote. *(reduce, decline, diminish, lessen, curtail, ease, deduct, belittle.)*

border—n. brink, rim, edge, circumference, limit, boundry, perimeter, hem, confine, enclosure, brim, band. *(tract, space, middle, center, land, inside, interior.)*

border on—v. be adjacent to, adjoin, be conterminous with, approach, come near. *(be remote from, be away from.)*

botch—v. jumble, mar, blunder, fumble, patch, disconcert, muff, cabble, spoil, mess, fail. *(trim, mend, perform, embroider, master, harmonize, beautify, handle, manipulate, perfect.)*

bother—n. worry, fuss, excitement, confusion, flurry, trouble. *(orderliness, quiet, comfort, calm, composure, peace, solace.)*

boundless—adj. infinite, illimitable, immense, unlimited, endless, unbounded, immeasurable. *(limited, circumscribed, restricted, small, confined, narrow, bounded.)*

bounty—n. benevolence, donation, charity, assistance, munificence, gratuity, liberality, gift, generosity, aid. *(closeness, stinginess, niggardliness, avarice, hardness, churlishness, greed.)*

brag—v. swagger, extol, bully, boast, crow, vaunt. *(whimper, deprecate, cringe, whine.)*

branch—n. bough, member, limb, channel, shoot, twig, ramification, relative, tributary, scion, bifurcation, offspring. *(house, trunk, stock, race, family, mass, stem, conglomerate.)*

brave—adj. courageous, valiant, heroic, dauntless, unafraid, plucky, fearless, stalwart. *(cowardly, fearful, craven, timid, timorous, frightened, faint hearted.)*

break—v. rupture, shatter, destroy, fragment, demolish, fracture, tame, burst, mangle, infringe, violate, subdue, smash, shiver, sever, split, tear. *(conjoin, observe, obey, repair, heal, conserve, rally, service, protect, piece.)*

breath—n. inspiration, respiration, exhalation, aspiration, expiration, inhalation. *(passing, death, perishing, cessation, departure, dying.)*

breeding—n. education, training, nurture, manners, air, decorum, discipline, gentility, culture. *(ill-training, ill-manners, ill-breeding, ignorance, ill-behavior.)*

brevity—*n.* compendiousness, abbreviation, terseness, curtness, shortness, conciseness, closeness, briefness, pointedness. *(diffuseness, tediousness, verbosity, length, elongation, prolixity, extension, garrulity.)*

bright—*adj.* luminous, happy, joyous, glowing, shining, cheerful, brilliant, intense, burnished, lucid, witty, radiant, sparkling, vivid. *(dull, joyless, imbecile, pallid, opaque, dead, sullen, cheerless, morose, muddy, slow, stupid.)*

brilliant—*adj.* shining, beaming, glorious, gleaming, flashing, radiant, luminous, resplendent, sparkling, lustrous. *(opaque, dull, tarnished, lusterless, lifeless.)*

bring—*v.* convey, bear, import, transport, fetch, carry, induce, produce, initiate, procure, cause. *(debar, prevent, subtract, quash, remove, exclude, dispel, abstract, export.)*

brisk—*adj.* vivacious, alert, quick, animated, vigorous, lively, active, prompt, spry, spirited, nimble, sprightly. *(dull, indolent, lethargic, slow,*

stagnant, heavy, lazy, inactive, unenergetic.)*

broad—*adj.* expansive, liberal, indelicate, voluminous, wide, coarse, extensive, spacious, generic, unreserved, ample. *(confined, prejudiced, narrow-minded, slender, restricted, pointed, delicate, veiled, shaded, precise, specific, enigmatical, illiberal, reserved, bigoted.)*

brotherhood—*n.* association, fellowship, society, affiliation, sodality, comradeship. *(no antonyms).*

brutal—*adj.* inhuman, violent, intemperate, fierce, savage, rude, bloodthirsty, stolid, cruel, primitive, unfeeling, vindictive, dense, ignorant, barbarous, brutish, sensual. *(civilized, self-controlled, sympathetic, generous, chivalrous, polished, intelligent, conscientious, merciful.)*

bubble—*n.* fancy, trash, effervescence, conceit, froth, percolate, trifle, toy, bead. *(treasure, good, advantage, be flat, reality, verity, acquisition, substance, prize, jewel.)*

budge—*v.* change, influence, persuade, sway, convince, shift. *(remain, stay, stick, halt, pause.)*

bugbear—*n.* goblin, ghoul, ogre, specter, bugaboo,

scarecrow, spook, spirit, hobgoblin.

building—*n.* architecture, fabric, structure, house, erection, frame, construction, domicile. *(dismantlement, delapidation, demolition, ruin, destruction.)*

bulk—*n.* entirety, mass, body, bigness, weight, dimension, largeness, bigness, enormity, whole, integrity, volume, magnitude, majority, size, greatness. *(diminution, atom, disintegration, tenuity, lesser part, smallest part, minority, portion, section.*

bungler—*n.* fumbler, novice, clown, blunderer, botcher, muffer, lubber. *(artist, professor, expert, master, proficient, adept, workman, adroit.)*

buoyant—*adj.* vivacious, light, spirited, floating, elated, sprightly, energetic, lively, joyous, elastic, hopeful. *(moody, heavy, cheerless, sullen, joyless, depressed, doleful, dejected, desponding.)*

burden—*n.* incubus, load, grief, stress, weight, affliction, hamper, difficulty, obstruction, oppression. *(expedition, lightness, ease, abjugation, free, facility, consolation, mitigation, airiness, alleviation, lighten, facility,*

disburdenment, assuagement, light-heartedness.)

burn—*v.* brand, cauterize, flash, scorch, ignite, consume, cremate, glow, singe, kindle, rage, incinerate, smoulder, blaze. *(cool, wane, pale, chill, lower, extinguish, soothe, glimmer, stifle.)*

bury—*v.* conceal, suppress, cancel, compose, screen, hush, entomb, inter, obliterate, repress, veil. *(resuscitate, bruit, expose, reveal, exhume, aggravate, excavate, air.)*

business—*n.* profession, affair, office, concern, career, trade, duty, interest, occupation, calling, activity, vocation, employment, matter. *(inactivity, hobby, leisure, stagnation, avocation.)*

bustle—*n.* stir, commotion, excitement, scramble, business, flurry, haste, energy, dash, eagerness, hurry. *(indifference, calm, stagnation, procrastinate, idleness, inactivity, indolence, quiet, loaf, desertion, vacation, coolness.)*

busy—*adj.* diligent, engaged, industrious, laboring, occupied, toiling, assiduous. *(indolent, slothful, relaxed, idle, unoccupied, lazy.)*

but—*conj.* except, yet, moreover, save, beside, excluding, notwithstanding, still, though, barring. *(nevertheless, not withstanding, inclusive, with, including, however.)*

C

cage—*n.* coop, pen, receptacle, cell, enclosure, box. *(free, liberate, let out.)*

calamity—*n.* misfortune, trouble, mishap, fatality, disaster, catastrophe, affliction, tragedy, reverse. *(blessing, luck, boon, God-send.)*

calculate—*v.* weigh, reckon, apportion, consider, compute, estimate, investigate, count, rate, gauge, proportion. *(chance, stake, guess, hit, risk, speculate, conjecture, miscalculate.)*

calculation—*n.* consideration, regard, care, judgement, estimation, balance, caution, apportionment, vigilance, investigation, watchfulness, anticipation, reckoning, computation, forethought, thought. *(exception, inconsideration, carelessness, incaution, omission, exclusion, inconsiderateness, indiscretion, miscalculation, misconception, supposition, mistake.)*

calibre—*n.* diameter, capacity, force, endowment, character, strength, quality, power, scope.

called—*v.* denominated, termed, named, designated. *(misnamed, unnamed, misdesignated, undesignated.)*

calm—*v.* compose, still, appease, sedate, smooth, tranquilize, assuage, quiet, soothe, allay, relax. *(agitate, lash, stir, disconcert, tense, ruffle, heat, discompose, excite.)*

calumny—*n.* libel, opprobrium, slander, aspersion, defamation, back-biting, traducement, detraction, scandal. *(eulogy, panegyric, vindication, testimonial, clearance.)*

cancel—*v.* annul, obliterate, erase, delete, efface, nullify, discharge, abolish, repeal, blot out, expunge, countervail, quash, rescind, abrogate, revoke. *(ratify, contract, enforce, confirm, perpetuate, re-enact, enact.)*

candid—*adj.* frank, aboveboard, plain, ingenious, blunt, open, fair, unreserved, impartial, transparent, honest, artless, just. *(biased, jesuitical, unfair, mysterious, shuffling, reserved, disingenuous, close, insincere.)*

candidate—*n.* claimant, aspirant, petitioner, solicitor, canvasser, applicant, nominee, contender. *(abjurer, decliner, waiver, abandoner, resigner, noncompetitor.)*

cantankerous—*adj.* crotchety, cranky, irritable, cross, contrary, bad-tempered, quarrelsome, perverse. *(serene, affable, pleasant, equable, debonair, good-humored.)*

canvass—*v.* examine, request, question, challenge, discuss, sift, test, analyze, ventilate, investigate, contemplate, solicit. *(admit, pretermit, pass, allow, disregard, misexamine, ignore, misinvestigate.)*

capacity—*n.* volume, space, scope, calibre, talents, comprehensiveness, magnitude, accommodation, range, parts, competency, cleverness, tonnage, aptitude, size, ability, faculty. *(restriction, coarctation, contractedness, narrowness, incapacity.)*

capital—*n.* important, high, wealth, chief, cleverness, wherewithal, cardinal, principal. *(minor, defective, inferior, poor, unimportant, subordinate, awful.)*

capricious—*adj.* humorsome, uncertain, erratic, wayward, crotchety, whimsical, fanciful, fitful, inconstant, changeful, fickle, giddy. *(unchanging, constant, steadfast, firm, inflexible, unswerving, decided.)*

captivated—*adj.* smitten, enslaved, taken, enthralled, enchanted, captured, charmed. *(free, unscathed, insensitive, uninfluenced, unaffected, insensible, unfeeling.)*

capability—*n.* capacity, skill, competence, power, talent, flair, knack, qualification, attainment. *(inadequacy, impotency, inability, ineptitude, incompetence.)*

care—*n.* prudence, attention, thrift, consideration, pains, economy, heed, wariness, anxiety, foresight, effort, caution, preservation, custody, regard, solicitude, circumspection, prevention, trouble, concern. *(unguardedness, neglect, incaution, recklessness, inattention, improvidence, disregard, remissness, indifference, temerity, carelessness, abandon.)*

career—*n.* walk, progress, way of life, employment, course, race, history, passage, activity. *(unsuccess, miscarriage, avocation, misproceeding, misdeportment.)*

caress—*n.* stroking, embrace, endearment, wheedling, blandishment, fondling.

(annoyance, persecution, melancholy, vexation, provocation, irritation, teasing.)

careless—*adj.* negligent, rash, thoughtless, heedless, slack, unthinking, inconsiderate, slipshod. *(cautious, alert, careful, wary, mindful, diligent, concerned, neat, orderly.)*

caricature—*n.* parody, farce, mimicry, travesty, satire, extravagance, burlesque, exaggeration, hyperbole, monstrosity. *(justice, representation, portraiture, resemblance, truthfulness, fidility, likeness.)*

carnival—*n.* festivity, revel, masquerade, rout, celebration. *(mortification, retirement, fast, lent.)*

carpet—*n.* consideration, table, consultation, board, mat. *(disposal, rejection, oblivion, shelf, discharge.)*

carriage—*n.* bearing, vehicle, gait, transportation, coach, conveyance, deportment, bearing, behavior, walk, mien, conduct, manner, stance. *(misconduct, misconveyance, miscarriage, misconsignment.)*

case—*n.* contingency, plight, episode, condition, fact, instance, predicament, occurrence, circumstance, event, incident. *(supposition,*

hypothesis, presumption, theory, fancy, conjecture.)

cast—*v.* throw, fling, frame, construct, pattern, mold, hurl, impel, project, pitch, send down. *(dissipate, approve, retain, ignore, dismember, misprovide, erect, raise, dislocate, break, recover, elevate, accept, carry, miscalculate.)*

cast—*n.* plight, fact, event, condition, subject, instance, occurrence, predicament, contingency, catapult. *(supposition, theory, hypothesis, fancy, conjecture, speculation.)*

caste—*n.* rank, blood, order, station, class, lineage, race, respect, dignity. *(taboo, reproach, degradation, disrepute, abasement, depravation.)*

casual—*adj.* occasional, contingent, fortuitous, accidental, chance, incidental, unforeseen. *(ordinary, fixed, systematic, calculated, regular, certain, periodic.)*

catastrophe—*n.* disaster, blow, misadventure, visitation, calamity, devastation, revolution, reverse, misfortune, tragedy. *(triumph, success, benefit, blessing, godsend, felicitation, ovation, achievement, victory.)*

catch—v. capture, corner, snag, grab, seize, arrest, apprehend, snare, trap. *(free, liberate, let go, fumble, lose, release, give up, drop.)*

cause—n. agent, inducement, suit, reason, action, source, motive, producer, stimulus, object, origin, creator, account, purpose, principle, motivation. *(result, end, production, issue, preventive, effect, accomplishment, conclusion.)*

cease—v. desist, pause, quit, stop, leave off, adjourn, intermit, abstain, refrain, end, discontinue. *(commence, persist.)*

celebrated—adj. notable, renowned, distinguished, exalted, popular, famed, eminent, noted, famous, glorious. *(disgraced, obscure, mean, insignificant, unrenowned, unknown, nondescript.)*

celebrity—n. eminence, honor, renown, fame, notoriety, personality, notability, distinction, star, glory. *(cipher, obscurity, ingloriousness, indolence, meaness, ignominy, disgrace, nobody, contempt.)*

celestial—adj. ethereal, elysian, heavenly, atmospheric, blissful, godlike, supernatural, radiant, angelic, immortal, divine. *(hellish, earth-*

ly, mundane, infernal, mortal, terrene, sublunary, human, wordly.)

censure—n. reprimand, blame, dispraise, stricture, rebuke, reproach, criticism, disapproval, admonition. *(eulogy, encouragement, praise, approbation, support, commendation.)*

ceremonial—adj. functional, imposing, scenic, ritualistic, pompous, sumptuous, official, ministerial. *(unostentatious, private, casual, undramatic, unimposing, ordinary.)*

certain—adj. regular, infallible, sure, actual, convinced, real, confident, unfailing, unmistakable, indubitable, incontrovertible, undoubtful, true, fixed, established, secure, reliable. *(undecided, casual, dubious, irregular, unsettled, uncertain, occasional, doubtful, exceptional, vacillating, unsure, fallible.)*

certify—v. prove, aver, vouch, demonstrate, protest, assure, inform, ratify, evidence, testify, acknowledge, avow, declare, avouch, underwrite. *(misinform, repudiate, disprove, misadvise, disavow.)*

challenge—v. dare, question, brave, demand, defy, investigate, canvass, summon. *(allow, believe, pass, grant, acquiesce, concede, yield.)*

chance—*n.* hazard, luck, fate, fortuity, befallment, accident, haphazard, casualty, destiny, fortune. *(design, consequence, rule, intent, certainty, law, causation, sequence, purpose, premeditation, casualty.)*

changeless—*adj.* settled, firm, consistent, constant, immovable, reliable, regular, uniform, immutable, steady, stationary, undeviating, resolute, fixed, abiding. *(mutable, irregular, plastic, unsettled, wavering, fluctuating, vacillating, capricious, unsteady, irresolute, variable.)*

character—*n.* mark, symbol, sign, record, letter, figure, nature, type, genius, class, quality, tone, part, disposition, temperament, repute, cast, kind, order, individuality, species, stamp, makeup. *(vagueness, non-description, dishonesty, anonymousness, disrepute, dishonor.)*

characteristic—*n.* singularity, distinction, specialty, peculiarity, idiosyncrasy, individuality, personality. *(miscellany, nondescription, mannerism, generality, abstractedness.)*

charge—*v.* command, instruct, bid, direct, call, order, accuse, incriminate, assign, indict, blame. *(vindicate, pardon, withdraw, retreat, imply, absolve, exonerate, acquit.)*

charitable—*adj.* benevolent, kind, inextreme, forgiving, liberal, compassionate, generous, placable, philanthropic, considerate, inexacting, benign. *(extreme, harsh, revengeful, exacting, stingy, retaliative, uncharitable, selfish, censorious, uncompassionate, unforgiving, illiberal, unkind, parsimonious.)*

charm—*v.* enchant, subdue, transport, delight, captivate, attract, entrance, bewitch, fascinate, soothe, entice, lay, mesmerize, gratify. *(irritate, rouse, annoy, disgust, terrify, excite, offend, disenchant, disturb, disillusionize, repel, alarm.)*

charm—*n.* attraction, incantation, allurement, spell, magnetism, spell, enchantment. *(repulsion, disgust, fear, disenchantment, displeasure.)*

chaste—*adj.* uncontaminated, nice, pure, virtuous, modest, celibate, incorrupt, unaffected, undefiled, simple, spotless, wholesome. *(meretricious, flashy, impure, lewd,*

45

corrupt, gaudy, overdecorated.)

cheap—*adj.* low-priced, mean, inexpensive, vile, economical, common, uncostly, worthless. *(worthy, honorable, valuable, high, costly, expensive, rare, noble.)*

cheat—*v.* fleece, inveigle, gull, silence, beguile, hoodwink, dissemble, deceive, overreach, victimize, prevaricate, trick, cozen, defraud, juggle, dupe, deprive, shuffle, swindle.

cheat—*n.* charlatan, fraud, imposter, artifice, fake.

check—*v.* halt, constrain, brake, curb, harness, arrest, prevent, stay, restrain, suppress, retard, impede, thwart. *(initiate, unleash, encourage, aid, support, begin, accelerate, spur, foster, help, abet.)*

cheer—*n.* conviviality, hope, comfort, hospitality, plenty, happiness, optimism. *(unsociableness, dejection, gloom, niggardliness, pessimism, sullenness, churlishness, dearth, inhospitableness, starvation.)*

cheerful—*adj.* joyous, lively, happy, sprightly, joyful, merry, jovial, gay, buoyant, blithe, in good spirits, bonny, glad, enlivening, pleasant, bright. *(despiriting, lifeless, unhappy, depressing, dull, dejected, melancholy, gloomy, morose, sullen, joyless, depressed.)*

chief—*n.* boss, administrator, supervisor, master, chairman, overseer, chieftain, overlord, monarch, potentate, director. *(underling, subject, subordinate, secondary, subsidiary, follower.)*

childish—*adj.* silly, paltry, foolish, infantine, adolescent, weak, trivial, trifling, imbecile, puerile. *(chivalrous, judicious, strong, polite, mature, resolute, wise, manly, sagacious, profound.)*

chivalrous—*adj.* generous, heroic, gallant, valiant, courtly, high-minded, spirited, handsome, courageous, adventurous, knightly, polite. *(dirty, ungenerous, unhandsome, sneaking, ungentlemanly, recreant, scrubby, dastardly, pettifogging, borish, cruel.)*

choice—*n.* preference, selection, option, election, discretion, alternative, adoption. *(indifference, refusal, compulsion, rejection, refuse, coercion, necessity, unimportance.)*

chuckle—*v.* cackle, laugh, grin, crow, chortle. *(grumble,* *wail, whine, cry, whimper, moan.)*

churlish—*adj.* brusque, crusty, petulant, irritable, bilious, sour, rude, grouchy, sullen. *(amiable, kind, pleasant, gallant, noble, cultivated, humble, polite.)*

cipher—*n.* dot, button (fig.), rush, straw, nonentity, naught, pin, nothing, trifle, mole-hill, nil. *(colossus, notability, triton, star, somebody, infinity, something, bigwig, celebrity.)*

circumstance—*n.* feature, point, event, incident, position, topic, episode, detail, specialty, condition, particular, occurrence, situation, fact. *(case, deed, transaction, performance.)*

civil—*adj.* political, polite, respectful, well-mannered, civilized, affable, obliging, accommodating, courteous, well-bred, complaisant, cordial. *(unaccommodating, boorish, churlish, impolite, uncivil, clownish, disrespectful, disobliging.)*

claim—*v.* ask, insist, privilege, maintain, profess, demand, require, title, right, pretense, request, avow. *(abandon, surrender, waive, deny, abjure, disavow, concede, repudiate, disclaim, forego.)*

claim—*n.* vindication, demand, right, assertion, pretension, title, arrogation, request, privilege. *(surrender, abjuration, waiving, disclaimer, denial.)*

claimant—*n.* appellant, assertor, vindicator, petitioner, litigant. *(conceder, abjurer, relinquisher, quiter, resigner, waiver, renouncer.)*

classification—*n.* nature, sect, designation, genus, order, section, division, species, character, description, assortment, category, kind, group, cast, stamp. *(isolation, division, heterogeneity, specialty, individuality, compartment, exclusion, alienation, singularity, distinction.)*

clause—*n.* paragraph, article, section, chapter, passage, portion, term, stipulation, proviso, condition, provision. *(instrument, document, muniment, charter.)*

clear—*v.* exonerate, disentangle, clarify, emancipate, extricate, whitewash, disencumber, set free, disembarrass, liberate, absolve, retrieve, acquit, justify, exculpate, eliminate, release, rid. *(pollute, embarrass, clog, implicate, contaminate, condemn, encumber, involve, befowl.)*

clear—*adj.* intelligible, pure, lucid, transparent, obvious, open, plain, free, unobstructed, patent, unequivocal, conspicuous, manifest, apparent, evident, unclowded, serene, acquitted, absolved, disentangled, disengaged, disencumbered. *(condemned, dubious, muddy, thick, opague, fowl, entangled, convicted, encumbered, blurred, indistinct, turbid, unintelligible, limpid.)*

clemency—*n.* mercy, compassion, leniency, forbearance, tolerance, charity, understanding, sympathy, benevolence. *(vindictiveness, cruelty, illwill, vengefulness, intolerance, brutality.)*

clever—*adj.* talented, gifted, expert, well-contrived, adroit, nimble, able, skillful, ingenious, quick-witted, dexterous, quick, ready. *(botched, weak, clumsy, dull, slow, awkward, incompetent, bungling, stupid, ill-contrived, uninventive, doltish, inept.)*

cling—*v.* adhere, hug, hang, fasten, embrace, linger, hold, twine, cleave, stick. *(surrender, drop, relax, swerve, abandon, forsake, apostatize, forego, secede, recede.)*

cloak—*v.* extenuate, conceal, screen, mask, disguise, cover, mitigate, camouflage, veil, palliate, hide. *(propound, exhibit, promulge, expose, reveal, protray, unmask, aggravate, demonstrate.)*

close—*adj.* condensed, compressed, dense, niggardly, secret, narrow, fast, limited, adjacent, restricted, shut, reserved, firm, compact, packed, solid. *(liberal, ample, frank, wide, spacious, rarefied, vaporous, public, roomy, open, advertised, open- handed, patent, airy, subtle, dispersed, unconfined.)*

cloudy—*adj.* misty, smoky, gray, overcast, hazy, vaporous, soupy, dreary, gloomy. *(clear, fair, bright, sunny, cloudless, azure, transparent.)*

clownish—*adj.* foolish, cloddish, bucolic, clumsy, comical, rude, rustic, untutored, boorish, awkward. *(intelligent, civil, polite, educated, urbane, high-bred, sedate, courtly, affable, graceful, polished, refined.)*

clumsy—*adj.* uncouth, bungling, unhandy, botching, ill-shaped, awkward, inept, unwieldy, inexpert, maladroit, unskillful. *(dexterous, artistic, adroit, neat, expert, workmanlike, handy, nimble, skillful.)*

coarse—*adj.* indelicate, rough, immodest, unrefined, crude, vulgar, common, unpolished, ordinary, gross, rude. *(choice, refined, elegant, delicate, gentle, fine, polished.)*

cognizance—*n.* recognition, notice, observation, knowledge, perception, experience. *(oversight, neglect, connivance, inadventure, ignorance, unawareness, inexperience.)*

coherent—*adj.* complete, compact, consecutive, united, close, sensible, logical, consistent, adhering. *(illogical, loose, inconsecutive, discursive, rambling, confused, aberrant, disunited, silly, inconsistent.)*

coincide—*v.* square, tally, agree, accord, harmonize, dovetail, correspond, equal, meet. *(diverge, conflict, differ, disagree, clash.)*

coincidence—*n.* consent, casualty, contemporaneousness, chance, agreement, fortuity, simultaneous, concurrence, harmony, correspondence, commensurateness. *(purpose, difference, incommensurateness, design, variation, premeditation, adaption, discordance, disharmony, asynchronism, anachronism.)*

colleague—*n.* adjutant, partner, helper, associate, assessor, companion, ally, collaborator, confederate, coadjutor, assistant. *(com-petitor, co-rival, counter-agent, adversary, co- opponent, co- antagonist.)*

collect—*v.* gather, sum, muster, accumulate, collate, marshal, garner, convoke, glean, convene, amass, congregate, infer, learn, assemble. *(arrange, sort, dispose, classify, deal, scatter, dispense, distribute, divide.)*

collection—*n.* store, assemblage, collation, gathering, compilation, assembly. *(disposal, division, classification, arrangement, distribution, assortment, dispersion, dispensation.)*

color—*n.* complexion, speciousness, falsification, perversion, hue, pretense, pigment, varnish, tint, distortion, garbling, tinge. *(transparency, achromatism, pallor, nakedness, paleness, openness, truthfulness, genuineness.)*

combination—*n.* association, coalition, co-operation, cabal, blending, union, synthesis, alliance, league, confederacy, concert, consortment. *(analysis, resistance, inter-repellence, separation, division, opposition, disunion, disruption, dispersion, dissolution.)*

comely—*adj.* becoming, tasteful, proper, pleasant,

charming, appealing, unaffected, decorous, nice, simple. *(homely, unsightly, ugly, faded, unattractive, improper, repulsive, affected, plain, unbecoming.)*

comfortable—*adj.* convenient, snug, consoled, satisfied, agreeable, congenial, commodious, cozy, pleasant. *(disagreeable, uncomfortable, forlorn, unhappy, dissatisfied, unsuitable, cheerless, wretched, troubled, miserable.)*

command—*v.* govern, conduct, guide, supervise, administer, rule, boss, direct, superintend. *(supplicate, follow, plead, beg, deter, discourage, repel, obey.)*

commerce—*n.* merchandize, barter, dealing, trade, intercourse, communication, exchange, business, industry, traffic. *(interdict, stagnation, dullness, inactivity, embargo, standstill, exclusion.)*

commodious—*adj.* ill- contrived, discommodious, inconvenient, cramped, incommensurate, incommodious, narrow. *(suitable, easy, comfortable, convenient, ample, spacious, luxurious.)*

common—*adj.* everyday, universal, ordinary, mean, habitual, low, prevalent, familiar, coarse, frequent, vulgar. *(exceptional, rare,*

egregious, unusual, excellent, peculiar, scarce, uncommon, partial, refined, sporadic, infrequent.)

community—*n.* association, unity, aggregation, homogeneity, polity, society, brotherhood, co-ordination, fellowship, similarity, nationality, commonwealth, fraternity, class, order, sympathy. *(contrariance, segregation, heterogeneity, hostility, estrangement, secession, polarity, animosity, independence, disconnection, dissociation, dissimilarity, rivalry.)*

company—*n.* union, aggregation, firm, sodality, concourse, assembly, order, congregation, association, audience, society, fraternity, corporation, guild, assemblage, community, gang, troop, posse, crew, establishment. *(antagonism, competition, counter-association, rivalry, isolation, opposition, counter-agency, disqualification.)*

compass—*v.* complete, circumvent, encompass, effectuate, embrace, consummate, surround, enclose, achieve, circumscribe. *(misconceive, liberate, expand, miscontrive, mismanage, despond, discard, fail, exclude, amplify,* *display, dismiss, bungle, unfold.)*

compatible—*adj.* consentaneous, consonant, consistent, congenial, harmonious, sympathetic, co-existent, agreeable, accordant, congruous. *(inter-repugnant, impossible, contradictory, divergent, incompatible, destructive, hostile, insupposable, adverse, incongruous, antagonistic, discordant, inconsistent.)*

compel—*v.* coerce, force, blind, make, oblige, constrain, domineer, drive, necessitate. *(cozen, persuade, liberate, induce, thwart, release, convince, egg, tempt, coax, seduce, acquit, allure.)*

compensation—*n.* restoration, pay, damages, remuneration, restitution, indemnification, amercement, equivalent, settlement, wages, allowance, satisfaction, atonement, expiation. *(fraudulence, deprivation, damage, loss, injury, donation, non-payment, gratuity.)*

competition—*n.* emulation, race, rivalry, contention, two of a trade, conflict. *(colleagueship, confederation, association, copartnership, collaboration, alliance, teamwork.)*

complacement—*adj.* kind, mannerly, pleased, amiable, acquiescent, affable, easygoing, satisfied, content, pleasant. *(morose, austere, grudging, dissatisfied, sullen, irritated, unmannerly, churlish.)*

complaint—*n.* repining, disease, murmur, lamentation, criticism, discontent, expostulation, sickness, annoyance, grievance. *(boon, sanity, benefit, congratulation, complacency, rejoicing, approbation, salve, applause, jubilee, health.)*

complement—*n.* totality, counterpart, completion, supply, fulfilment, correlative, supplement. *(defalcation, abatement, insufficiency, drawback, lessening, deficiency, diminution, deficit, detraction.)*

complete—*adj.* perfect, thorough, accomplished, full, exhaustive, intact, finished, total, consummate, adequate, entire. *(partial, imperfect, incomplete, inadequate, deficient, unfinished.)*

complexion—*n.* feature, indication, face, interpretation, makeup, aspect, hue, color, look, appearance, character. *(reticence, heart, unindicativeness, inexpression, core, concealment, reserve.)*

complicated—*adj.* involved, entangled, confused, perplexed, intricate, complex. *(simple, lucid, uninvolved, obvious, clear, unraveled.)*

compliment—*n.* courtesy, praise, homage, flattery, tribute. *(discourtesy, contempt, insolence, insult.)*

complimentary—*adj.* ecomiastic, lavish of praise, flattering, commendatory, laudatory, panegyrical, eulogistic. *(vituperative, condemnatory, disparaging, abusive, insulting, objurgatory, damnatory, reproachful, defamatory, denunciatory.)*

composition—*n.* combination, adjustment, commutation, mixture, settlement, compound, creation, conformation, compromise, structure. *(perpetuation, analysis, aggravation, criticism, segregation, discussion, examination, disturbance.)*

comprehend—*v.* embody, understand, apprehend, include, perceive, embrace, grasp, involve, enclose, comprise, conceive. *(misunderstand, reject, except, exclude.)*

comprehensive—*adj.* general, large, capacious, pregnant, embracing, inclusive, wide, extensive, all, universal, compendious, ample, significant, generic, brood. *(shallow, narrow, exceptive, exclusive, limited, restricted, adversative.)*

compromise—*v.* adjust, settle, implicate, involve, arbitrate, reconcile, compose, endanger. *(disengage exempt, exonerate, enfranchise, aggravate, extricate, excite, foster, perpetuate, arbitrate.)*

conceal—*v.* keep secret, screen, hide, disguise, suppress, shield, dissemble, secrete, camouflage. *(divulge, manifest, publish, reveal, promulgate, disclose, expose, exhibit, avow, confess.)*

concentrate—*v.* muster, convene, centralize, conglomerate, assemble, converge, cluster, localize, condense, draw, congregate. *(dismiss, disperse, scatter, decentralize, dissipate.)*

concerning—*prep.* relating, about, touching, with respect to, relative to, of, with regard to, apropos of, with reference to, respecting, in relation to, regarding. *(disregarding, omitting, neglecting.)*

concert—*n.* combination, union, co-operation, concord, agreement, collaboration, association, harmony. *(counteraction, dissociation, disconnection, opposition.)*

conciliate—v. appease, disarm, placate, mollify, soothe, pacify, arbitrate. *(arouse, stir up, antagonize, alienate.)*

concrete—adj. explicit, precise, specific, actual, tangible, definite, material. *(general, vague, abstract, intangible, immaterial.)*

condescension—n. graciousness, stooping, affability, favor, humility. *(pride, haughtiness, superciliousness, scorn, arrogance, superiority, disdain.)*

condition—n. mood, qualification, situation, plight, requisite, state, circumstances, proviso, case, mode, stipulation, predicament, term, shape. *(fulfilment, relation, circumstances, adaptation, dependence, connection, situation, concession.)*

conducive—adj. promotive, effective, contributive, caustive, calculated, subsidiary, productive. *(contrariant, destructive, counteractive, repugnant, hindering, preventive.)*

conduct—v. transfer, manage, guide, administer, lead, control, bring, behavior, carry, direct. *(misconduct, mislead, follow, miscarry, misadminister, mismanage.)*

confer—v. deliberate, present, compare, give, palaver, collate, discuss, consult, converse. *(contrast, withhold, hazard, withdraw, dissociate, deny, conjecture.)*

confession—n. catechism, tenets, subscription, creed, articles, doctrine, declaration, revelation, profession. *(renunciation, refutation, heresy, protest, concealment, apostasy, index, abjuration, condemnation.)*

confidant—n. advisor, confederate, confessor, trusty companion. *(betrayer, rival, traitor, turncoat.)*

confident—adj. assured, bold, certain, impudent, sure, positive, undaunted, sanguine. *(diffident, apprehensive, despondent, dubious, uncertain.)*

confidential—adj. trustworthy, private, intimate, secret, honorable. *(open, official, treacherous, insidious, disloyal, public, patent.)*

confirm—v. stabilitate, settle, substantiate, perpetuate, verify, strengthen, sanction, ratify, establish, corroborate, prove, fix. *(annul, refute, upset, weaken, abrogate, confute, nullify, shake, cancel, repeal.)*

conform—v. fit, harmonize, reconcile, correspond, adapt, comply, agree, acquiesce, submit. *(diverge, deviate, disagree, oppose, differ.)*

confront—*v.* face, resist, encounter, menace, challenge, intimidate, oppose. *(encourage, abet, evade, countenance, rally.)*

confused—*adj.* perplexed, dazed, disordered, promiscuous, abashed, chaotic, disarranged, embarrassed, involved, disconcerted, complex, disorganized. *(unembarrassed, unconfused, unabashed, systematic, arranged, organized.)*

congregate—*v.* get together, flock, assemble, collect, convene, rally, meet, throng. *(scatter, part, disperse, separate, spread out.)*

congress—*n.* parliament, convention, synod, conclave, assembly, conference, council, legislature. *(conclave, cabal, mob, session.)*

conjecture—*v.* divination, guess, supposition, notion, estimate, hypothesis, surmise, theory. *(calculation, proof, computation, certainty, inference, deduction, reckoning.)*

connection—*n.* relation, kindred, union, junction, relationship, conjunction, kinsman, association, coherence, communication, concatenation, affinity, relevance, intercourse. *(irrelevance, disunion, disconnection, separation, disjunction, independence, dissociation.)*

conquer—*v.* vanquish, master, prevail over, subdue, surmount, subjugate, quell, crush, defeat, overthrow, overcome, overpower. *(forfeit, fail, cede, fall, resign, retreat, sacrifice, succumb, lose, capitulate, fly, submit, surrender.)*

conscious—*adj.* cognizant, alert, aware, sensible. *(unconscious, insensible, asleep, unaware.)*

consecutive—*adj.* coherent, continuous, orderly, subsequent, arranged. *(undigested, discursive, rambling, disordered, simultaneous, inconsecutive, inconsequent, incoherent.)*

consent—*v.* agree, concur, acquiesce, submit. *(disagree, refuse, dissent, disapprove, resist, decline.)*

consequence—*n.* dignity, effect, moment, issue, note, result, importance, inference, sequel, coherence, outcome, deduction, conclusion. *(paltriness, cause, meanness, antecedence, causation, irrelevance, inconsecutiveness, premise, inconse-*

quence, precursor, origin, in-significance, unimportance, axiom, postulate, datum.)

consider—*v.* revolve, think, deem, weigh, attend, ponder, judge, deliberate, mediate, cogitate, deduce, infer, investigate, reflect, opine, observe, regard, contemplate. *(hazard, disregard, conjecture, ignore, guess, pretermit, despise, omit.)*

considerate—*adj.* cautious, patient, thoughtful, careful, attentive, reflective, forbearing, circumspect, prudent, unselfish, judicious, serious. *(careless, rash, thoughtless, inconsiderate, injudicious, inattentive, rude, overbearing, heedless, selfish.)*

consistency—*n.* proportion, mass, consistence, analogy, congruity, harmony, composition, uniformity, substance, coherence, material, compactness, amalgamation, compound, density, closeness, compatibility, solidity. *(contrariety, volatility, subtility, contradiction, vaporousness, disproportion, incongruity, tenuity, variance, sublimation, incoherence, inconsistency.)*

consistent—*adj.* harmonious, congruous, compatible, accordant, agreeing, consonant, congenial. *(not*

agreeing with, incongruous, inharmonious, at variance with, incompatible, illogical.)

conspicuous—*adj.* magnified, uniform, noticeable, visible, seen, observable, easily, prominent, salient, noted, eminent, famous, manifest, distinguished, evident. *(microscopic, invisible, unobservable, inconspicuous, noticeable, shrouded.)*

constant—*adj.* regular, trustworthy, true, uniform, faithful, perpetual, immutable, firm, continuous, stalwart, fixed, steady, invariable. *(exceptional, false, irregular, treacherous, variable, untrustworthy, faithless, fickle, vacillating, casual, incidental, accidental, broke, interrupted, inconsistent.)*

constitution—*n.* frame, regulation, temperament, law, structure, habit, temper, organization, texture, character, substance, nature, government, composition, state, consistence, policy. *(destruction, accident, demolition, habituation, disorganization, modification, dissipation, interference, change, revolution, anarchy, depotism, rebellion, tyranny.)*

construction—*n.* view, composition, interpretation, fabrication, fabric, creation, explanation, reading, rendering, understanding, erection, edifice. *(misconception, dislocation, misinterpretation, dismemberment, razing, demolition, misunderstanding, displacement, misconstruction, misplacement.)*

consult—*v.* ask advice of, confer, promote, interrogate, care for, canvass, consider, question, advise, deliberate, regard, counsel. *(contravene, resolve, counteract, explain, dictate, expound, instruct, direct, bypass.)*

consumption—*n.* lessening, decay, decrease, decline, waste, decrement, expenditure, depletion. *(development, growth, augmentation, conservation, enlargement.)*

contact—*n.* continuity, adjunction, touch, contiguity, collision, apposition. *(adjacence, non-contact, proximity, isolation, distance, interruption, separation, disconnection.)*

contagious—*adj.* infectious, catching, epidemic, transmitted, pestilential, communicated, transferred, spreading. *(preventive, sporadic, antipathetic, endemic, noninfectious.)*

contaminate—*v.* taint, corrupt, soil, pollute, defile, sully, befoul. *(chasten, purify, sanctify, cleanse, clarify, lave, ameliorate.)*

contemplate—*v.* project, mediate, intend, behold, design, survey, observe, purpose, study, ponder. *(waive, overlook, ignore, disregard, abandon.)*

contemptible—*adj.* trivial, mean, despicable, vile, paltry, pitiful, disreputable, trifling, detestable. *(venerable, grave, important, weighty, respectable, honorable, laudable.)*

content—*adj.* satisfied, gratified, resigned, full, willing, pleased, contented, happy. *(reluctant, unwilling, unsatisfied, discontented, dissatisfied, restless.)*

contentious—*adj.* perverse, exceptious, litigious, wayward, quarrelsome, splenetic, cantankerous. *(obliging, easy, pacific, obsequious, considerate, accommodating, harmonious.)*

contingent—*adj.* incidental, conditional, dependent, uncertain, provisional, co-efficient, hypothetical. *(irrespective, positive, uncontrolled, absolute, unaffected, unmodified, independent, contrived.)*

continually—*adv.* persistently, ever, repeatedly, continuously, frequently, constantly, always, perpetually, incessantly, unceasingly. *(intermittently, casually, fitfully, occasionally, rarely, spasmodically, sometimes, contingently.)*

contract—*v.* lessen, curtail, form, retrench, abridge, compress, diminish, abbreviate, agree, decrease, reduce, narrow. *(dilate, elongate, cancel, abandon, magnify, expand, amplify, reverse.)*

contract—*n.* agreement, compact, bargain, pact, covenant, treaty, bond, stipulation. *(assurance, promise, parole, discourse.)*

contradict—*v.* negate, refute, contravene, oppose, controvert, impugn, dissent, deny, confute, disprove. *(propound, argue, affirm, state, maintain, endorse, corroborate, confirm.)*

contrary—*adj.* incompatible, opposed, inconsistent, repugnant, opposite, adverse, antagonistic, negative. *(coincident, agreeing, kindred, consentaneous, consistent, obstinate, compatible.)*

contribute—*v.* supply, add, give, assist, cooperate, tend, conduce, bestow, subscribe. *(misapply, refuse, contravene, withhold, deny, misconduce.)*

contrive—*v.* arrange, plan, adjust, scheme, design, intrigue, fabricate, concert, devise, manage, adapt. *(overdo, hazard, chance, over-vault, demolish, bungle, hit, venture, run.)*

control—*v.* administer, curb, coerce, govern, manipulate, check, manage, restrain, regulate, guide, moderate, repress. *(liberate, abandon, misconduct, neglect, mismanage, license, release.)*

convenient—*adj.* seasonable, apt, opportune, handy, timely, fitted, adapted, useful, helpful, commodious, suitable, beneficial. *(untimely, awkward, inopportune, inconvenient, useless, unseasonable, obstructive, superfluous, unsuitable.)*

conventional—*adj.* usual, prevalent, customary, social, ordinary, traditional, stipulated. *(unsocial, natural, invariable, unusual, innovative, legal, immutable, statutable, compulsory.)*

conversant—*adj.* proficient, learned, familiar, versed, experienced, acquainted. *(strange, unfamiliar, inconversant, unacquainted, unversed, ignorant, unlearned.)*

convertible—*adj.* identical, equivalent, commensurate, equipollent, conterminous, transformable. *(contradictory,*

57

variant, contrariant, incommensurate, contrary, unequivalent, converse.)

conviction—*n.* persuasion, faith, assurance, belief. *(misgiving, doubt, skepticism, disbelief.)*

co-operate—*v.* abet, concur, work together, conspire, assist, collaborate, help, contribute. *(oppose, rival, thwart, nullify, counteract.)*

copy—*n.* portraiture, transcript, image, imitation, likeness, reproduction, duplicate, counterfeit, facsimile. *(example, original, prototype, pattern, model, creation.)*

cordial—*adj.* earnest, hearty, invigorating, warm, sincere, affectionate, reviving, genial. *(formal, cold, hostile, distant, ceremonious.)*

corner—*n.* hole, recess, retreat, nook, cavity, confound. *(protection, coin, convexity, abutment, prominence, angle, elbow, protrusion, salience.)*

corpulent—*adj.* lusty, stout, fat, gross, fleshy, obese, plethoric, portly, burly. *(attenuated, emaciated, lean, slight, thin, gaunt.)*

correct—*adj.* exact, accurate, decorous, true, right, faultess, proper, strict. *(un-*

true, wrong, falsify, imprecise, false, incorrect.)

correct—*v.* rectify, amend, set right, chasten, remedy, punish, improve, redress, emend, reform. *(ruin, falsify, corrupt, spare.)*

correction—*n.* discipline, chastisement, amendment, punishment, emendation, reparation. *(retrogradation, deterioration, recompense, debasement, reward, compensation.)*

correspond—*v.* fit, harmonize, agree, match, answer, correlate, suit, tally. *(disagree, vary, clash, jar, differ, deviate.)*

correspondence—*n.* adaptation, match, fitness, answerableness, letter, correlation, depatches, agreement, congruity, congeniality, writing, communication. *(colloquy, reservation, difference, withholding, conversation, repugnance, withdrawal, confabulation, dissimilarity, nonintercourse.)*

corrupt—*adj.* polluted, depraved, tainted, contaminated, defiled, vitiated, wicked, decayed, putrid, profligate, infected, rotten. *(undefiled, pure, moral, uncorrupt.)*

corruption—*n.* putrescence, taint, putrefaction,

decomposition, evil, contamination, decay, debasement, adulteration, deterioration, depravity, rottenness, perversion, defilement. *(purification, vitality, amelioration, morality, organization, purity.)*

cost—*v.* absorb, amount to, consume, require. *(produce, return, afford, yield, fetch, bring, obtain.)*

cost—*n.* outlay, expense, payment, expenditure, worth, outgoings, precious, charge, price, compensation, disbursement, *(emolument, profit, revenue, return, income, resources, perquisite, receipt.)*

costly—*adj.* expensive, precious, high-priced, exorbitant, valuable, rich, sumptuous. *(cheap, beggarly, mean, valueless, paltry, worthless, reasonable, low-priced.)*

council—*n.* consultation, parliament, synod, convocation, cabinet, convention, bureau, company, conference, chamber, conclave, meeting, congress, assembly, legislature. *(conspiracy, mob, crowd, league, cabal, intrigue, multitude, alliance.)*

counsel—*n.* instruction, monition, warning, recommendation, advice, admoni-

tion, consultation. *(misinstruction, betrayal, subversion, misguidance.)*

count—*v.* enumerate, reckon, compute, calculate, estimate, sum, total, number. *(conjecture, confound, guess, exclude, hazard, lump.)*

countenance—*v.* favor, support, help, encourage, patronize, abet, sanction, tolerate, aid. *(discourage, confront, discountenance, oppose, browbeat, condemn.)*

countenance—*n.* encourage, aid, support, visage, abet. *(discountenance, disapproval, thwart.)*

counteract—*v.* counterfoil, baffle, thwart, hinder, neutralize, counterinfluence, foil, negate, rival, oppose. *(conserve, promote, co-operate, aid, subserve, help, encourage, abet.)*

counterpart—*n.* fellow, brother, correlative, supplement, match, parallel, tally, complement, twin, copy. *(reverse, opposite, contradiction, counter-agent, contrary, opponent, observe, antithesis, contrast.)*

countryman—*n.* husbandman, clown, compatriot, yeoman, native, inhabitant, swain, rustic, citizen, boor, subject, fellow-citizen, provincial, fellow-subject, peasant, fellow-countryman, laborer, agriculturist. *(townsman, alien, cockney, oppidan, foreigner, stranger, emigrant.)*

couple—*v.* conjoin, bracket, unite, button, brace, yoke, link, connect, tie, buckle, splice, clasp, amalgamate, pair. *(part, separate, untie, loosen, detach, divorce, sever, uncouple, unclasp, isolate.)*

courage—*n.* fortitude, gallantry, intrepidity, boldness, pluck, heroism, bravery, fearlessness, resolution, valor. *(poltroonery, timidity, pusillanimity, cowardice, faintheartedness, dastardliness.)*

course—*n.* sequence, direction, race, order, method, continuity, conduct, plain, trail, manner, line, progress, succession, series, passage, route, mode, career, way, round, road. *(solution, disorder, conjecture, caprice, deviation, interruption, speculation, error, discursion, hazard, hindrance, cogitation.)*

courtly—*adj.* polished, aristocratic, mannerly, dignified, refined, high-bred, elegant. *(rough, awkward, unrefined, rustic, unmannerly, vulgar, undignified, coarse, unpolished, plebeian, boorish.)*

covetous—*adj.* avaricious, greedy, rapacious, acquisitive, lustful, grasping. *(bountiful, unselfish, profuse, generous, liberal, charitable, self-sacrificing.)*

coward—*n.* dastard, poltroon, renegade, craven, recreant, milquetoast. *(daredevil, champion, desperado, hero, lion.)*

coxcomb—*n.* puppy, pedant, fop, prig, dandy, dude. *(philosopher, savant, genius, sage, celebrity, authority, prophet.)*

coy—*adj.* shrinking, modest, shy, bashful, sheepish, reserved, retreating. *(rompish, bold, hoydenish, saucy, forward.)*

crabbed—*adj.* morose, petulant, irritable, crusty, sour, complicated, churlish, cross-grained. *(conversable, hearty, pleasant, cordial, precise, warm, open, genial, easy.)*

craft—*n.* underhandedness, art, dodge, artifice, chicanery, guile, intrigue, ingenuity, cunning, stratagem, wiliness, maneuver, duplicity, trickery. *(ingenuousness, candor, openness, straightforwardness, fairness, reliability, honesty, frankness, sincerity, artlessness.)*

cram—*v.* squeeze, gorge, ram, compress, stuff, choke, pack. *(vent, empty, unload, eliminate, deplete, disgorge, eviscerate, discharge, unpack.)*

crash—*n.* clang, resonance, clash. *(babble, din, murmur, silence, reverberation, whisper, rumbling.)*

crave—*v.* pine for, desire, want, covet, require, need, yearn for, wish for. *(repudiate, spurn, detest, abominate, despise, scorn, abhor.)*

cream—*n.* pith, acme, gist, marrow. *(offal, dross, garbage, refuse, dregs.)*

credential or credentials—*n.* seal, diploma, vouchers, missive, recommendation, title, letter, testament, warrant, certificates, testimonials. *(self-appointment, self license, autocracy, self constitution, self-derived power.)*

credit—*n.* trustworthiness, faith, honor, relief, reputation, merit, reliance, confidence, praise, security. *(insecurity, disbelief, untrustworthiness, disgrace, skepticism, distrust, shame, censure.)*

creed—*n.* articles, subscription, catechism, belief, doctrine, confession. *(abjuration, disbelief, protest, recantation, non-subscription, retractation, rejection.)*

criminal—*adj.* felonious, wrong, sinful, nefarious, indictable, flagitious, guilty, illegal, vicious, iniquitous, immoral, culpable. *(virtuous, laudable, right, lawful, honorable, just, blameless, praise-worthy, innocent, meritorious, moral, creditable.)*

critical—*adj.* exact, censorious, momentous, precarious, severe, nice, hazardous, important, delicate, crucial, fastidious, accurate, discriminating, dubious, ticklish. *(settled, popular, redressed, inexact, retrieved, supportive, loose, easy, determined, undiscriminating, safe, decided.)*

criticism—*n.* censure, evaluation, animadversion, stricture. *(praise, approval, acclaim, rave.)*

cross-grained—*adj.* wayward, peevish, cantankerous, obdurate, perverse, morose, ill-conditioned. *(pleasant, jolly, accommodating, genial, obliging, agreeable, gratifying.)*

crude—*adj.* undigested, unrefined, raw, half-studied, unchastened, unfinished, unconsidered, harsh, illprepared, unshaped, churlish.

(well-digested, artistic, well-prepared, highly-wrought, ripe, classical, well-considered, elaborate, well-adapted, refined, finished, classical, well-expressed, elegant.)

cruel—*adj.* barbarous, truculent, malignant, inhuman, maleficent, sanguinary, savage, brutal, unmerciful, pitiless, ruthless, unrelenting, inexorable, hard-hearted, harsh. *(forbearing, beneficent, humane, generous, forgiving, benevolent, beneficial, merciful.)*

crush—*v.* pound, crumble, pulverize, demolish, granulate, triturate, bray, overpower. *(compact, aggrandize, consolidate, solidify, liberate, stabilitate, compress, upraise, amalgamate, cake.)*

cuff—*v.* box, punch, buffet, slap, smack, pummel, hustle, smite. *(flagellate, cane, lash, whip, cudgel, thrash, strap, maul.)*

cultivate—*v.* foster, improve, till, improve, nourish, advance, cherish, promote, study, nurture, civilize, refine, fertilize. *(desert, uproot, neglect, extirpate, abandon, prevent, paralyze, stifle, abolish, discourage, impair, blight, blast, eradicate.)*

cupidity—*n.* acquisitiveness, stinginess, avarice, repacity, covetousness. *(extravagance, prodigality, generosity, liberality.)*

cure—*n.* restorative, renovation, convalescence, medication, remedy, heal-all, alleviation, restoration, amelioration, reinstatement. *(confirmation, disease, inoculation, corruption, aggravation, inflamation, complaint, ailment, contagion.)*

curiosity—*n.* interest, marvel, lion, celebrity, prying, wonder, inquisitiveness, interrogativeness, phenomenon, oddity, rarity. *(heedlessness, drug, song, abstraction, disregard, dirt, apathy, bagatelle, indifference, cipher, absence, weed.)*

curious—*adj.* inquisitive, odd, inquiring, recondite, meddling, unique, questioning, scrutinizing, rare, prying, peering, searching, peeping, singular. *(uninquiring, trite, superficial, blasé, indifferent, incurious, common, uninterested.)*

current—*adj.* prevalent, exoteric, general, running, vulgar, floating, widespread, ordinary, popular, present. *(private, secret, confined, obsolete, rejected, previous, esoteric, exploded.)*

custody—*n.* guardianship, care, conservation, protection, keeping. *(betrayal, jeopardy, abandonment, liberation, release, neglect, discharge, desertion, exposure.)*

cynical—*adj.* snarling, sneering, currish, cross-grained, sarcastic, contemptuous, snappish, carping. *(complaisant, lenient, sanguine, urbane, genial.)*

D

daft—*adj.* innocent, silly, light-headed, lunatic, foolish, idiotic, cracked. *(sensible, sane, practical, shrewd, palpable, deft, sound.)*

dainty—*adj.* rare, tasty, epicurean, choice, refined, delicate, luxurious, exquisite. *(unrelishing, dirty, gluttonous, nasty, greedy, gross, common, omnivorous, coarse.)*

damage—*n.* harm, impairment, injury, defacement, mutilation, loss, ruin, destruction. *(reparation, mend, improvement, betterment, repair.)*

damp—*adj.* moist, drizzly, humid, dewy, wet, vaporous.

dapper—*adj.* neat, smart, dashing, spruce, natty. *(un-wieldy, untidy, slovenly, sloppy, awkward.)*

daring—*adj.* fearless, valorous, adventurous, intrepid, dashing, brave, bold, imprudent, courageous, foolhardy, venturesome, dauntless. *(timid, prudent, cautious, inadventurous.)*

dark—*adj.* sable, obscure, recondite, blind, benighted, inexplicable, dismal, sombre, sorrowful, opaque, black, swarthy, abstruse, ignorant, dim, secret, nebulous, joyless, dingy, dusky, enigmatical, besotted, unintelligible, shadowy, mysterious, hidden, murky, cheerless, gloomy, mournful. *(fair, luminous, white, radiant, festive, illumined, light, dazzling, radiant, glaring, brilliant, enlightened, bright, intelligible, lucid, transparent, crystalline.)*

dash—*v.* throw, scatter, hurl, course, fly, cast, shatter, subvert, drive, send, strike, dart, speed, rush, detrude. *(erect, lag, raise, support, reinstate, creep, hobble, crawl.)*

daunt—*v.* scare, intimidate, terrify, confront, frighten, appall, alarm, dishearten, cow. *(encourage, inspirit, countenance, fortify, rally.)*

dawdle—v. dally, lag, loiter, idle, loaf. (speed, rush, fag, hustle, work, haste, dash.)

dead—adj. departed, inanimate, still, deserted, spiritless, heavy, defunct, inert, torpid, deceased, cheerless, dull, unconscious, insensible, gone, lifeless. (thronged, living, susceptible, joyous, bustling, stirring, responsive, vivacious, vital, animate, alive.)

deadly—adj. venomous, fatal, pernicious, destructive, murderous, mortal, implacable, malignant, destructive, noxious, baneful. (healthful, vital, wholesome, nutritious, innocuous, life-giving.)

deaf—adj. disinclined, averse, dead, inaudible, surd, heedless, hard of hearing, inexorable, rumbling, insensible, inattentive. (interested, acute, disposed, susceptible, alive, listening, sensible, willing, attentive, penetrating.)

dear—adj. costly, beloved, loved, precious, priceless, expensive, high-priced. (inexpensive, vile, nominal, cheap, misliked.)

death—n. decease, exit, fall, expiration, departure, release, demise, cessation, dissolution, mortality, failure, eradication, termination. (life, auspices, rise, inauguration, commencement, vigor, birth, existence, spirit, operation, animation, activity, vitality, action, growth.)

debatable—adj. problematical, unsettled, doubtful, disputable, undecided, dubious, floating, uncertain, inestimable. (sure, incontestible, certain, unquestionable, self-evident, settled, indisputable.)

debauch—v., debauchery—n. revel, orgies, gluttony, riot, excess, boisterous. (fast, meal, frugality, maceration, moderation, abstinence, asceticism, refraining.)

debase—v. disgrace, corrupt, adulterate, desecrate, lower, degrade, defile, befowl, corrupt, deteriorate. (elevate, heighten, enhance, improve, uplift.)

debt—n. liability, obligation, something due, debit, score, default, claim, bill. (assets, gift, grace, accommodation, gratuity, credit, liquidation, trust, favor, obligation, grant.)

decay—v. sink, wither, decrease, perish, decline, waste, wane, dwindle, ebb, rot, shrivel. (grow, enlarge, rise, expand, flourish, increase, luxuriate, vegetate.)

decay—n. waning, decadence, wasting, declension, dry rot, decline, sinking, corruption, putrefaction, consumption, rottenness, decrease, collapse. *(growth, increase, exuberance, prosperity, rise, birth, fertility, luxuriance, vigor.)*

deceit—*n.* imposition, fraud, artifice, hypocrisy, cunning, cheat, sham, trick, duplicity, deception, guile, indirection, double-dealing, circumvention, insidiousness, treachery, beguilement, delusion. *(honesty, verity, reality, openness, instruction, guidance, fair dealing, enlightenment, candor.)*

deceitful—*adj.* delusive, fallacious, deceptive, dishonest, fraudulent. *(fair, veracious, open, honest, truthful, delude.)*

deceive—*v.* beguile, gull, entrap, take in, trick, circumvent, ensnare, overreach, mislead, betray, cheat, dupe, delude. *(advise, deliver, illumine, be honest to, enlighten, guide, undeceive, disabuse.)*

decide—*v.* settle, terminate, resolve, determine, fix, adjudicate, arbitrate. *(drop, misdetermine, waive, raise, misjudge, suspend, waver, vacillate, moot, doubt.)*

decipher—*v.* spell, solve, unravel, unfold, read, explain, interpret, translate. *(sym-*

bolize, mystify, enigmatize, cipher, impuzzle, illustrate.)

decision—*n.* resolve, conviction, determination, firmness, will, strength, perseverance, certainty, decisiveness. *(vagueness, weakness, vacillation, uncertainty, evasion, indecisiveness.)*

declaration—*n.* exhibition, avowal, manifestation, ordinance, affirmation, profession, assertion, statement, testimony. *(concealment, denial, retraction, suppression.)*

decompose—*v.* individualize, dissolve, analyse, segregate, spoil, resolve. *(mix, organize, compound, concoct, compose, brew.)*

decorum—*n.* propriety, order, good manners, modesty, seemliness, respectability, dignity, good behavior. *(impropriety, disorder, rudeness, unseemliness, disturbance.)*

decrease—*v.* lessen, abate, decline, curtail, wane, diminish, abbreviate, subside, lower, retrench, reduce. *(grow, expand, extend, enlarge, increase, escalate, amplify, augment.)*

decrepit—*adj.* weak, enfeebled, aged, infirm, superannuated, broken down, dilapidated, effete, tottering, crippled. *(robust, agile, youthful, strong, active, in good shape.)*

dedicate—*v.* consecrate, assign, set, devote, set apart, separate, hallow, apportion, offer, apply. *(misconvert, alienate, misapply, misuse, devolve, misappropriate, desecrate.)*

deed—*n.* commission, instrument, muniment, act, feat, action, accomplishment, achievement, document, perpetration, exploit. *(failure, recall, undoing, omission, reversion, abortion, non-per formance, false-witness, innocent, disproof, cancelling, invalidation, retraction, impossiblity, collapse.)*

deep—*adj.* subterranean, thick, heartfelt, occult, obscure, penetrating, profound, abstruse, submerged, learned, designing, recondite, sagacious, mysterious, intense, subtle. *(superficial, familiar, commonplace, undesigning, shallow, artless, obvious.)*

deface—*v.* spoil, disfigure, mar, destroy, damage, injure, mutilate, deform. *(adorn, embellish, beautify, decorate.)*

defame—*v.* libel, disparage, vilify, insult, slander, discredit, malign, stigmatize, belittle. *(flatter, laud, applaud,* extol, compliment, boost, praise.)*

default—*n.* forfeit, delinquency, want, lapse, failure, defect, absence, omission. *(appearance, supply, maintenance, presence, compliance, plea, forthcoming, satisfaction.)*

defeat—*n.* discomfiture, frustration, disaster, overthrow. *(triumph, success, killing, victory.)*

defeat—*v.* worst, foil, baffle, conquer, frustrate, rout, overcome, vanquish, overthrow, overpower. *(establish, promote, advance, secure, aid, speed, insure, strengthen.)*

defect—*n.* blemish, shortcoming, want, fault, flaw, omission, deficiency, imperfection. *(sufficiency, virtue, emendation, complement, supply, ornament, strength, compensation.)*

defective—*adj.* insufficient, short, faulty, wanting, inadequate, imperfect, deficient. *(complete, ample, perfect, satisfactory, correct, sufficient, abundant, full.)*

defense—*n.* protection, excuse, apology, resistance, rampart, preservation, vindication, plea, justification, shelter, bulwark. *(surrender,* exposure, prosecution, abandonment, betrayal.)

defer—v. postpone, adjourn, put off, prolong, delay, retard, waive, procrastinate, shelve, prorogue, hinder, protract. *(hasten, press, hurry, expedite, dispatch, urge, quicken, overdrive, facilitate.)*

deference—n. consideration, honor, allegiance, respect, condescension, homage, contention, obedience, esteem, regard, reverence, submission, veneration. *(contumacy, defiance, attention, disrespect, contumely, disregard, impudence, rudeness, non-allegiance, slight, disobedience.)*

defiant—adj. mutinous, fractious, rebellious, ungovernable, lawless, willful, audacious, bold, stubborn. *(obedient, dutiful, meek, submissive, timid, docile.)*

definite—adj. specified, certain, clear, positive, limited, exact, determined, precise, bounded, definitive, specific, fixed, concrete, ascertained, restricted. *(confused, vague, obscure, unspecified, ambiguous, undetermined, intermingled, indefinite.)*

definition—n. specification, determination, restriction, clarification, limitation.

(vagueness, misconception, confusion, misstatement, ambiguity, acceptation, explanation, description.)

defray—v. liquidate, bear, quit, discharge, meet, settle, pay, dispose of. *(misappropriate, repudiate, embezzle, dishonor, dissatisfy, swindle.)*

defy—v. challenge, despite, brave, scorn, provoke, spurn. *(agree, comply, obey, cooperate, submit, yield.)*

degree—n. stage, amount, grade, quantity, rank, station, step, order, class, limit, extent, mark, position, quality, level, rate, measure, range. *(magnitude, numbers, space, size, mass, volume.)*

deliberate—v. meditate, perpend, ponder, consider, reflect, debate, consult, weigh, contemplate. *(discard, risk, shelve, hazard, burke, haphazard, chance.)*

deliberate—adj. intentional, resolute, unbiased, determined, grave, unprejudiced, thoughtful, earnest, designed, purposed. *(playful, biased, jocose, prejudiced, facetious, instigated, irresolute, dictated, spontaneous, suggested, dubious, unresolved, compulsory, undetermined.)*

delicious—*adj.* luxurious, choice, exquisite, dainty, savory, delightful. *(common, nauseous, loathsome, unpalatable, coarse, unsavory, inedible.)*

delight—*n.* pleasure, happiness, esctasy, bliss, gratification, enjoyment, rapture, joy, transport, gladness, felicity. *(suffering, trouble, discontent, dissatisfaction, pain, sorrow, melancholy, misery, distress, displeasure, depression, discomfort, disappointment, dejection, disgust.)*

delinquent—*n.* culprit, criminal, violator, offender. *(paragon, worthy, pattern, model.)*

deliver—*v.* free, utter, consign, liberate, entrust, save, give up, set free, hand, surrender, give, yield, pronounce, rescue, transmit, concede, distribute. *(misdeliver, confine, suppress, appropriate, retain, assume, betray, withdraw, conserve.)*

deluxe—*adj.* choice, prime, posh, grand, luxurious, select, costly, sumptuous, elegant, splendid. *(ordinary, everyday, common, run of the mill, mediocre, cheap.)*

democratic—*adj.* autonomous, popular, republican, leveling, destructive, radical, unlicensed, subversive, anarchical. *(despotic, regal, autocratic, imperial, tyrannical, conservative, oligarchical, dictatorial, constitutional, aristocratic.)*

demonstrate—*v.* show, manifest, illustrate, describe, prove, exhibit, evince. *(conceal, obscure, misexemplify, disprove, misdemonstrate.)*

demure—*adj.* grave, discreet, sedate, prudish, staid, dispassionate, modest, sober, downcast, retiring. *(vivacious, indiscreet, boisterous, lively, hoydenish, facetious, wanton, noisy, rompish, wild, aggressive.)*

denial—*n.* rejection, declination, negation, refusal, veto, repulsion, prohibition, rebuff. *(acceptance, approval, permission, allowance, yes, affirmation.)*

denomination—*n.* designation, appellation, class, name, order, description, category, kind. *(misnomer, pseudonym, non-description.)*

dense—*adj.* thick, solid, stout, consolidated, thick-set, slow, stupid, dull, compact, close, condensed, stolid. *(uncompacted, quick, sparse, intelligent, clever, rare, meager, rarefied.)*

deny—*v.* withhold, oppose, refuse, disclaim, disown, reject, disavow, contradict, nullify, gainsay, negative. *(accept, indulge, afford, yield, grant, concede, affirm, acquiesce, confirm, admit.)*

department—*n.* division, portion, line, section, province, dominion, branch, function, office. *(establishment, body, society, institution, community, art, organization, whole, service, science, state, literature, conformity.)*

dependent—*adj.* contingent, resting, relative, hanging, relying, trusting, subject, subordinate. *(irrelative, free, independent, absolute, autonomous, irrespective.)*

deplorable—*adj.* lamentable, sorry, calamitous, regrettable, distressing, unfortunate, grievous, ill-fated, miserable. *(happy, felicitious, cheering, fortunate, gratifying, pleasant, agreeable.)*

depression—*n.* degradation, valley, dip, discouragement, hollow, dejection, despondency. *(prominence, raising, mound, elevation, eminence, exaltation, rising, promotion, encouragement, amelioration, preferment, rallying, optimism.)*

deprive—*v.* bereave, rob, hinder, despoil, dispossess, prevent, depose, strip, divest, abridge, confiscate. *(indemnify, invest, present, compensate, reinstate, endow, supply, enrich, furnish.)*

derision—*n.* contempt, irony, disrespect, scorn, contumely, sarcasm, mockery, isdain. *(admiration, respect, reverence, regard, esteem.)*

descendant—*n.* progeny, lineage, branch, offspring, family, stock, house, scion, posterity, issue, seed. *(source, progenitor, parent, author, origin, root, founder, ancestor, stock, forebear.)*

describe—*v.* explain, draw, depict, delineate, recount, picture, narrate, illustrate, define, relate, portray, represent, chronicle. *(confuse, distort, confound, caricature, mystify, misrepresent, contort.)*

desert—*n.* wilderness, void, wild, waste, solitude. *(field, pasture, oasis, civilization, enclosure, garden.)*

design—*v.* purpose, plan, project, contemplate, intend, prepare, fashion. *(conjecture, miscontrive, risk, hit, fluke guess, misconceive, chance, peril.)*

design—*n.* intention, sketch, plan, artifice, scheme, contemplation, pattern, project, purpose, intent, preparation, contrivance, draft, delineation, guile, drawing, artfulness, cunning. *(performance, accident, execution, change, result, simplicity, sincerity, issue, artlessness, construction, openness, candor, structure, fairness, frankness.)*

desirable—*adj.* advisable, beneficial, valuable, expedient, judicious, profitable, acceptable, delightful, good, proper, enviable, worthwhile. *(unadvisable, evil, improper, undesirable, deplorable, injudicious, inexpedient, objectionable, unprofitable.)*

desire—*n.* affection, craving; appetency, yearning, concupiscence, longing, propension. *(abomination, loathing, reject, hate, repugnance, aversion, disgust, horror.)*

despair—*n.* despondency, alienation, desperation, hopelessness. *(expectation, hilarity, hopefulness, anticipation, elation, optimism, confidence, sanguineness.)*

desperate—*adj.* inextricable, audacious, frantic, irremediable, daring, hopeless, determined, mad, desponding, reckless, regardless, abandoned, furious, rash, despairing, heedless. *(propitious, cool, promising, calm, hopeful, shy, remediable, prudent, irresolute, timid, cautious.)*

despotic—*adj.* arbitrary, cruel, tyrannical, autocratic, self-willed, absolute, irresponsible, domineering, arrogant, dictatorial, imperious. *(constitutional, merciful, limited, yielding, humane.)*

destination—*n.* design, aim, end, purpose, goal, intention, location, design, point, consignment, scope, appointment, object, use, application, fate, doom, aspiration. *(effort, operation, project, tendency, initiation, exercise, design, action, movement, activity.)*

destiny—*n.* doom, fate, end, decree, necessity, fortune, lot, predestination, providence. *(volition, freedom, free will, choice, will, deliberation, selection.)*

destroy—*v.* annihilate, ruin, consume, demolish, waste, overthrow, subvert, undo, extinguish. *(construct, restore, repair, create, fabricate, make, reinstate, erect.)*

destructive—*adj.* hurtful, baleful, damaging, detrimental, subversive, deleterious, ruinous, injurious, baneful, noxious. *(conservative, restorative, constructive, wholesome, preservative, beneficial, subsidiary, reparatory.)*

determination—*n.* settlement, verdict, decision, arbitration, judgement, verification, corroboration, confirmation, resolution, authentication. *(uncertainty, vacillation, indecision, irresolution, hesitation, spinelessness.)*

detraction—*n.* backbiting, slander, diminution, depreciation, derogation, aspersion, deterioration. *(compliment, eulogy, augmentation, flattery, respect, improvement, enhancement.)*

detriment—*n.* prejudice, harm, inconvenience, loss, damage, hurt, disadvantage, deterioration, impairment, injury, disservice. *(improvement, remedy, augmentation, repair, benefit, reinstatement, enhancement.)*

detrimental—*adj.* hurtful, pernicious, prejudicial, injurious. *(profitable, augmentative, beneficial, advantageous.)*

develop—*v.* eliminate, expand, educe, enlarge, enucleate, amplify, lay open, enunciate, disclose, clear, unravel, unfold, mature. *(wrap, involve, narrow, envelop, conceal, obscure, compress, mystify, contract, restrict, condense, recede.)*

device—*n.* expedient, emblem, show, cognizance, invention, artifice, contrivance, design, implement, symbol, stratagem, project, plan. *(hazard, incognito, fairdealing, abortion, openness, fortune, miscontrivance, hit, luck, camouflage.)*

devil—*n.* lucifer, arch-fiend, demon, satan, foul fiend, fiend, villain. *(angel, cherub, saint, archangel, seraph.)*

devise—*v.* plan, concert, manage, contrive, maneuver, create. *(mismanage, disorder, miscontrive.)*

devoid—*adj.* destitute, unprovided, void, unendowed, wanting, depleted. *(supplied, gifted, provided, furnished, replete, laden.)*

devotion—*n.* love, attachment, piety, self-sacrifice, devoutness, dedication, religiousness, loyalty, self-abandonment, ardor, consecration, self-surrender. *(apathy, impiety, indiference, profanity, alienation, selfishness, antipathy, coolness.)*

devour—*v.* consume, gorge, absorb, eat, bolt, swallow, gulp. *(vomit, regurgitate, disgorge.)*

dictate—*v.* suggest, order, decree, command, prompt, enjoin, rule, prescribe, instruct, direct, propose. *(obey, follow, answer, submit to, repeat, echo.)*

dictatorial—*adj.* domineering, autocratic, despotic, bossy. *(democratic, liberal, reasonable, tolerant, flexible, open-minded.)*

die—*v.* decay, cease, expire, perish, decrease, languish, sink, decline, disappear, wane, fade, wither, succumb. *(originate, regetate, begin, rise, luxuriate, live, strenghten, grow, blossom, flourish, develop.)*

difference—*n.* dissimilarity, dissent, variety, dissimilitude, separation, destruction, dissonance, estrangement, distinction, contrariety, unlikeness, discord, disagreement, individuality. *(consociation, identity, community, uniformity, condonation, reconciliation, similarity, harmony, consentaneousness, consonance, sympathy, likeness, agreement, resemblance.)*

difficult—*adj.* intricate, opposed, perplexing, reserved, hard, obscure, unamenable, complicated, involved, uphill, unmanageable, troublesome, enigmatical, arduous, trying. *(unreserved, plain, favorable, easy, amenable, lucid, tractable, categorical, straight, simple, complaisant.)*

digest—*v.* arrange, tabulate, sort, methodize, dispose, convert, order, incorporate, classify, ponder, prepare, assimilate, consider, study, recapitulate. *(disturb, discompose, displace, complicate, reject, eject, confound, derange, refuse, disorder, dislocate.)*

dignity—*n.* honor, loftiness, worth, stateliness, worthiness, grandeur, excellence, solemnity, behavior, decorum. *(disrepute, ignobility, shame, guilt, humility, lowness, unimportance.)*

dilemma—*n.* quandry, doubt, scrape, fix, difficulty, hobble, plight. *(rebutment, retort, superiority, solution, extrication, freedom, escape, solvent.)*

diligence—*n.* attention, industry, care, heed, assiduity, application, meticulousness. *(desultoriness, indifference, idleness, neglect, carelessness, inattention, inertness, heedlessness, lethargy.)*

dingy—*adj.* rusty, sombre, bright, dull, bedimmed, soiled, dusky, obscure, tarnished, colorless, dead, dirty, shabby. *(gleaming, burnished, lustrous, bright, luminous, high-colored, glossy, radiant, sparkling.)*

diplomacy—*n.* circumvention, tact, ministry, contrivance, negotiation, out- witting, ambassadorship, management, discretion, savoir-faire. *(recall, miscontrivance, self-defeat, mismanagement, cancel, ineptness, crassness, self-entanglement, mal-administration, over vaulting.)*

diplomatic—*adj.* sagacious, wise, well-managed, judicious, prudent, politic, astute, clever, well- contrived, discreet, delicate, knowing, well-planned. *(bungling, rude, ill-managed, injudicious, stultifying, undiplomatic, tactless.)*

direction—*n.* tendency, line, order, course, superscription, address, command, control, inclination, bearing, charge, trend. *(miscontrol, deviation, misinstruction, aberration, departure, alteration.)*

directly—*adv.* immediately, at once, quickly, straightaway, soon, promptly, instantly, speedily, precisely. *(by-and-by, indirectly, eventually, there-after, later.)*

dirty—*adj.* soiled, stained, foul, contaminated, polluted, unclean, filthy, grimy, tarnished, messy. *(spotless, clean, immaculate, pure, decent, respectable, washed.)*

disability—*n.* impotency, forfeiture, incompetency, infirmity, defect, incapacity, disqualification. *(fitness, merit, qualification, recom-* mendation, capacity, deserving, strength.)

disappoint—*v.* defeat, frustrate, foil, deluxe, betray, delude, baffle, mortify, vex, deceive, thwart. *(justify, fulfil, gratify, encourage, realize, satisfy, please, delight, verify.)*

discern—*v.* understand, discover, notice, behold, ascertain, note, recognize, apprehend, observe, perceive, distinguish. *(disregard, slight, neglect, overlook, pass by, fail to see.)*

discharge—*v.* remove, unburden, debark, unload, activate, explode, detonate, launch, propel, project. *(detain, keep, hire, load, maintain, fill, stow, burden.)*

discipline—*n.* strictness, drilling, coercion, organization, order, government, chastisement, rule, training, punishment, control. *(confusion, reward, disorganization, mutiny, disorder, chaos, turbulence, encouragement, rebellion.)*

discomfort—*n.* vexation, trouble, disagreeableness, disquiet, ache, annoyance, anguish, unpleasantness. *(ease, pleasure, agreeableness, comfort, pleasantness.)*

disconcert—*v.* confuse, derange, thwart, defeat, interrupt, ruffle, embarrass, frustrate, disorder, vex, abash, confound, upset, perplex, disturb, fret, unsettle, baffle, discompose. *(scheme, design, rally, encourage, prepare, order, hatch, reassure, countenance, pacify, aid, arrange, contrive, concoct.)*

discourtesy—*n.* incivility, rudeness, impoliteness, brusqueness, insolence, surliness, impudence, boorishness. *(civility, refinement, politeness, graciousness.)*

discreet—*adj.* wise, circumspect, wary, sensible, discerning, prudent, judicious, regulative, cautious, tactful, guarded. *(injudicious, blind, silly, foolish, indiscreet, reckless, undiscerning, insensitive, imprudent, unrestrained.)*

discrimination—*n.* discernment, sagacity, distinction, penetration, judgement, insight, acuteness, shrewdness, perception, acumen. *(hebetude, dullness, shortsightedness, carelessness, fairness, insensitivity, indescernment, confusedness.)*

disease—*n.* malady, complaint, sickness, affliction, disorder, ailment, illness, distemper, indisposition. *(sanity, health, vitality, convalescence, salubrity, strength.)*

disgrace—*n.* discredit, dishonor, disfavor, reproach, debase, infamy, degradation, tarnish, embarrassment, blemish. *(credit, glory, pride, reverence, honor, distinguish.)*

disgust—*n.* loathing, abhorrence, repugnance, nausea, dislike, irritate, abomination, aversion, distaste, revolt. *(liking, relish, fondness, avidity, desire, partiality, delight, longing, please, affection.)*

dismal—*adj.* tragic, dreary, sad, lonesome, melancholy, blank, funereal, somber, gloomy, depressed, foreboding, cheerless, doleful, pessimistic, sorrowful. *(ridiculous, gay, lively, promising, comic, elated, propitious, cheerful, exhilarating, joyous, pleasing.)*

dispatch—*v.* send, execute, conclude, hasten, expedite, accelerate, settle, push. *(obstruct, retard, stall, impede, detain, delay.)*

dispel—*v.* scatter, dissipate, dismiss, disperse, banish, drive away, disseminate, rout. *(mass, summon, congregate, recall, convene, assemble, collect, accumulate, conglomerate.)*

disperse—*v.* separate, dispel, distribute, dealout, disseminate, dissipate, scatter, dissolve, break up, spread abroad. *(summon, gather, meet, collect, concentrate, recall, congregate.)*

dispute—*v.* question, contest, quarrel, difference, argue, canvass, debate, altercation, controvert, challenge, squabble, contend, controversy, gainsay, impugn. *(forego, waive, allow, acquiesce, concede, agree.)*

dissemble—*v.* feign, repress, cloak, smother, disguise, restrain, conceal, pretend. *(manifest, feign, proclaim, pretend, exhibit, protrude, expose, evidence, vaunt, simulate, assume, profess, show.)*

dissiminate—*v.* propagate, claim, circulate, spread, promulgate, distribute, scatter, preach. *(suppress, extirpate, repress, eradicate, discountenance, stifle, quell, annihilate.)*

dissolute—*adj.* profligate, wanton, abandoned, loose, vicious, libertine, licentious, rakish. *(self-controlled, upright, correct, virtuous, strict, conscientious.)*

distance—*n.* absence, removal, remoteness, length, interspace, interval, aloofness, separation, space, gap. *(neighborhood, contact, proximity, adjacency, presence,* nearness, propinquity, closeness, warmth, contiguity.)

distinct—*adj.* independent, unlike, conspicuous, perspicuous, plain, separate, unconnected, disjoined, clear, obvious, dissimilar, detached, definite, different, transparent. *(confused, united, conjoined, indistinct, dim, one, consolidated, obscure, blurred, indefinite.)*

distinction—*n.* separation, dignity, eminence, characteristic, mark, difference. *(debasement, unity, insignificance, identity, degradation, anonymity.)*

distinguish—*v.* perceive, know, separate, discern, discriminate, divide, make famous, differentiate, descry, dissimilate, see, discover, characterize, isolate. *(confound, miss, overlook, confuse, oversee.)*

distinguished—*adj.* noted, famous, illustrious, celebrated, eminent, conspicuous, marked, dignified. *(inconspicuous, hidden, obscure, not famous, mediocre.)*

distress—*v.* embarrass, worry, disturb, afflict, harass, trouble, pain, vex, annoy, mortify, grieve, perturb, sadden. *(gratify, console, comfort, soothe, please, gladden,* *elate, compose, solace, sustain.)*

disturb—*v.* discompose, disquiet, derange, molest, disorder, vex, discommode, worry, plague, confuse, interrupt, rouse, trouble, agitate, annoy, upset, distract. *(collocate, soothe, leave, order, pacify, compose, arrange, quiet, organize.)*

diversion—*n.* divergence, detour, enjoyment, pastime, sport, deviation, recreation, amusement, entertainment. *(procedure, task, avocation, study, continuity, directness, labor, work, business, drudgery.)*

divide—*v.* dissect, portion, part, segregate, sunder, disunite, allot, keep apart, distribute, part among, multiply, separate, bisect, divorce, sever, deal out, partition. *(consociate, unite, join, collocate, convene, conglomerate, classify, congregate, conglutinate, co-ordinate, commingle, cement, splice.)*

divorce—*n.* divert, separate, alienate, dissever, disconnect, dissolution. *(unite, apply, reunite, conjoin, connect, reconcile, fusion.)*

do—*v.* accomplish, work, achieve, complete, finish, act, execute, perform, transact, enact, produce. *(mar, omit, neglect, undo, fail.)*

docile—*adj.* amenable, managed, yielding, quiet, tractable, tame, teachable, pliant, gentle, easily, compliant, submissive. *(obstinate, intractable, self-willed, dogged, stubborn, defiant.)*

dogmatic—*adj.* theological, arrogant, positive, magisterial, doctrinal, imperious, dictatorial, settled, authoritative, self-opinionated. *(active, diffident, vacillating, modest, practical, moderate, uncertain.)*

doleful—*adj.* rueful, piteous, somber, sorrowful, dismal, dolorous, melancholy, woebegone, mournful. *(joyful, blithe, gay, merry, beaming, cheerful.)*

dominion—*n.* tyranny, power, rule, government, empire, realm, jurisdiction, supremacy, territory, sway, control, despotism, authority. *(inferiority, weakness, servitude, subjugation, submission, docility.)*

dormant—*adj.* slumbering, quiescent, sleeping, latent, inert, oblivious, undeveloped. *(wakeful, energetic, vigilant, active, developed, operative, functioning.)*

doubt—*n.* scruple, suspense, distrust, indecision,

biousness, hesitation, sus-
cion, difficulty, uncertainty,
mbiguity, perplexity, chal-
nge, demur. *(clearness, de-
rmination, satisfaction, cer-
inty, precision, conviction,
ecision, belief, trust.)*

dowdy—*adj.* shabby, slov-
nly, unfashionable, seedy,
umpy, unfashionable, slop-
y, drab, bedraggled, unat-
active. *(smart, stylish, chic,
'egant, fashionable, modish,
dy, trim.)*

drain—*v.* percolate, ex-
aust, dry, draw, drip, strain,
rop, empty, withdraw, dis-
harge. *(supply, moisten, fill,
undate, swill, replenish,
our, energize, drown,
rench, stimulate.)*

dramatize—*v.* intensify,
ighlight, punctuate, exagger-
te, rant, embroider, spout,
mbellish, emote, color, inter-
ret. *(play down, minimize,
nderstate.)*

draw—*v.* pull, induce,
ketch, entice, describe, de-
neate, rouse, inhale, drag,
aul, attract, solicit. *(propel,
rive, thrust, push, throw, car-
y, compel, repel, impel,
hove, disperse.)*

dreadful—*adj.* monstrous,
errible, awful, horrible, fear-
al, dire, shocking, alarming,
rightful, terrific, distressing,
agic. *(assuring, hopeful, pro-*

mising, encouraging, suitable, inspiriting, cheerful.)*

dreamy—*adj.* visionary, absent, fanciful, speculative,
foggy, abstracted, fabulous,
rapt. *(earnest, practical, collected, attentive, awake, energetic, active, vigilant, aware.)*

dregs—*n.* sediment, lees,
trash, refuse, offal, dross, out-
casts, off-scouring, debris.
*(pickings, flower, cream, sam-
ple, pink, bouquet, exemplification.)*

dress—*n.* preparation, ac-
coutrements, garniture, vest-
ments, clothing, don, lively,
habiliments, uniform, apparel,
raiment, investiture, garb,
costume, array, arrangement,
garments, drape, ornament.
*(disorder, undress, nudity,
disarrangement, deshabille,
disrobe, divest.)*

drift—*n.* direction, tenor,
scope, issue, conclusion,
course, aim, tendency, motion, meaning, design, purport, intention, object, purpose, result, end, inference,
vein. *(vagueness, indefiniteness, pointlessness, aberran-
cy, unmeaningness, con-
fusedness, aimlessness,
motionlessness, inertia.)*

drink—*v.* guaff, absorb,
draught, imbibe, drain, guzzle,
swallow, gulp. *(replenish, ex-*

ude, water, disgorge, moisten, pour, dampen.)

drivel—n. nonsense, snivel, fatuity, trifling, babble, rambling. (coherence, solidity, soundness, substance, essence.)

droll—adj. queer, funny, comic, farcical, whimsical, odd, quaint, fantastic, amusing, comical, laughable. (lugubrious, sad, funereal, lamentable, ordinary, tragic.)

drop—v. emanate, percolate, fall, faint, decline, descend, ooze, droop, trickle, distil. (rise, recover, soar, rally, evaporate, climb, ascend.)

drown—v. overwhelm, submerge, deluge, sink, swamp, engulf, perish, inundate, immerse, overflow. (drain, ventilate, dry, expose, air, rescue, perserve.)

dry—adj. parched, monotonous, dull, arid, juiceless, sarcastic, tame, moistureless, uninteresting, vapid, evaporated, barren, lifeless, tedious, withered. (fresh, lively, damp, entertaining, juicy, soaked, moist.)

due—adj. unpaid, payable, mature, accrued, owed, owing, outstanding, in arrears, demandable. (unsuitable, inapt, wrong, undeserved, inappropriate.)

dull—adj. stolid, insensible, heavy, dismal, turbid, dowdy, sad, commonplace, stupid, dead, doltish, callous, gloomy, clowdy, opaque, sluggish, tiresome, faded, muted. (clever, animated, bright, burnished, exhilarating, sharp, lively, sensible, transparent, brilliant, cheerful, keen, intense.)

durable—adj. permanent, firm, abiding, continuing, lasting, stable, sturdy, persistent, constant. (transient, unstable, impermanent, perishable, evanescent.)

duty—n. part, responsiblity, function, province, trust, service, liability, obligation, business, allegiance, office, calling, commission, task. (exemption, license, desertion, freedom, direliction, dispensation, immunity, liberation.)

dwindle—v. diminish, fall off, melt, pine, decline, waste, decrease, lessen, degenerate. (enlarge, grow, flourish, expand, develop, augment, strenghten, increase, multiply.)

dynamic—adj. vigorous, energetic, vital, forceful, active, oscillating, impelling, powerful. (fixed, still, inert, stable, dead, passive, weak, enverated.)

E

early—*adj.* forward, quickly, anon, beforehand, soon, first, betimes, matutinal, shortly, premature. *(backward, belated, late, vespertinal, tardily, retarded.)*

earn—*v.* acquire, obtain, gain, realize, merit, achieve, win, deserve, collect. *(forego, lose, squander, forfeit, waste, spend, exhaust, dissipate.)*

earnest—*adj.* serious, determined, solemn, warm, ardent, eager, fervent, intent, strenuous, grave, intense, devoted. *(playful, unearnest, jesting, indifferent, flippant, idle, desultory, irresolute, sportive, superficial.)*

easy—*adj.* comfortable, indulgent, lenient, gentle, self-possessed, not difficult, unconcerned, quiet, manageable, facile, unpretentious. *(disturbed, difficult, hard, embarrassed, uneasy, exacting, anxious, painful, unmanageable, awkward, uncomfortable.)*

ebb—*v.* recede, fall, decline, wane, lessen, shrink, dwindle, sink, diminish, weaken, decrease. *(grow, wax, enlarge, increase, swell, prosper, flowish, build.)*

economical—*adj.* thrifty, spare, frugal, saving, prudent, chary, careful, parsimonious, cheap, scrimping. *(prodigal, lavish, improvident, spendthrift, elaborate, ample, generous, liberal.)*

economy—*n.* dispensation, rule, administration, management, distribution, arrangement, frugality, thrift. *(waste, mismanagement, prodigality, misrule, disorder, maladministration, imprudence, extravagance.)*

ecstasy—*n.* inspiration, frenzy, emotion, delight, happiness, rapture, fervor, enthusiasm, joy, transport, exhilaration. *(coolness, weariness, tedium, fidget, misery, bore, dullness, indifference, sorrow.)*

edifice—*n.* building, tenement, structure, house, fabric, institute. *(heap, dismantlement, ruin, demolition, devastation.)*

educate—*v.* nurture, train, develop, school, initiate, teach, instruct, discipline, ground, enlighten, cultivate. *(misinstruct, misnurture, miseducate, mistrain.)*

effective—*adj.* conducive, cogent, able, powerful, telling, talented, efficient, effectual, serviceable, operative, patent, efficacious, competent. *(futile, nugatory, ineffective, inoperative, weak, inconducive, inadequate, useless.)*

effete—*adj.* barren, sterile, exhausted, worn-out, sere, unproductive, decadent, morally, decayed, spent, deteriorated. *(fruitful, inventive, prolific, creative, teeming, vital, vigorous, youthful.)*

effort—*n.* attempt, exertion, trial, endeavor, struggle, stress. *(misadventure, facility, spontaneity, ease, failure, unsuccess, futility, inactivity, frustration, collapse.)*

egotism—*n.* vanity, self-assertion, conceit, self-exaltation, pride, self-praise, narcissism, arrogance. *(deference, modesty, self-abnegation, considerateness.)*

ejaculation—*n.* utterance, cry, exclamation, vaciferation. *(silence, speech, dumbfoundedness, obmutescence, speechlessness, drawl, oration, address.)*

elastic—*adj.* extensile, resilient, flexible, springy, modifiable, buoyant, ductile, alterable, supple. *(unchangeable, inert, tough, brittle, rigid, inflexible, obstinate, dull, crystallized.)*

elated—*adj.* inspirited, proud, cheered, inflated, joyed, gleeful, jubilant. *(dis-*

pirited, dejected, disappointed, depressed, sad, humiliated, gloomy, abashed, confounded.)*

elegance—*n.* refinement, taste, grandeur, beauty, symmetry, gracefulness, luxuriousness. *(awkwardness, rudeness, ungracefulness, plainness, deformity, coarseness, crudeness, disproportion.)*

elegant—*adj.* lovely, well made, accomplished, refined, graceful, handsome, symetrical, polished, luxurious, well formed, graud. *(deformed, coarse, rude, unsymmetrical, plain, ungraceful, inelegant, crude.)*

elementary—*adj.* material, simple, ultimate, physical, constituent, primary, physical, basic, natural, component, inchoate, fundamental. *(incorporeal, compound, aggregate, organized, complicated, immaterial, collective, impalpable, developed, complex.)*

elevate—*v.* basic, fundamental, elemental, rudimentary, primary, original, initial, simple, primitive. *(debase, belittle, degrade, reduce, weaken, impair, depreciate.)*

eligible—*adj.* suitable, desirable, choice, preferable, capable, prime, worthy, chosen, proper. *(worthless, ordinary, indifferent, unprofitable, undesirable, unacceptable, ineligible, unsuitable.)*

eloquent—*adj.* forceful, fluent, articulate, inspired, passionate, persuasive, cogent, inspired, vivid, emphatic. *(inarticulate, dull, hesitant, clumsy, routine, commonplace, prosaic, weak.)*

elude—*v.* avoid, baffle, parry, frustrate, wade, eschew, shun, escape, fence, dodge, mock, flee. *(court, defy, encounter, confront, dare, meet, challenge.)*

emaciated—*adj.* wasted, thin, scrawny, famished, gaunt, haggard, frail, atrophied, wizened, skeletal. *(well-fed, fat, corpulent, plump, obese, hardy, robust.)*

embarrass—*v.* desconcert, confuse, clog, entangle, puzzle, encumber, distress, trouble, hamper, perplex, mortify. *(expedite, assist, extricate, disencumber, liberate, facilitate, accelerate, put at ease.)*

embezzle—*v.* confuse, piculate, appropriate, falsify, misappropriate, pilfer, steal. *(balance, square, recompense, clear, remunerate.)*

embody—*v.* methodize, codify, aggregate, compact, enlist, express, systematize, incorporate, integrate, introduce, combine, consolidate. *(segregate, dissipate, dismember, disband, eliminate, analyse, disintegrate, colliquate, disembody, divide, disunite.)*

embrace—*v.* comprehend, hug, contain, incorporate, clasp, close, encompass, include, comprise, embody. *(reject, except, repudiate, exclude, decline.)*

emergency—*n.* conjuncture, strait, exigency, difficulty, crisis, casualty, pitch, necessity, embarrassment, tension. *(solution, provision, arrangement, rescue, anticipation, subsidence, deliverance, stability.)*

eminent—*adj.* excellent, foremost, outstanding, esteemed, celebrated, noted, renowned, distinguished, honored, famous, laureate, paramount. *(obscure, humble, mediocre, undistinguished, unknown, modest, unpretentious, petty.)*

emotion—*n.* feeling, agitation, trepidation, passion, excitement, tremor, perturbation, worry, turmoil. *(impassiveness, peace, stoicism, in-*

difference, harmony, insensibility, imperturbability.)

emphatic—*adj.* forceable, energetic, positive, special, consummate, earnest, strong, impressive, important, egregious, decisive. *(cool, ordinary, commonplace, mild, unnoticeable, unimpassioned, unimportant, hesitant.)*

employ—*v.* apply, occupy, engross, use, economize, engage, hire, enlist. *(dismiss, misemploy, discard, misuse, discharge, fire.)*

empower—*v.* commission, qualify, warrant, direct, enable, encourage, delegate, sanction, authorize, permit. *(prevent, disable, disqualify, hinder, discourage, forbid, disbar.)*

empty—*adj.* void, unobstructed, waste, unfrequented, vacuous, unfilled, untenanted, deficient, silly, senseless, vacant, idle, unencumbered, unoccupied, devoid, uninhabited, destitute, unfurnished, evacuated, weak, frivolous. *(occupied, obstructed, substantial, colonized, informed, experienced, significant, important, full, encumbered, abundant, sensible, cultivated, inhabited, well-instructed, forcible.)*

enamor—*v.* fascinate, charm, bewitch, captivate, enchain, enslave, endear, infatuate. *(disgust, disenchant, repel, horrify, estrange, revolt.)*

enclose—*v.* encircle, afforest, include, envelop, shut, circumscribe, wrap, surround. *(disclose, bare, develop, open, exclude, expose, disencircle, boycott, disenclose.)*

encourage—*v.* rally, abet, inspirit, embolden, enhearten, incite, urge, foster, promote, advance, impel, forward, animate, prompt, reassure, countenance, cherish, stimulate, cheer, advocate. *(discourage, dispirit, deter, dissuade, dishearten, daunt.)*

end—*n.* stop, terminus, limit, tip, boundary, point, finish, close, conclusion, finale, cessation, point, expiration, aftermath. *(origin, beginning, source, start, commencement, infancy, inception, outset.)*

endanger—*v.* risk, imperil, jeopardize, peril, commit, expose, hazard, compromise. *(defend, screen, cover, protect, safeguard, shield.)*

endear—*v.* gain, attach, make dear, conciliate, idolize, treasure. *(alienate, embitter, estrange, provoke.)*

endless—*adj.* illimitable, eternal, unceasing, deathless, infinite, everlasting, interminable, unending, perpetual, boundless, imperishable, immortal. *(temporary, transient, ephemeral, finite, terminable, limited, brief, periodic, fugitive, measured.)*

endowment—*n.* provision, capacity, qualification, gift, benefaction, donation, benefit, attainment, grant. *(incapacity, impoverishment, lack, loss, poverty, detriment, drawback, harm.)*

enforce—*v.* compel, exact, strain, urge, require, exert, administer, impose. *(forego, abandon, relax, disregard, waive, remit, default.)*

engage—*v.* vouch, promise, buy, involve, undertake, employ, occupy, attract, adopt, agree, hire, gain, stipulate, commit, pledge, enlist. *(refuse, dismiss, extricate, disengage, decline, withdraw, discard, fire, cancel.)*

enhance—*v.* magnify, intensify, heighten, elevate, lift, boast, embellish, augment, fortify, escalate. *(diminish, detract, undermine, reduce, lessen, depreciate, minimize, weaken.)*

enigmatical—*adj.* perplexing, elusive, mystic, puzzling, obscure, cryptic. *(explana-*

tory, self-evident, lucid, plain, candid, frank.)

enlarge—*v.* expand, broaden, stretch out, dilate, augment, swell, increase, extend, amplify, magnify, widen. *(lessen, restrict, curtail, narrow, reduce, contract, diminish, dwindle, condense.)*

enlighten—*v.* edify, illuminate, teach, illumine, instruct, inform, educate, apprise. *(darken, obscure, perplex, mislead, mystify, confound, delude, deceive.)*

enlist—*v.* register, embody, enroll, enter, incorporate, recruit, obtain. *(erase, dismiss, retire, disembody, withdraw, expunge, disband, resign.)*

enmity—*n.* asperity, bitterness, animosity, malignity, maliciousness, hostility, discord, hate, malevolence, aversion, ill-feeling, opposition, acrimony, malice, antipathy. *(love, esteem, cordiality, friendship, affection, friendliness, harmony, amicability.)*

enormous—*adj.* immense, gross, colossal, vast, monstrous, huge, prodigious, elephantine, gigantic, astronomic. *(insignificant, venial, ordinary, trivial, diminutive, regular, average, puny, undersized.)*

enough—*adj.* ample, abundance, plenty, sufficient, adequate. *(scant, inadequate, short, bare, insufficient, deficient.)*

ensue—*v.* accrue, befall, follow, supervene, result. *(threaten, forewarn, precede, herald, premonish.)*

ensure—*v.* determine, seal, secure, fix, guarantee. *(hazard, forfeit, imperil, jeopardize, endanger.)*

enterprising—*adj.* bold, dashing, active, adventurous, forceful, speculative, venturesome, daring. *(inadventurous, inactive, cautious, timid, apathetic.)*

entertain—*v.* maintain, foster, recreate, harbor, amuse, receive, conceive, engross. *(exclude, debar, tire, weary, eject, deny, bore, annoy, ignore.)*

enthusiasm—*n.* frenzy, passion, fervor, devotion, excitement, sensation, transport, warmth, vehemence, ardor, inspiration, zeal, rapture, fervency, ebullience. *(callousness, disaffection, alienation, coldness, contempt, repugnance, indifference, apathy.)*

entire—*adj.* complete, total, all, undiminished, solid, whole, integral, unimpaired, full, perfect, intact. *(impaired, partial, broken, incomplete, fragmentary.)*

entitle—*v.* empower, characterize, denominate, qualify, fit, name, designate, style, enable, permit. *(disable, disqualify, not characterize, desentitle, not designate, unfit.)*

entreat—*v.* obsecrate, beseech, crave, supplicate, ask, petition, implore, beg, importune, solicit, pray, urge, plead with. *(insist, enjoin, bid, command, demand.)*

enumerate—*v.* name, recount, reckon, calculate, over, specify, number, detail, compute, call, list. *(miscount, miscalculate, misreckon, confound.)*

ephemeral—*adj.* evanescent, fugacious, momentary, transient, fleeting, fugitive, temporary. *(persistent, perpetual, perennial, abiding, immortal, external, permanent, lasting.)*

equable—*adj.* regular, even, easy, smooth, uniform, tranquil, proportionate. *(uneasy, desultory, fitful, irregular, agitated, variable, disjointed.)*

equal—*adj.* commensurate, alike, even, sufficient, co- extensive, uniform, smooth, impartial, co-ordinate, identical, adequate, equivalent, equable. *(incommensurate, inadequate, unequal, partial, incoordinate, variable, disparate.)*

equitable—*adj.* proportionate, fair, honest, reasonable, just, proper, even-handed, impartial, upright honorable. *(disproportionate, unfair, partial, biased, unjust.)*

erase—*v.* efface, blot, eradicate, cancel, expunge, obliterate. *(write, stamp, delineate, mark.)*

erect—*v.* institute, establish, set up, elevate, manufacture, raise, build plant, found, construct, uplift. *(supplant, remove, demolish, raze, subvert, destroy, depress, lower.)*

erratic—*adj.* aberrant, capricious, desultory, abnormal, changeful, unpredictable, flighty. *(normal, calculable, undeviating, regular, predictable, methodical, steady, unalterable.)*

error—*n.* mistake, deception, untruth, fault, hallucination, blunder, misunderstanding, falsity, fallacy. *(correctness, soundness, truth, rectification, correction, flawlessness, accuracy.)*

escape—*v.* decamp, avoid, fly, elude, evade, shun, flee, abscond. *(meet, confront, suffer, trap, incur, encounter.)*

esoteric—*adj.* cryptic, obscure, arcane, abstruese, inscrutable, mysterious, private, veiled, occult, hidden. *(clear, simple, open, exoteric, obvious, plain.)*

essential—*adj.* inherent, leading, immanent, innate, requisite, crucial, necessary, indispensable, vital, key, main. *(qualitative, option, promotive, induced, ascititious, superfluous, adventitious, minimal, accidental, quantitative, regulative, imported, redundant.)*

establish—*v.* settle, substantiate, plant, found, prove, organize, inaugurate, confirm, fix, demonstrate, institute. *(presume, surmise, guess, supplant, break-up, misstate, refute, subvert, conjecture, suppose, unsettle, disestablish, upset, confute, invalidate.)*

esteem—*n.* value, deem, believe, think, affect, revere, respect, venerate, love, price, consider, admiration, like, admire, honor, appreciate, regard, judge, estimate, prize, treasure. *(disconsider, dislike, underrate, deprecate, disregard, disaffect, undervalue, decry, contempt.)*

eternal—*adj.* endless, deathless, never-dying, everliving, undying, infinite, unceasing, immortal, perpetual, ceaseless, everlasting, imperishable, constant. *(temporal, fleeting, ephemeral, evanescent, mortal, transient, perishable.)*

etiquette—*n.* fashion, manners, conventionality, protocal, breeding, decorum. *(rudeness, singularity, nonconformance, boorishness, vulgarity, misobservance.)*

evaporate—*v.* exhale, colliquate, distil, melt, liquefy, dissolve, vaporize, dehydrate, disappear. *(crystallize, solidify, consolidate, indurate, condense, compact.)*

even—*adj.* level, smooth, flush, regular, straight, flat, uniform, tranquil, serene, calm. *(jagged, askew, unfair, uneven, rough, lumpy, jumpy, unstable, biased.)*

event—*n.* circumstance, adventure, accident, fact, occurence, incident, happening, issue, episode, result. *(predisposition, cause, tendency, antecedent, union, convergence, contribution, operation, inducement.)*

eventful—*adj.* memorable, marked, critical, notable, remarkable, signal, active, stirring, noted, important. *(unmarked, trivial, ordinary, unimportant, empty, character-less, uninteresting, eventless.)*

evidence—*n.* attraction, testimony, declaration, sign, proof, exemplification, token, illustration, manifestation, averment, disposition, appearance, corroboration, indication. *(conjecture, fallacy, surmise, counter-evidence, refutation, suppression, disproof, concealment, misindication, disguising.)*

evident—*adj.* visible, manifest, obvious, palpable, plain, clear, incontrovertible, indisputable, conspicuous, apparent. *(questionable, doubtful, dubious, obscure, uncertain, unsure.)*

evil—*adj.* deleterious, bad, hurtful, unhappy, unpropitious, corrupt, unfair, miserable, ill, sorrowful, noxious, wrong, mischievous, sinful, adverse, wicked, harmful, notorious, immoral. *(beneficial, virtuous, pure, fortunate, joyous, grateful, welcome, good, wholesome, right, holy, happy, felicitous, noble.)*

exactly—*adv.* correspondently, truly, precisely, accurately, literally. *(inadequately, loosely, otherwise, approximately, differently, incorrectly.)*

exaggerate—*v.* enlarge, magnify, overdraw, over-paint, strain, overestimate, embellishment, amplify, heighten, overstate, inflate. *(attenuate, lenify, soften, modify, disparage, palliate, mitigate, qualify, understate, minimize, underestimate.)*

examine—*v.* ponder, perpend, scrutinize, prove, discuss, search, explore, weigh, inspect, overhaul, inquire, study, test, criticize, investigate, survey. *(conjecture, slur, guess, discard, misinvestigate, misconsider, ignore.)*

example—*n.* specimen, model, copy, illustration, issue, development, sample, pattern, instance, standard. *(material, law, stock, character, substance, rule, case, principle, quality, system, anomaly.)*

excellent—*adj.* superior, great, fine, splendid, exceptional, superb, remarkable, outstanding, magnificent, choice. *(average, inadequate, mediocre, deficient, rotten, worthless, so-so, inferior.)*

except—*v.* save, segregate, exclude, bar, negate, omit, ignore. *(include, state, propound, admit, count, reckon, classify, affirm, attest.)*

exceptional—*adj.* peculiar, unusual, rare, uncommon, irregular, abnormal, outstanding. *(regular, ordinary, common, normal, usual, typical.)*

excessive—*adj.* undue, overmuch, extravagant, immoderate, enormous, inordinate, exorbitant, unreasonable, superfluous, superabundant, extreme. *(scant, inadequate, insufficient, want, shortage.)*

excuse—*v.* pardon, exculpate, condone, exonerate, release, absolve, extenuate, defend, forgive, vindicate, overlook, remit, mitigate, indulge, free, justify, acquit, exempt, alibi. *(inculpate, sentence, strain, charge, condemn, exact, accuse, blame, criticize.)*

exemplary—*adj.* praiseworthy, honorable, meritorious, excellent, laudable, conspicuous, wary, worthy, commendable. *(objectionable, regrettable, exceptionable, detestable, worthless.)*

exempt—*adj.* irresponsible, free, clear, privileged, unamenable, absolved, liberated, special, responsible, liable, amenable, subject, accountable.

exercise—*n.* use, application, drill, employment, exertion, training, practice, discipline, preparation. *(idleness, ease, recreation, relaxation, inactivity, rest.)*

exhaust—*v.* spend, weaken, void, drain, debilitate, deplete, weary, waste, empty, consume. *(replenish, refresh, obtain, fill, invigorate, augment.)*

existence—*n.* entity, creature, being, subsistence, life. *(non-existence, chimera, nothingness, nonenity.)*

expand—*v.* dilate, open, spread, amplify, unfold, distend, swell, enlarge, diffuse, extend, develop. *(curtail, restrict, contract, diminish, condense, attenuate, deflate.)*

expect—*v.* await, forebode, anticipate, wait for, foresee, forecast, contemplate, hope, rely on, predict. *(recognize, realize, welcome, fear, greet, hail, dread.)*

expediency—*n.* advantage, aptness, utility, interest, usefulness. *(disadvantage, inutility, idealism, detriment, inexpediency.)*

expend—*v.* disburse, waste, use, exhaust, spend, lay out, consume, dissipate. *(economize, preserve, husband, save, hoard.)*

expense—*n.* cost, payment, outlay, price, amount, charge, expenditure. *(receipt, income, proceeds, profit, gain.)*

experience—*v.* feel, encounter, suffer, try, undergo, endure, perceive. *(miss, evade, foil, escape, lose, baffle.)*

experience—*n.* test, proof, habit, knowledge, experiment trial, observation. *(theory, surmise, inexperience.)*

explain—*v.* teach, decipher, interpret, expound, elucidate, illustrate, demonstrate, clear up, describe. *(obscure, bewilder, mystify, confuse, misinterpret, darken.)*

explanation—*n.* interpretation, description, explication, sense, exposition, reason, analysis. *(obscuration, misinterpretation, mystification, confusion, complication.)*

explicit—*adj.* detailed, declaratory, stated, determinate, express, plain, precise, inobscure, categorical, distinctly, definite. *(implied, vague, obscure, implicit, hinted, suggestive.)*

expression—*n.* indication, term, lineament, phrase, delivery, countenance, feature, look, face. *(enigma, suppression, falsification, solecism, restraint, misstatement.)*

exquisite—*adj.* refined, perfect, intense, delicious, choice, elegant, rare, consummate, matchless, delicate. *(coarse, ordinary, gross, common, uncouth.)*

extend—*v.* expand, increase, reach, apply, spread, avail, prolong, augment, unfurl, stretch, amplify, enlarge. *(contract, narrow, fail, return, curtail, constrict, miss, restrict, limit, recur, shorten.)*

extinguish—*v.* quench, put out, abolish, extirpate, annihilate, destroy, eradicate, kill, douse, smother. *(replenish, promote, propagate, confirm, implant, secure, establish, ignite, cherish, invigorate, light*

extraneous—*adj.* irrelevant, extra, immaterial, incidental, external, accidental, superfluous, nonessential, peripheral. *(apropos, apt, inherent, germane, pertinent, relevant, essential.)*

extraordinary—*adj.* uncommon, preposterous, unwonted, wonderful, strange, monstrous, unprecedented, peculiar, marvelous, prodigious, amazing, unusual, remarkable. *(unimportant, frequent, wonted, usual customary, common, ordinary, unremarkable, expected.)*

extravagant—*adj.* abnormal, wild, profuse, monstrous, lavish, wasteful, profligate, reckless, prodigal, absurd, preposterous, excessive. *(usual, frugal, sound, consistent, fair, sober careful, thrifty, economical, regular, rational.)*

extreme—*adj.* ultimate, final, distant, immoderate, severe, terminal, remote, extravagant, last, utmost, farthest, most violent. *(moderate, judicious, initial, primal, average, mild.)*

F

fable—*n.* fiction, falsehood, romance, fabrication, romance, parable, apologue, fantasy, allegory, untruth, novel, invention. *(narrative, truth, history, fact, authenticity.)*

fabrication—*n.* deceit, fiction, forgery, lie, deception, fib, untruth, prevarication, creation. *(fact, verity, destruction, truth, reality, actuality.)*

facetious—*adj.* jocular, droll, pungent, comical, jesting, humorous, clever, flippant, witty, funny. *(matter-of-fact, saturnine, lugubrious, grave, heavy, sombre, dull, serious, sedate, sad.)*

facile—*adj.* tractable, indulgent, irrisolute, affable, pliable, docile, characterless, easy, weak, flexible, manageable, dexterous. *(obstinate, crusty, self-willed, self-reliant, sturdy, determined, inflexible, resolue, independent, pig-headed, arduous.)*

facility—*n.* address, quickness, dexterity, adroitness, proficiency, ease, readiness, pliancy, skill. *(awkwardness, labor, ineptness, difficulty, exertion.)*

fact—*n.* deed, certainty, event, truth, reality, incident, occurence, circumstance. *(supposition, unreality, delusion, romance, fiction, opinion, falsehood, invention, lie, chimera.)*

fade—*v.* decline, etiolate, pale, vanish, fall, droop, dissolve, set, fail, bleach, dwindle, change, blur, taper. *(increase, endure, bloom, stand, rise, brighten, grown, flourish, last, abide.)*

failure—*n.* lapse, miscarriage, decline, disappointment, collapse, ruin, insolvency, defeat, bankruptcy. *(victory, conquest, prosperity, luck, success, hit, fortune.)*

faint—*adj.* languid, inconspicuous, weak, fatigued, irresolute, exhausted, obscure, faded, collapse, unenergetic, feeble, timid, pale, half-hearted, dim. *(glaring, strong, fresh, vigorous, conspicuous, energetic, marked, resolute, daring, courageous, prominent.)*

fair—*adj.* clear, unspotted, reasonable, serene, just, equitable, open, impartial, attractive, spotless, untarnished, unblemished, beautiful, honorable. *(fraudulent, dull, disfigured, lowering, fowl, inclement, unfair, ugly, dishonorable.)*

faithful—*adj.* firm, loyal, close, correspondent, equivalent, incorruptible, true, staunch, attached, accurate, consistent, exact, trustworthy. *(fickle, inexact, false, capricious, faithless, treacherous, untrue, wavering, inaccurate.)*

fallacy—*n.* error, misconception, chimera, fiction, saphistry, blunder, delusion, bugbear, deception. *(verity, logic, proof, axiom, truth, certainty, fact, argument, postulate, soundness.)*

false—*adj.* faithless, untrue, fiction, fallacious, spurious, fabrication, mendacious, mock, unfaithful, falsity, dishonorable, fib, bagus, sham, counterfeit, deceptive, sophistical, hypocritical, erroneous. *(correct, faith-*

ful, true, sound, authentic, genuine, real, honorable, candid, conclusive, staunch.)

falsify—*v.* misinterpret, cook, mistake, garble, misrepresent, betray, distort, belie. *(correct, declare, verify, expose, rectify, publicate, confirm, exhibit, check, justify, certify.)*

falter—*v.* hesitate, slip, flinch, halt, vacillate, fluctuate, hobble, dubitate, demur, stammer, waver. *(career, proceed, resolve, run, persevere, speed, persist, flow, determine, discourse.)*

fame—*n.* renown, eminence, repute, notice, reputation, prominence, notability, esteem, notoriety. *(anonymity, seclusion, retirement, oblivion, dishonor, infamy.)*

familiar—*adj.* common, intimate, household, conversant, free, apprised, accustomed, frank, well- acquainted, affable, every- day. *(rare, unfamiliar, new, unaccustomed, uncommon, extraordinary, strange, ignorant, unacquainted, inconversant.)*

famous—*adj.* glorious, eminent, celebrated, prominent, illustrious. *(obscure, unknown, unsung, inglorious, humble.)*

fanciful—*adj.* chimerical, fitful, grotesque, unreal, quaint, absurd, whimsical, erroneous, imaginary, eccentric, humorous, freakish, capricious, erratic, fantastic. *(literal, calculable, natural, regular, sober, real, truthful, correct, ordinary, accurate, orderly, prosaic.)*

fancy—*n.* belief, supposition, idea, caprice, conceit, inclination, humor, desire, thought, illusion, imagination, notion, vagary, whim, predilection. *(horror, object, fact, aversion, subject, verity, reality, unadorned, system, order, law, truth.)*

far—*adj.* remote, removed, long-distant, estranged, alienated, faraway, separated, yonder. *(close, adjacent, near, familiar, neighboring, contiguous, handy, convenient.)*

fashion—*n.* mold, shape, ceremony, form, vague, way, guise, manner, style, usage, appearance, figure, practice, character, custom, mode. *(strangeness, work, outlandishness, person, speech, eccentricity, dress, derangement, shapelessness, formlessness.)*

fast—*adj.* gay, firm, dissipated, secure, reckless, fixed, wild, constant, accelerated, steadfast, rapid, stable, unswerving, unyielding, immovable. *(virtuous, loose, slow, sober, insecure, tardy, steady, tenuous, wavering.)*

fastidious—*adj.* dainty, critical, squeamish, over-nice, particular, censorious, punctilious, over-refined, meticulous. *(omnivorous, easy, uncritical, neglectful, coarse, indulgent.)*

fat—*adj.* oleaginous, corpulent, obese, fleshy, unctuous, brawny, pursy, fertile, rich, stout, luxuriant, portly, rotund. *(anatomical, lean, exsanguineous, slender, scant, attenuated, poor, emacinated, barren, marrowless, gaunt, cadaverous.)*

fatal—*adj.* lethal, calamitous, mortal, deadly, destructive, terminal, pernicious. *(harmful, beneficial, superficial, wholesome, slight, nutritious, restorative, salubrious, vitalizing, nonlethal.)*

fate—*n.* doom, necessity, fortune, lot, destiny, end, providence. *(independence, choice, freedom, will, chance, decision.)*

fault—*n.* error, drawback, flow, defect, want, imperfection, misdeed, omission, failure. *(perfection, sufficiency, goodness, completeness, correctness.)*

favor—*n.* patronage, permission, countenance, grace, boon, gift, concession, preference, civility, accomodation, condescension, goodwill, regard, predilection, benefit, kindness. *(discountenance, refusal, withholding, injury, denial, frown, prohibition, disfavor, withdrawal, malice, disapproval.)*

favorable—*adj.* friendly, fond, permissive, auspicious, partial, indulgent, liberal, propitious, concessive, advantageous, beneficial. *(unpropitious, impartial, contrary, unsatisfactory, reluctant, unfavorable.)*

fear—*n.* solicitude, awe, fright, apprehension, timidity, alarm, dread, trepidation, horror, dismay, panic, terror, consternation, misgiving. *(boldness, fearlessness, assurance, bravery, confidence, trust, courage.)*

feasible—*adj.* practicable, attainable, possible, suitable, practical, operable, reasonable, expedient, desirable. *(impractical, unworkable, unsuitable, impossible, unfeasible.)*

feeble—*adj.* scanty, weak, vain, pitiable, wretched, fruitless, poor, frail, incomplete, infirm, debilitated, dull, invalid, forceless, faint, puny, enervated, enfeebled, nerveless. *(robust, effective, abundant, vigorous, strong, active, successful.)*

feeling—*n.* sensation, passion, touch, sensitiveness, pathos, sentiment, contact, emotion, tenderness, impression, sensibility, awareness, consiousness. *(insensateness, callousness, coldness, apathy, insensibility, inexcitability, imperturbability, numbness.)*

felicitous—*adj.* timely, opportune, happy, successful, joyous, appropriate, apropos. *(unhappy, sad, unsuccessful, unfortunate, inopportune, irrelevant, disastrous, untimely.)*

feminine—*adj.* womanly, modest, delicate, soft, tender, gentle, ladylike. *(manly, rude, unfeminine, robust, indelicate, rough, masculine.)*

ferment—*v.* stir up, incite, agitate, trouble, disturb, rouse, shake, seethe, fester, perturb, provoke, effervesce, foam. *(soothe, relax, calm, compose, allay, still, quiet.)*

fertile—*adj.* inventive, rich, copious, ingenious, luxuriant, fruitful, teeming, fecund, productive, prolific, exuberant, causative, pregnant, fraught, conducive. *(unimaginative, poor, uninventive, sterile, in-operative, barren, fruitless, inconducive, ineffective, unproductive, unyielding.)*

fickle—*adj.* unstable, fanciful, inconstant, fitful, restless, capricious, variable, irresolute, shifting, unpredicitable, changeable, veering, unrealiable, vacillating, mutable. *(uniform, sober, steady, orderly, trustworthy, reliable, calculable, well-regulated, faithful.)*

fiction—*n.* myth, invention, romance, fabrication, falsehood, creation, fable, fantasy, figment. *(truth, reality, accuracy, fact, verity.)*

fidelity—*n.* attachment, loyalty, truthfulness, integrity, fealty, honesty, allegiance, faithfulness, devotion, accuracy, exactness, closeness. *(disloyalty, infidelity, treachery, inexactness, disaffection, inaccuracy, untruthfulness, unrealiability.)*

fierce—*adj.* furious, cruel, enraged, violent, ravenous, extreme, savage, ferocious, brutal. *(gentle, docile, mild, harmless, moderate, meek, calm, submissive, placid, domesticated.)*

fiery—*adj.* hot-brained, vehement, irritable, hot, impassioned, ardent, fervid, fervent, glowing, fierce, smoldering, enkindled, passionate, excited, irascible, choleric. *(tame, cold, quenched, icy, extinguished, indifferent, mild, apathetic, unimpassioned, passionless, phlegmatic.)*

fight—*n.* engagement, battle, action, struggle, encounter, contention, skirmish, conflict, combat, contest. *(reconciliation, compromise, pacification, appeasement.)*

figure—*n.* illustration, aspect, delineation, shape, likeness, emblem, metaphor, type, symbol, imagine, form, appearance, condition, silhouette. *(deformity, defigurement, malformation, misrepresentation.)*

fill—*v.* content, expand, replenish, increase, glow, supply, swell, satisfy, rise, gorge, store, glut, appoint, occupy, stuff, saturate. *(diminish, exhaust, evaporate, deprive, ebb, drain, shrink, dissatisfy, subside, stint, misappoint, vacate, empty.)*

filthy—*adj.* polluted, foul, dirty, putrid, sordid, stained, unclean, unwashed, slimy, piggish, squalid. *(washed, hygienic, cleansed, purified, sanitary, decent, virtuous, pure.)*

final—*adj.* terminal, last, decisive, ultimate, latest, irrevocable, definite, conclusive, extreme, developed.

(rudimental, open, nascent, initiative, inchoate, unconcluded, inaugural, dynamic, incipient, current, continuous, progressive.)

find—*v.* confront, furnish, meet, invent, ascertain, discover, experience, observe, perceive. *(elude, miscontrive, overlook, miss, withdraw, lose, withhold, misplace.)*

fine—*adj.* minute, casuistical, thin, subtle, slender, nice, delicate, high, presumptuous, pure, ostentatious, grand, elegant, noble, showy, pretty, sensitive, beautiful, refined, generous, handsome, honorable, dull, exemplary, pretentious, excellent, superior, finished, smooth, choice, filmy, artistic, gauzy, keen, pulverized. *(indissective, coarse, unreflective, large, unanalytical, rough, plainspoken, blunt, rude, categorical, unfinished, affable, mean, unaffected, petty, modest, illiberal, unimposing, paltry, mediocre.)*

finesse—*n.* tact, savoir faire, discretion, skill, polish, artfulness, cleverness, diplomacy, adroitness, delicacy. *(clumsiness, stupidy, ineptitude, crudeness, tactlessness, maladroitness.)*

finical—*adj.* dandyish, euphuistic, affected, fac

titious, over nice, foppish, spruce, dallying, over-fastidious. *(coarse, genuine, unaffected, rude, outspoken, effective, blunt, practical, real, natural, energetic, competent.)*

finish—v. terminate, complete, shape, perfect, end, accomplish, achieve, conclude, cease, desist. *(commence, botch, miscontrive, begin, mar, start, mismanage, undertake, fail, launch.)*

first—adj. onmost, leading, chief, primary, highest, pristine, primeval, original, principal, foremost, primitive, earliest. *(secondary, hindmost, subsequent, last, subordinate, unimportant, subservient, lowest, terminating, concluding.)*

fit—adj. befitting, proper, decent, ripe, expedient, meet, contrived, apt, calculated, fitting, adequate, adapted, prepared, seemly, suitable, appropriate, particular, becoming, peculiar, decorous, congruous, qualified, germane. *(improper, awkward, unfit, ungainly, inexpedient, misfitting, miscontrived, ill-suited, miscalculated, unseemly, inadequate, inappropriate, unprepared, amiss, unsuitable, out of place.)*

fix—v. fasten, secure, attach, plant, decide, place, determine, settle, position, link, root, locate, establish, tie, immobilize. *(unsettle, change, shake, remove, transfer, disestablish, unfix, displace, uproot, disconnect, reverse, disarrange, transplant, weaken, disturb.)*

flagrant—adj. brazen, scandalous, outrageous, glaring, indecent, blatant, disgraceful, shocking, shameless, notorious, infamous, audacious. *(clandestine, sneaky, concealed, hidden, surreptitious, undercover.)*

flat—adj. insipid, mawkish, dull, level, lifeless, tame, vapid, tasteless, downright, horizontal, even, spiritless, absolute, uniform. *(rugged, interesting, sensational, exciting, thrilling, animated.)*

flexible—adj. lithe, yielding, elastic, ductile, pliable, easy, pliant, indulgent, rubbery, supple. *(hard, inelastic, inexorable, rigid, tough, inflexible, brittle.)*

flimsy—adj. thin, superficial, gauzy, shallow, poor, weak, fragile, transparent, trifling, puerile, trivial, inane, slight. *(substantial, sound, irrefragable, cogent, durable, solid.)*

flippant—*adj.* forward, malapert, thoughtless, pert, saucy, brazen, superficial. *(deferential, servile, accurate, complimentary, flattering, respectful, polite, obsequious, considerate.)*

flood—*n.* abundance, drench, inundation, deluge, shower. *(ebb, subsidence, drought, scarcity, drain, shortage.)*

florid—*adj.* sanguine, overwrought, rubicund, meretricious, flowery, embellished, ornate. *(exsanguineous, unadorned, sober, pallid, nude, understated, chaste, bare.)*

flounder—*v.* blunder, wallow, roll, bungle, tumble, struggle, boggle. *(career, rise, emerge, skim, course, flow, emanate, speed, flourish.)*

flourish—*v.* thrive, triumph, wave, flower, prosper, speed, brandish. *(decline, ground, arrest, fail, miscarry, sheathe, wither, fade, founder.)*

flow—*v.* issue, course, run, surge, stream, career, glide, progress. *(stick, hesitate, halt, recoil, abate, regurgitate, stint, ebb, stickle, stop, fail, beat.)*

fluent—*adj.* facile, flowing, glib, graceful, articulate, smooth, ready, effusive, uninterrupted, expert, constrained. *(halting, hesitant, limping, constrained, stammering, uneven.)*

flurry—*v.* ruffle, excite, fluster, agitate, disturbance, worry. *(compose, calm, soothe, tranquilize, mesmerize, quiet.)*

foible—*n.* failing, weakness, peccadillo, infirmity, defect, fault. *(atrocity, sin, crime, strength, enormity.)*

follow—*v.* accompany, succeed, attend, copy, pursue, observe, chase, shadow, ensue, supplant, obey, imitate, result. *(elude, abandon, quit, produce, forerun, shun, cause avoid, disobey, precede.)*

folly—*n.* nonsense, imbecility, absurdity, madness, silliness, misconduct, weakness, irrationality, foolishness, imprudence. *(wisdom, judgment, sobriety, sense prudence, allay, rationality.)*

foment—*v.* cherish, propagate, fan, agitate, encourage, excite. *(extinguish, extirpate, allay, quench, discourage, hinder.)*

fond—*adj.* attached, foolish, weak, empty, devoted, silly, loving, doting, enamored, affectionate, friendly. *(sensible, unloving, undemonstrative, averse, hostile, well-*

groomed, unaffectionate, rational, strong-minded, austere.)

foolish—*adj.* idiotic, shallow, simple, ridiculous, senseless, crazed, weak, asinine, nonsensical, injudicious, contemptible, absurd, brainless, witless, preposterous, silly, imbecile, objectionable, irrational. *(sane, advisable, deep, sensible, eligible, clearsighted, wise, calculating, sagacious, intelligent, strongminded, judicious, prudent, sound.)*

forbearance—*n.* restraint, sympathy, meekness, mildness, temperance, gentleness, mercy, clemency, patience, tolerance, self-control. *(vindictiveness, rancor, ruthlessness, impatience, intolerance, vengefulness.)*

forbidding—*adj.* deterrent, offensive, repulsive, prohibitory, menacing. *(encouraging, permissive, attractive, cordial, alluring, seductive.)*

force—*n.* strength, instrumentality, cogency, violent, coercion, power, agency, validity, compulsion, army duress, host, vehemence, pressure, dint, might, vigor. *(counteraction, inefficiency, pointlessness, inconclusiveness, weakness, debility,* feebleness, impotence, neutralization.)*

foreign—*adj.* outlandish, strange, extraneous, exotic, alien, imported, irrelevant. *(native, pertinent, domestic, germane, indigenous, congenial.)*

forfeit—*n.* mulct, loss, penalty, damages, transgress, amercement, fine. *(reward, douceur, compensation, gratuity, entice, premium, remuneration, bribe.)*

forget—*v.* unlearn, overlook, lose, oblivate, pretermit, unintentionally. *(learn, recollect, mind, treasure, reminisce, retain, acquire, remember.)*

form—*v.* mould, constitue, frame, devise, produce, create, shape, fashion, contrive, make, scheme, arrange, construct. *(analyze, deform, distort, disorganize, disintegrate, dislocate, dissipate, derange, dismember, subvert.)*

formal—*adj.* complete, sufficient, stately, ceremonious, stiff, explicit, affected, systematic, methodical, exact, regular, shapely, precise, pompous, dignified, correct. *(incomplete, easy, unceremonious, irregular, informal, nonconformist, inadequate, unassuming, incorrect.)*

formality—*n.* parade, stateliness, ritualism, punctiliousness, ceremony, etiquette, affectation. *(casualness, ease, nonconformism, eccentricity, informality.)*

former—*adj.* antecedent, ancient, anterior, foregoing, preceding, previous, preliminary, bygone, first- mentioned, prior, earlier. *(subsequent, latter, succeeding, future, modern, ensuing, posterior, coming.)*

fortunate—*adj.* propitious, happy, felicitous, auspicious, successful, blessed, lucky, prosperous, providental. *(unhappy, disastrous, unlucky, infelicitous, unfortunate.)*

forthright—*adj.* direct, candid, blunt, honest, frank, sincere, explicit, plain, straightforward, truthful. *(guarded, equivocal, misleading, devious, indirect, circuitous.)*

forward—*adj.* ready, anxious, bold, self-assertive, presumptuous, advanced, eager, brash, obtrusive, impertinent, confident, progressive, onward. *(reluctant, slow, modest, timid, backward, tardy, retiring, indifferent.)*

found—*v.* institute, fix, root, ground, establish, set, endow, plant, originate, build, base, setup, rest. *(supplant, uproot, disestablish, annihilate, subvert.)*

foundation—*n.* establishment, basis, ground, rudiments, underlying, institution, footing, skeleton, base, origin, groundwork, principle, substratum. *(superstructure, pinnacle, disestablishment, summit.)*

fragrant—*adj.* scented, balmy, aromatic, odoriferous, redolent, odorous, perfumed, sweet-smelling, sweet-scented, spicy. *(scentless, fetid, malodorous, inodorous, mephitic.)*

frail—*adj.* erring, delicate, mutable, irresolute, wispy. *(virtuous, robust, lasting, resolute, vigorous.)*

frank—*adj.* candid, unreserved, free, honest, sincere, plain, evident, ingenious, open, artless, familiar, easy, outspoken. *(close, guarded, disingenious, reserved, devious.)*

freakish—*adj.* whimsical, erratic, sportful, capricious, grotesque, frisky, fanciful, strange. *(sober, unwhimsical, reliable, uniform, temperate, equable, demure, consistent, unfanciful, steady.)*

free—*adj.* playing, open, unoccupied, unimpeded, unhindered, gratuitous, at liberty, liberal, unconfined, loose, munificent, frank, gratis, generous, detached, operating, unobstructed, permitted, exempt, unconditional, bounteous, clear, untrammelled, careless, easy, unreserved, bountiful. *(stingy, qualified, intern, amenable, unlawful, impeded, occupied, restricted, bound, biased, enslaved, subservient, shocked, clogged, obstructed, compulsory, liable, conditional, niggardly.)*

frequent—*adj.* repeated, recurrent, continual, common, many, numerous, usual, habitual, general. *(solitary, scanty, few, sporadic, casual, rare.)*

fresh—*adj.* young, cool, renewed, untarnished, blooming, novel, modern, flourishing, unskilled, untried, ruddy, unfaded, new, unimpaired, recent, vigorous. *(stale, weary, stagnant, original, tarnished, decayed, sickly, mouldy, fusty, polluted, musty, putrid, pallid, faded, impaired, ordinary, former, old, jaded.)*

fretful—*adj.* fractious, impatient, waspish, cranky, petulant, peevish, irritable. *(forbearing, meek, unmurmuring, agreeable, patient, contented, resigned.)*

friction—*n.* grating, abrasion, rubbing, attrition, contact, grinding. *(detachment, harmony, lubrication, isolation, compatibility.)*

friend—*n.* companion, familiar, chum, coadjutor, adherent, ally, intimate, confidant, messmate, acquaintance, associate. *(foe, antagonist, rival, opponent, adversary, enemy, competitor.)*

friendly—*adj.* well-disposed, kindly, neighborly, affectionate, cordial, comradely, well-inclined, amicable, social, sociable, favorable. *(ill-disposed, inimical, distant, antagonistic, averse, hostile, aloof, ill-inclined.)*

frightful—*adj.* horrible, ugly, monstrous direful, shockful, terrific, norrendous, horrid, awful, dreadful, hideous, grim, alarming, terrible. *(attractive, fair, lovely, charming, encouraging, beautiful, pleasing.)*

frivolous—*adj.* silly, petty, worthless, flighty, trifling, trivial, giddy. *(earnest, grave, significant, important, serious.)*

frolic—*n.* game, festivity, gambol, lark, merry-making, play, sport, entertainment, gayety, spree, prank, outing. *(undertaking, engagement,* *obligation, study, occupation, purpose.)*

frugal—*adj.* economical, abstinent, temperate, thrifty, sparing, provident, parsimonious, abstemious, saving, cautious. *(luxurious, prodigal, intemperate, generous, self-indulgent, extravagant, profuse.)*

fruitful—*adj.* prolific, fraught, effectual, successful, abundant, fecund, productive, pregnant, causative, useful, fertile, plenteous, plentiful, valuable. *(sterile, fruitless, useless, futile, abortive, ineffectual, barren, unproductive.)*

fulfill—*v.* complete, verify, achieve, effect, consummate, execute, fill, accomplish, discharge. *(sober, delicate, nice, chaste, abandon.)*

fulsome—*adj.* gross, nauseous, fawning, extravagant, offensive, sickening, loathsome, excessive. *(sober, delicate, tempered, chaste, nice.)*

function—*n.* part, capacity, duty, administration, operation, power, office, character, business, role, discharge, exercise, employment, pursuit. *(maladministration, misdemeanor, misconduct, misdeed.)*

fundamental—*adj.* important, essential, primary, foremost, indispensable. *(unimportant, ascititious, secondary, superficial, nonessential, adventitious.)*

funny—*adj.* droll, laughable, jocose, ludicrous, ridiculous, amusing, diverting, humorous, comical, sportive. *(tedious, lugubrious, grave, sad, sober, lamentable, serious, dismal, mournful, dull.)*

furnish—*v.* provide, afford, bestow, give, provide, purvey, yield, equip, supply. *(withdraw, demolish, dismantle, withhold.)*

fuss—*n.* excitement, worry, ado, bustle, fidget, flurry, tumult, stir, agitation. *(peace, tranquility, silence, calm, quiet, composure, sedateness.)*

future—*n.* coming, destiny, advenient, forthcoming, forecast. *(bygone, previous, past, gone, prior.)*

G

gabby—*adj.* loquacious, wordy, chatty, talkative, garrulous, windy, talky, glib, talkative, voluble. *(terse, quiet, taciturn, reticent, laconic, reserved.)*

gain—*v.* get, procure, reach, profit, earn, realize, reap, acquire, win, accomplish, obtain, benefit, attain, achieve. *(suffer, deplete, forfeit, lose, squander.)*

gallant—*adj.* chivalrous, courteous, fearless, valiant, splendid, gay, undaunted, showy, bold, courageous, heroic, intrepid, brave. *(discourteous, timid, churlish, cowardly, fearful.)*

game—*n.* recreation, amusement, diversion, contest, play, frolic, pastime, sport. *(labor, duty, flagging, weariness, study, trust, toil, business, occupation.)*

garble—*v.* misquote, cook, color, pervert, misstate, distort, falsify, dress, misrepresent, mutilate. *(recite, quote, cite, clarify, extract.)*

gather—*v.* assemble, mass, store, accumulate, muster, collect, marshal, congregate, group, deduce, pile. *(disperse, scatter, separate, distribute, spread, dissipate, allot.)*

gaudy—*adj.* fine, bespangled, gay, showy, garish, ostentatious, showy, tawdry, meretricious. *(simple, chaste, fine, subtle, rich, handsome.)*

gauge—*v.* fathom, probe, assess, measure, evaluate, appraise, calculate. *(conjecture, scan, observe, survey, view, guess, mismeasure, analyze.)*

gawky—*adj.* ungainly, clumsy, awkward, foolish, uncouth, clownish. *(handy, handsome, polished, neat, graceful.)*

gay—*adj.* merry, lively, sportive, smart, gladsome, cheerful, blithe, joyous, jolly, sprightly, festive, pleasuresome. *(melancholy, sad, sombre, dowdy, miserable, heavy, grave, dull.)*

general—*adj.* universal, comprehensive, broad, prevalent, common, impartial, collective, generic, panoramic, vague, categorical. *(exclusive, limited, individual, local, specific, precise, explicit.)*

generous—*adj.* chivalrous, honorable, disinterested, magnanimous, munificent, noble, benevolent, liberal, bountiful, open-hearted. *(ignoble, selfish, mean, illiberal, churlish, stingy, petty.)*

genial—*adj.* cordial, cheering, festive, hearty, restorative, warm, balmy, merry, joyous, revivifying, affable. *(cutting, deleterious, deadly, destructive, lethal, cold, surly, harsh, noxious, blighting, uncongenial.)*

genteel—*adj.* well-bred, courteous, elegant, polished, cultured, polite, refined, aristocratic, graceful, fashionable. *(boorish, clownish, unpolished, plebeian, rude, ill-bred, churlish, unfashionable, inelegant.)*

gentle—*adj.* polite, mild, tame, amiable, soft, tender, serene, placid, meek, docile, bland, high-bred, courteous. *(rude, fierce, heartless, savage, coarse, rough.)*

genuine—*adj.* true, pure, natural, sincere, veritable, proven, real, authentic, unalloyed, unaffected, sound, unadulterated. *(apocryphal, fictitious, counterfeit, spurious, adulterated, fake.)*

get—*v.* procure, earn, attain, achieve, acquire, secure, obtain, gain, receive. *(forfeit, forego, lose, avoid, surrender.)*

ghastly—*adj.* wan, cadaverous, pallid, shocking, hideous, spectral, grim, deathlike, appalling. *(blooming, buxom, ruddy, seemly, fresh, comely, beautiful.)*

giddy—*adj.* vertiginous, inconstant, lofty, dizzy, flighty, whirling, thoughtless, unsteady, faint, beetling, harebrained. *(slow, thoughtful, steady, unelevated, circumspect, serious, wary, low,*

earnest, ponderous, stationary.)

gift—*n.* present, boon, benefaction, talent, alms, donation, douceur, faculty, endowment, gratuity, grant, contribution. *(refusal, purchase, compensation, inanity, forfeit, fine, penalty, reservation, wages, earnings, remuneration, stupidy, surrender, confiscation.)*

gigantic—*adj.* huge, enormous, mammoth, collosal, tremendous, immense, gargantuan, vast, stupendous, prodigious. *(miniature, tiny, dwarfish, small, microscopic, infinitesimal.)*

gist—*n.* pith, substance, force, essence, main point, marrow, kernel, core, meaning. *(redundancy, environment, garb, surplusage, additament, accessories, clothing, excess.)*

give—*v.* grant, impart, produce, concede, afford, furnish, donate, bestow, confer, yield, surrender, present, communicate. *(withdraw, retain, fail, deny, accept, withhold, refuse, grasp, restrain.)*

glad—*adj.* joyous, gratified, gleeful, delighted, elated, happy, merry, joyful, cheerful, gladsome, blithesome, pleased. *(sorrowful, disap-*

pointed, tearful, dismal, sorry, unhappy, disastrous.)

glare—v. shine, ray, glow, stare, dazzle, beam, gleam, radiate. (scintillate, smoulder, glisten, sparkle, flicker, glance, shimmer, glitter, glimmer, glister, flash.)

glassy—adj. smooth, glacial, brittle, crystalline, limpid, silken, expressionless, glossy, pellucid, transparent, glabrous, polished, vitreous. (scabrous, muddy, opaque, pliant, uneven, bright, rough, rugged, tough, luteous, turbid.)

gloom—n. depression, despair, woe, melancholy, despondency, sorrow, pessimism, misery, sadness, dejection. (glee, happiness, joy, delight, mirth, frivolity, cheerfulness.)

glory—n. radiance, honor, fame, pomp, magnificence, renown, prestige, splendor, luster, celebrity, brightness, effulgence. (igonominy, dishonor, obscurity, cloud, degradation, infamy.)

glut—v. fill, cram, cloy, gorge, satiate, surfeit, stuff, devour. (empty, disgorge, vacant, void.)

glut—n. redundancy, overstock, surplus, deluge, superfluity, saturation. (drain-

age, dearth, scantiness, exhaustion, deficiency, scarcity, failure.)

go—v. depart, travel, reach, evaporate, move, budge, pass, vanish, extend, stir, set out. (stay, remain, abide, endure, fail, approach, lack, stand, come, persist, rest.)

good—adj. complete, sound, pious, propitious, suitable, sufficient, valid, actual, honorable, righteous, true, just, efficient, excellent, right, virtuous, benevolent, serviceable, admirable, competent, real, considerable, reputable, proper, upright. (imperfect, vicious, evil, niggardly, unserviceable, inefficient, incompetent, fictitious, inconsiderable, disgraceful, bad, mediocre, disreputable, mean, supposititious, invalid, inadequate, unsuitable, unpropitious, profane, unsound, wrong.)

good—n. benefit, gain, mercy, prosperity, profit, welfare, enjoyment, interest, boon, weal, advantage, blessing, virtue. (loss, disadvantage, calamity, hurt, catastrophe, curse, ill, injury, infliction, evil, detriment.)

goodly—adj. desirable, fair, fine, personable, pleasant, excellent, comely, graceful, considerable. (uncomely, *unpleasant, inconsiderable, disagreeable, undesirable.)*

goodness—*n.* honesty, integrity, morality, virtue, righteousness, merit, innocence, benevolence, worth, quality. *(dishonesty, vice, evil, wickedness, corruption, malice, imperfection, cruelty, spite.)*

gorgeous—*adj.* splendid, rich, grand, magnificent, glorious, costly, superb, strong, beautiful. *(naked, bare, dingy, poor, homely, threadbare, cheap.)*

govern—*v.* direct, moderate, conduct, manage, rule, influence, control, guide, sway, command, supervise. *(misdirect, misrule, submit, comply, miscontrol, follow.)*

grace—*n.* beauty, kindness, charm, pardon, favor, refinement, condescension, elegance, mercy, excellence. *(deformity, pride, awkwardness, ugliness, gawkiness, inelegance, unkindness, disfavor.)*

gracious—*adj.* courteous, kind, condescending, friendly, gentle, affable, beneficent, compassionate, benignant, civil, merciful, tender. *(discourteous, churlish, uncivil, haughty, illdisposed, ungracious, austere.)*

gradual—*adj.* step by step, slow, progressive, continuous, steady, gradational, unintermittent, successive. *(instantaneous, recurrent, disconnected, abrupt, sudden, broken, intermittent, momentary, periodic, hasty, discontinuous.)*

grand—*adj.* dignified, important, magnificent, majestic, exalted, impressive, splendid, elevated, gorgeous, superb, large, imposing, eventful, grandly, august, stately, lofty, pompous, sublime. *(undignified, secondary, unimportant, little, ignoble, insignificant, mean, paltry, unimposing, inferior, petty, beggarly, common.)*

grant—*v.* award, accord, bestow, donate, impart, confer, allow, give, yield, concede, apportion, allocate. *(refuse, deny, reject, renounce, forbid, despite, repel, withdraw, disclaim, withhold.)*

graphic—*adj.* illustrative, pictorial, vivid, described, striking, forcible, picturesque, descriptive, emphatic, comprehensible. *(unrealistic, dull, undescriptive, unpicturesque, hazy, unillustrative, dubious.)*

grateful—*adj.* acceptable, thankful, welcome, pleasant, appreciative, agreeable, obliged. *(disagreeable, rude, disobliged, unpleasant, careless, ungrateful.)*

gratify—*v.* satisfy, humor, charm, please, delight, indulge, regale, exhilarate. *(dissatisfy, stint, curb, inure, deprive, displease, deny, disappoint, discipline, harden, frustrate.)*

gratitude—*n.* gratefulness, obligation, thankfulness, acknowledgment, thanks, recognition. *(resentment, ingratitude, indignation, unthankfulness, beholdenness, thanklessness.)*

grave—*adj.* serious, weighty, sedate, thoughtful, sombre, important, heavy, sad, cogent, subdued, momentous, pressing, demure, sober, solemn, aggravated. *(merry, unimportant, trivial, frivolous, joyous, inconsequential, futile, light, ridiculous, facetious.)*

great—*adj.* huge, protracted, large, bulky, gigantic, grand, august, magnanimous, powerful, noticeable, stupendous, big, numerous, wide, excellent, immense, majestic, vast, sublime, eminent, noble, exalted. *(narrow, scanty, short, ignoble, unimportant, little, few, diminutive, puny, mean, weak.)*

greedy—*adj.* voracious, desirous, gluttonous, mercenary, avaricious, hungry. *(abstinent, contented, philanthropic, abstemious, indifferent.)*

grief—*n.* tribulation, mourning, affliction, sadness, heartbreak, trouble, woe, regret, sorrow. *(exultation, elation, bliss, joy, hilarity, solace, delight.)*

grieve—*v.* burden, distress, wound, sorrow, affict, lament, deplore, weep, trouble, annoy, bewail, pain, hurt, mourn, complain. *(console, please, exult, alleviate, gladden, ease, soothe, rejoice, gratify.)*

grim—*adj.* ferocious, hideous, ghastly, stern, fierce, terrible, savage, ugly, sullen. *(docile, placid, mild., amiable, benign, attractive.)*

groan—*v.* whine, grumble, moan, lament, growl, complain. *(cackle, titter, chuckle, laugh, giggle, snicker.)*

gross—*adj.* flagrant, deplorable, grievous, shocking, glaring, dreadful, outrageous, obvious, unmitigated. *(minor, trivial, small, graceful, elegant, refined, cultivated, inoffensive.)*

groundless—*adj.* suppositious, baseless, gratuitous, false, unwarranted, vain, unfounded, fanciful, chimerical. *(substantial, actual, authentic, well-founded, logical, authoritative, justified.)*

group—*n.* bunch, assemblage, class, clump, assembly, order, cluster, knot, collection, congregation, collocation. *(individual, confusion, isolation, crowd, medley, disperse.)*

grudge—*v.* retain, envy, spare, resent, covet, withhold, stint. *(welcome, spend, impart, gratify, please, satisfy.)*

grudge—*n.* grievance, rancor, pique, discontent, spite, aversion, resentment, refusal, dissatisfaction, hatred. *(satisfaction, bestowal, approval, benefaction, liberality, complacency, welcome, contentment.)*

gruff—*adj.* surly, harsh, blunt, impolite, rough, bearish, rude. *(mild, courteous, genial, affable, smooth.)*

guess—*v.* surmise, suppose, fancy, estimate, imagine, suspect, conjecture, divine. *(prove, establish, deduce, elaborate, examine, certainty, investigate, demonstrate.)*

guide—*v.* direct, pilot, superintend, train, lead, manage, shield, conduct, regulate, influence. *(misconduct, mismanage, misguide, betray, mislead, dupe, deceive, miseducate, misregulate, misdirect, ensore.)*

gush—*v.* stream, gush, rush, flow-out, burst, eject, flow, pour out, spout. *(drop, trickle, drain, filter, drip, dribble, ooze, percolate, strain, discharge.)*

guttural—*adj.* harsh, gruff, deep, hoarse, rasping, cracked, rough, gargling, throaty, inarticulate. *(high, ringing, musical, clear, pleasant, dulcet, nasal, squeaky.)*

H

habit—*n.* custom, association, usage, way, routine, manner, practice, inurement, familiarity, habituation. *(inexperience, desuetude, irregularity, dishabituation, inconversance.)*

habitual—*adj.* ordinary, customary, familiar, wonted, chronic, regular, perpetual, usual, accustomed. *(extraordinary, unusual, rare, sporadic, irregular, occasional, exceptional.)*

hail—*v.* salute, applaud, greet, acclaim, cheer, call, honor, signal, summon, accost, welcome. *(ignore, avoid,*

shun, neglect, pass over, disregard, rebuff, insult.)

half—n. bisection, partial,
dimidiation, moiety, divided.
(entirety, whole, total, integrity, totality, aggregate.)

halt—v. rest, falter, stammer, dubitate, hold, still,
restrain, stop, limp, hammer,
demur, pause, stand still.
(decide, speed, career, continue, advance, determine,
flow.)

handsome—adj. good-
looking, liberal, ample, graceful, elegant, stately, comely,
generous, beautiful, pretty,
lovely. (ill-looking, illiberal,
uncomely, unhandsome, re-
pulsive, ungenerous.)

handy—adj. convenient,
helpful, dexterous, expert, accessible, near, useful, manageable, ready. (inconvenient,
useless, unwieldy, worthless,
remote, awkward, cumbrous,
unhandy.)

haphazard—adj. aimless,
random, accidental, purposeless, casual, fortuitous, incidental, arbitrary, unmethod-
ical, unsystematic. (controlled, planned, deliberate, intentional, designed, organized,
thoughtful, premeditated,
systematic.)

happy—adj. fortunate, successful, joyous, blithesome,
glad, ecstatic, lucky, felicitious, delighted, merry, prosperous, blissful. (unfortunate,
sorry, unsuccessful, unlucky,
unhappy, lugubrious,
ecstatic, infelicitous, sorrowful, disappointed, dull,
desponding.)

hard—adj. dense, compact,
impenetrable, difficult, distressing, oppressive, un-
feeling, born, forced, inexplicable, severe, obdurate,
callous, hardened, cruel, flinty, constrained, harsh, stubborn, exacting, rigorous, firm,
grievous, arduous, unyielding,
solid, formidable. (fluid,
elastic, penetrable, mild,
tender, uninvolved, intelligible, soft, liquid, brittle, easy,
pliable, lenient, ductile, simple, perspicuous, resilient.)

hardship—n. burden, grievance, infliction, affliction,
ordeal, endurance, calamity,
annoyance, trouble. (amusement, recreation, relief,
facilitation, treat, pleasure,
happiness, alleviation, boon,
gratification, assuagement.)

hardy—adj. robust, resolute, stout-hearted, intrepid,
manly, sturdy, valiant, brave,
vigorous, inured, strong. (un-
inured, irresolute, debilitated,
fragile, weak, delicate, enervated, tender, dainty.)

harm—*n.* mischief, detriment, evil, misfortune, mishap, injury, hurt, trauma, damage, wrong, ill. *(boon, improvement, compensation, remedy, benefit, amelioration, reparation, healing, welfare, cure.)*

harmonious—*adj.* accordant, uniform, musical, tuneful, peaceful, amicable, concordant, compatible, congruous, proportioned, melodious, dulcet, consistent, agreeable, friendly. *(discordant, unshapely, unmelodious, grating, riotous, quarrelsome, conflicting, incongruous, disproportioned, harsh, sharp, unfriendly, unpeaceful.)*

hasty—*adj.* rapid, hurried, impetuous, head-long, incomplete, immature, precipitate, passionate, quick, rash, prompt, speedy, superficial, irascible, reckless, crude, undeveloped, swift, fiery, slight, excitable, cursory. *(leisurely, close, developed, complete, thoughtful, meticulous, slow, careful, reflective, matured, deliberate, elaborate.)*

hateful—*adj.* detestable, odious, execrable, repulsive, offensive, abominable, vile, heinous, loathsome. *(lovely, delightful, enticing, tempting, agreeable, pleasant, lovable, desirable, attractive, enjoyable.)*

have—*v.* possess, entertain, bear, keep, acquire, own, feel, accept, enjoy. *(need, forego, reject, desiderate, desire, crave, want, lose, discard, miss, covet.)*

hazard—*n.* risk, danger, imperil, venture, dare, peril, jeopardy, chance. *(security, warrant, calculation, safety, assurance, protection, certainty, law.)*

hazy—*adj.* nebulous, filmy, cloudy, caliginous, smoky, murky, gauzy, misty, foggy. *(clear, transparent, distinct, crystalline, diaphanous.)*

head—*n.* crown, leader, mind, section, topic, culmination, leadership, commander, summit, superior, top, chief, ruler, source, division, gathering, crisis, guide, acme. *(bottom, servant, tail, subordinate, inferiority, bulk, continuation, worker, follower, retainer, subordination, body, subject.)*

healthy—*adj.* hale, sound, hearty, vigorous, in the pink, robust, virile, strong, hygienic, healing, lusty. *(sickly, ill, weak, delicate, feeble, emaciated, ailing, infirm, debilitated, unsound.)*

hearty—*adj.* robust, sound, honest, genuine, sincere, hale, generous, healthy, cordial, warm, earnest, well, heart felt. *(delicate, cold, frail, insincere, infirm, unhealthy.)*

heat—*n.* ardor, excitement, ebullition, temperature, intensity, fever, passion, warmth. *(indifference, calmness, reflection, tranquillity, composure, subsidence, coolness.)*

heavy—*adj.* ponderous, slow, inert, stupid, impenetrable, cumbrous, afflictive, burdensome, laborious, weighty, dull, stolid, grievous, oppressive, sluggish, depressed, substantial. *(trifling, agile, light, quick, alleviative, skimpy, buoyant, weightless, trivial, active, joyous, consolatory, animating.)*

heighten—*v.* increase, intensify, vivify, raise, lift up, strengthen, amplify, exalt, enhance, color, aggravate, exaggerate. *(depress, deteriorate, temper, extenuate, qualify, abate, lower, diminish, abase, tone, modify.)*

heinous—*adj.* hateful, detestable, atrocious, abominable, enormous, repugnant, flagrant, flagitious, odious, execrable. *(laudable, praiseworthy, justifiable, palliable, creditable, excellent, meri-torious, distinguished, excusable.)*

help—*v.* succor, prevent, assist, co-operate, second, befriend, aid, remedy, avoid, promote, relieve. *(obstruct, incur, hinder, aggravate, oppose.)*

herculean—*adj.* formidable, mighty, prodigious, heroic, titanic, exhausting, difficult, arduous, overwhelming, stupendous. *(feeble, delicate, weak, restful, effortless, frail, easy.)*

hereditary—*adj.* ancestral, inbred, lineal, inherited, congenital. *(won, conferred, acquired, earned.)*

heroism—*n.* bravery, valor, courage, daring, gallantry, prowess, boldness, chivalry. *(cowardice, timidity, meanness, weakness, baseness, cravenness.)*

hesitate—*v.* waver, scruple, stammer, doubt, tentative, dubitate, demur, falter, pause. *(determine, flow, positive, career, run, decide.)*

hide—*v.* secrete, dissemble, protect, ensconce, cover, camouflage, burrow, screen, disguise, store, mask, conceal. *(discover, manifest, strip, reveal, expose, exhibit, betray.)*

hideous—*adj.* unshapely, horrid, ugly, grim, repulsive, ghastly, grisly, horrible, monstrous, frightful. *(beautiful, charming, attractive, graceful, captivating.)*

high—*adj.* lofty, eminent, noble, violent, exalted, prominent, elevated, tall, excellent, haughty, proud. *(low, ignoble, mean, affable, insignificant, depressed, stunted, base.)*

hilarious—*adj.* laughable, comical, uproarious, riotous, gleeful, mirthful, boisterous, funny. *(serious, depressed, miserable, melancholy, sad, woebegone.)*

hinder—*v.* interrupt, retard, embarrass, thwart, stop, delay, block, impede, debar, obstruct, prevent. *(expedite, promote, accelerate, enable, support, facilitate, encourage.)*

hoarse—*adj.* grating, raucous, gruff, guttural, rough, harsh, husky. *(mellow, sweet, full, mellifluous, rich, melodious.)*

hold—*v.* grasp, support, defend, occupy, sustain, consider, have, continue, occupy, keep, retain, restrain, maintain, possess, regard, cohere. *(abandon, fail, desert, vacate, break, relinquish, cease, drop, surrender, release, forego, concede.)*

hollow—*adj.* concave, weak, insincere, unsubstantial, flimsy, senseless, unsound, empty, foolish, faithless, artificial, void, transparent, vacant, false, sunken. *(solid, strong, sincere, genuine, sound, cogent, full, wellstored, firm, true, substantial.)*

homely—*adj.* coarse, modest, uncomely, plain. *(beautiful, courtly, ostentatious, handsome, refined.)*

honest—*adj.* upright, proper, sincere, reliable, conscientious, honorable, virtuous, right. *(dishonorable, improper, wrong, deceitful, dishonest, vicious, insincere.)*

honor—*n.* reverence, dignity, reputation, high-mindedness, self-respect, grandeur, glory, esteem, respect, nobility, eminence, fame, spirit, renown. *(contempt, slight, degradation, abasement, cowardice, infamy, humiliation, disrespect, irreverence, obscurity, disgrace, demoralization, dishonor.)*

honorary—*adj.* unofficial, nominal, titular, complimentary, gratuitous, unremuneration. *(remuneration, jurisdictional, official, professional, skilled.)*

hope—*n.* prospect, longing, desire, trust, contemplation, anticipation, vision, confidence, expectation. *(despondency, disbelief, abjuration, doubt, abandonment, distrust, despair.)*

horrible—*adj.* destestable, fearful, ghastly, hateful, horrid, frightful, shocking, abominable, dreadful, hideous, terrific, direful, awful. *(desirable, attractive, fair, amiable, lovely, enjoyable, beautiful, pleasant, delightful.)*

hostility—*n.* enmity, will, dislike, animosity, defiance, spite, hatred, contempt, abhorrence, antagonism. *(goodwill, warmth, benevolence, cordiality, friendliness, affability.)*

huge—*adj.* monstrous, vast, large, prodigious, stupendous, mammoth, gigantic, immense, enormous, colossal, bulky, great. *(undersized, puny, petty, pigny, microscopic.)*

humane—*adj.* kind, merciful, compassionate, charitable, benign, tender, benevolent. *(cruel, inhuman, unkind, brutal, unmerciful.)*

humble—*adj.* lowly, meek, low, unassuming, submissive, obscure, modest, unpretending, insignificant. *(lofty, proud, high, arrogant, pretentious, eminent, boastful, assuming, haughty.)*

humor—*n.* temper, caprice, pleasantry, drollery, disposition, nonsense, fun, frame, jocoseness, mood. *(personality, will, purpose, nature, mind, seriousness, sadness.)*

hurt—*v.* bruise, injure, pain, ache, grieve, damage, wound, harm. *(soothe, repair, reinstate, benefit, alleviate, compensate, heal, console.)*

hurt—*n.* injury, wound, detriment, harm, laceration, mischief, damage. *(pleasure, benefit, content, comfort.)*

hurtful—*adj.* injurious, baleful, baneful, detrimental, harmful, mischievous, pernicious, deleterious, noxious, moleficent. *(remedial, good, advantageous, helpful.)*

hypocritical—*adj.* sanctimonious, smooth, unctuous, pharisaical, faultfinding, mincing, mealy, smug. *(candid, sincere, transparent, plainspoken, lenient, genuine, truthful.)*

hysterical—*adj.* distraught, crazed, frenzied, overwrought, distracted, ludicrous, droll. *(composed, poised, grave, sad, calm, somber, serious.)*

I

idea—*n.* notion, belief, supposition, fiction, thought, fan-

111

tasy, image, sentiment, opinion, fancy, doctrine, understanding, conception, impression. *(form, thing, fact, reality, subject, object, weight.)*

ideal—*adj.* notional, intellectual, spiritual, supposititious, unreal, chimerical, imaginative, visionary, mental, conception, creative, poetical, fictitious, fanciful, imaginary. *(visible, tangible, real, palpable, factual, substantial, physical, material, historical, actual.)*

identical—*adj.* same, uniform, twin, equal, duplicate, alike, one, synonymous, equivalent, substitute, indistinguishable. *(separate, diverse, contrary, different, divergent, opposite, unlike, distinct.)*

idle—*adj.* unoccupied, vain, empty, useless, lazy, jobless, indolent, void, waste, unemployed, inactive. *(occupied, filled, helpful, assiduous, industrious, tilled, populated, employed.)*

ignoble—*adj.* base, humble, lowly, unworthy, mean, dishonorable, plebeian, inferior. *(noble, exalted, grand, illustrious, admirable, honorable, eminent, lordly, notable.)*

ignominious—*adj.* scandalous, infamous, humiliat-

ing, shameful, dishonorable. *(reputable, honorable, worthy, creditable, estimable.)*

ignorant—*adj.* uneducated, stupid, unlearned, unlettered, untaught, uninformed, illiterate. *(learned, cultivated, intelligent, well-informed, wise, cultured.)*

illegal—*adj.* illicit, banned, wrong, unlawful, prohibited, criminal, felonious, unconstitutional, illegitimate. *(lawful, sanctioned, permitted, legal, authorized, permissible, licit.)*

illegible—*adj.* cramped, obscure, scribbled, unreadable, indecipherable, unintelligible. *(clear, plain, legible, readable, intelligible.)*

illusion—*n.* mockery, delusion, phantasm, myth, show, fallacy, mirage, dream, deception, error, hallucination, vision, false. *(reality, substance, actuality, form, body, truth.)*

illustrious—*adj.* glorious, exalted, eminent, celebrated, noble, famous, remarkable, renowned, brillant, conspicuous, splendid. *(disgraceful, inglorious, obscure, ignominious, infamous, notorious, disreputable.)*

ill-will—*n.* hatred, dislike, spite, antipathy, malevolence, malice, aversion. *(bene-*

ficence, favor, congeniality, good-will.)

imaginative—adj. conceptive, poetical, inventive, enterprising, original, creative, ideal, romantic. (practical, unpoetical, prosaic, unromantic, uninventive, matter-of-fact, realistic.)

imagine—v. suppose, understand, fabricate, presume, apprehend, think, create, conceive, deem, surmise, fancy, envision. (exhibit, prove, verify, validate, depict, represent, demonstrate, substantiate.)

imitate—v. copy, follow, depict, pattern, mock, counterfeit, after duplicate, mimic, represent, ape, resemble, portray, repeat, echo. (caricature, vary, differentiate, remodel, change, distort, misrepresent, alter, dissimilate, modify.)

immaculate—adj. spotless, clean, unsoiled, untarnished, stainless, untainted, spic-and-span. (unclean, soiled, tarnished, dirty, spotted, stained.)

immediate—adj. contigious, direct, next, closest, proximate, present, instant. (remote, mediate, indirect, distant, future.)

immoral—adj. bad, wicked, unprincipled, corrupt, evil, heinous, obscene, indecent, unethical. (good, ethical, honest, moral, decent, noble, virtuous, honorable, chaste.)

impair—v. injure, damage, vitiate, lessen, obstruct, deteriorate, reduce, enfeeble, diminish. (improve, repair, amend, enhance, augment, facilitate.)

impassive—adj. phlegmatic, calm, insensible, reserved, unmoved, unemotional, aloof, sedate, apathetic, indifferent. (theatrical, expressive, demonstrative, responsive, dramatic, emotional, perturbed.)

impediment—n. obstacle, barrier, stumbling block, hinderance, obstruction, delay. (help, succor, furthermore, relief, furtherance, support, assistance, aid, encouragement.)

imperative—adj. irresistable, inexorable, compulsory, mandatory, obligatory, urgent, dictatorial, peremptorily. (lenient, entreative, optional, voluntary, indulgent, mild, supplicatory, discretional.)

imperious—adj. exacting, haughty, authoritative, arrogant, lordly, insolent, domineering, dictatorial. *(submissive, docile, lenient, subservient, mild, yielding, compliant, ductile, gentle.)*

implement—*n.* utensil, appliance, instrument, tool, apparatus. *(work, art, labor, agriculture, manufacture, science.)*

implicate—*v.* associate, criminate, entangle, compromise, embroil, connect, charge, involve, infold. *(dissociate, extricate, exclude, acquit, disconnect.)*

imply—*v.* mean, suggest, denote, import, include, connote, hint, involve, indicate. *(pronounce, declare, express, describe, state.)*

importance—*n.* moment, significance, avail, import, concern, signification, weight, consequence. *(insignificance, immateriality, triviality, unimportance, nothingness.)*

important—*adj.* expressive, main, considerable, dignified, weighty, material, essential, serious, significant, relevant, leading, great, influential, momentous, grave. *(trivial, irrelevant, petty, uninfluential, negligible, unimportant, insignificant, minor, inex-*

pressive, inconsiderable, mean, secondary.)

Impotent—*adj.* powerless, feeble, nerveless, incapacitated, enfeebled, weak, useless, helpless. *(vigorous, virile, forceful, strong, powerful.)*

Impractical—*adj.* unfeasible, inoperable, unrealistic, ideal, unintelligent, careless, speculative, quixotic, romantic. *(practical, viable, prosaic, pragmatic, realistic, sensible, systematic.)*

Impressive—*adj.* solemn, grand, imposing, magnificent, important, forcible, affecting, effective. *(unimpressive, tame, dry, unimportant, ordinary, insignificant, weak, feeble, jejune, vapid.)*

Improvement—*n.* amendment, increase, proficiency, enrichment, advancement, progress, correction, beneficial. *(degeneration, debasement, retrogression, ruination, degeneracy, deterioration, retrogradation.)*

Impudent—*adj.* insolent, shameless, rude, immodest, presumptuous, impertinent, saucy, brazen, bold. *(obsequious, bashful, diffident, modest, timid, servile, sycophantic, retiring, deferential.)*

impulse—*n.* push, force, instigation, motive, stimulus, incentive, incitement, thought, feeling. *(repulse, denial, deliberation, premeditation, rebuff, rejection.)*

inactive—*adj.* inert, stationary, inoperative, dormant, dilatory, idle, languid, indolent, dull, sedentary. *(operative, active, functional, dynamic, vigorous, energetic, busy, industrious.)*

inadequate—*adj.* deficient, lacking, unequal, unqualified, unfit, imperfect, meager, scant, slight, incapable, inept. *(adequate, fit, abundant, enough, sufficient, competent, capable, ample, equal.)*

inadvertent—*adj.* accidental, fortuitous, chance, thoughtless, unobservant, inconsiderate, careless, involuntary, unpremeditated. *(deliberate, careful, intentional, aware, premeditated, calculated, planned, studied.)*

inaudible—*adj.* inarticulate, muttering, stifled, silent, low, muffled, suppressed, mumbling. *(outspoken, loud, articulate, ringing, clear, audible, sonorous, candid.)*

incapable—*adj.* unable, weak, feeble, insufficient, inadequate, unqualified, unfitted, disqualified, incompetent. *(able, clever, fitted, qualified, skilled, strong.)*

incidental—*adj.* occasional, concomitant, accidental, casual, subordinate, appertinent, concurrent, fortuituous. *(regular, disconnected, essential, inherent, invariable, fundamental, systematic, independent, irrelative, imminent, uniform.)*

incivility—*n.* ill-breeding, uncourteousness, ill-manners, discourtesy, rudeness, impudence. *(urbanity, politeness, good-manners, civility, respect.)*

inclement—*adj.* tyrannical, raw, unmerciful, stormy, rigorous, tempestuous, harsh, cruel, severe, rough. *(benign, genial, pleasant, merciful, clement, mild.)*

inclination—*n.* slope, disposition, aptness, bias, attachment, liking, leaning, tendency, wish, proneness, predelection, bent, affection, desire. *(inaptness, disinclination, dislike, distate, inaptitude, repulsion.)*

incoherent—*adj.* incongruous, loose, illogical, unconnected, inconsequential. *(connected, plain, coherent, articulate, clear.)*

incomparable—*adj.* unique, transcendent, matchless, superlative, consummate. *(ordinary, mediocre, average, common.)*

inconsistent—*adj.* incompatible, incoherent, contrary, opposed, careless, remiss, thoughtless, vacillating, volatile, changing. *(coherent, uniform, steady, reliable, homogeneous, orderly, suitable, constant.)*

inconsolable—*adj.* joyless, melancholy, disconsolate, forlorn, heartbroken, cheerless, spiritless, gloomy, comfortless, heartsick. *(hopeful, consolable, enthusiastic, cheerful.)*

inconstant—*adj.* mutable, fitful, unsteadfast, erractic, fickle, changeable, variable, unstable. *(reliable, steady, constant, steadfast, loyal.)*

incontestable—*adj.* impregnable, indisputable, unassailable, undeniable, unquestionable, irrefutable. *(questionable, supposititious, dubious, problematical, hypothetical, arbitrary, assumptive, unctuous.)*

inconvenient—*adj.* annoying, awkward, cumbersome, bothersome, troublesome, tiresome, inopportune, untimely, unwieldy. *(opportune,* helpful, convenient, handy, advantageous, timely.)

increase—*n.* advance, development, augmentation, extension, addition, expansion, grouth, enlargement, spread, benefit. *(diminution, loss, decrease, reduction, drop, contraction.)*

incredible—*adj.* belief, marvelous, remarkable, surpassing, fabulous, preposterous. *(believable, usual, ordinary, credible, common, unremarkable.)*

inculcate—*v.* urge, infuse, instill, implant, teach, impart, press, impress, enforce. *(suggest, disavow, denounce, intimate, insinuate, abjure.)*

incumbent—*adj.* binding, urgent, indispensable, devolvent, imperative, pressing, coercive, obligatory, persistent. *(discretional, exempt, optional, privileged.)*

incurable—*adj.* irredeemable, terminal, cureless, irremediable, hopeless. *(remediable, tractable, curable, removable, correctable.)*

indecent—*adj.* immodest, improper, distasteful, indelicate, lewd. *(proper, delicate, modest, virtuous, ethical.)*

ineffable— *adj.* inconceivable, indeclarable, exquisite, perfect, unutterable, inexpressible, insurpassable, indescribable. *(trivial, vulgar, colloquial, commonplace, frivolous, common, superficial, conversational, obvious.)*

Ineffectual—*adj.* useless, idle, abortive, ineffective, unsuccessful, fruitless, vain, unavailing, inoperative. *(successful, effective, profitable, effectual, useful.)*

Inexcusable—*adj.* unpardonable, unjustifiable, outrageous, unmitigated, indefensible, unforgiving. *(pliable, vindicable, pardonable, forgivable, mitigable, justifiable, defensible.)*

Inexhaustible—*adj.* unwearied, perennial, unlimited, illimitable, incessant, indefatigable. *(poor, measured, limited, scant, wearied.)*

Inexpedient—*adj.* inadvisable, imprudent, disadvantagious, undesirable, indiscreet. *(expedient, advisable, judicious, profitable.)*

Infallible—*adj.* perfect, sure, reliable, foolproof, dependable, all-wise, incontestable, tested, unimpeachable, certain. *(errant, dubious, refutable, uncertain, unsure, doubtful, unsure, contestable, unreliable.)*

Infamy—*n.* degradation, ignominy, extreme, dishonor, corruption, despair, disgrace, obloquy, vileness. *(reputation, glory, integrity, renown, honor, celebrity.)*

Inference—*n.* corollary, deduction, consequence, assumption, conclusion. *(enunciation, anticipation, proposition, statement.)*

Inferiority—*n.* minority, mediocrity, servitude, insignificance, poverty, subordination, subjection, depression, inadequacy. *(majority, edge, eminence, mastery, elevation, advantage, superiority, excellence, independence, exaltation.)*

Infidel—*n.* unbeliever, heretic, freethinker, pagan, skeptic. *(pietist, Christian, religionist, believer, devotee.)*

Infinitesimal—*adj.* tiny, wee, microscopic, diminutive, insignificant, imperceptible, minute. *(vast, colossal, huge, enormous, tremendous, gargantuan, great.)*

Inflame—*v.* kindle, rouse, fire, incense, infuriate, irritate, fan, anger, ignite, enrage, excite, madden, exasperate, imbitter. *(extinguish, cool, quiet, soothe, quench, allay, pacify.)*

Inflexible—*adj.* firm, steadfast, determined, rigid, mulish, resolute, adamant, stubborn, obstinate, stringent. *(elastic, resilient, pliable, supple, flexible, springy, malleable, fluid.)*

Influence—*n.* control, affection, power, character, weight, prestige, supremacy, authority, effect, causation, impulse, credit, sway, ascendancy. *(ineffectiveness, nullity, inefficacy, aloofness, inefficiency, inoperativeness, neutrality.)*

Influential—*adj.* powerful, forcible, controlling, considerable, inspiring, potent, efficacious, persuasive, guiding. *(ineffective, weak, inconsiderable, unpersuasive, impede, inoperative.)*

Information—*n.* advice, notice, knowledge, evidence, counsel, instruction, notification. *(occulatation, ignorance, unawareness, concealment, mystification, hiding.)*

Infringe—*v.* violate, contravene, intrude, break, transgress. *(conserve, satisfy, keep within bounds, observe, preserve.)*

Ingenious—*adj.* adept, inventive, frank, creative, skillful, clever, ready, sincere, imaginative. *(slow, unready, unskillful, clumsy, inept, uninventive.)*

Ingenuous—*adj.* candid, frank, straightforward, open, honest, unsophisticated, noble, generous, sincere, honorable, artless. *(reserved, subtle, disingenuous, insincere, sly, mean.)*

Ingrained—*adj.* innate, inborn, inherent, intrinsic, rooted, organic, inbred, implanted. *(surface, alien, external, superficial, learned, superimposed, acquired.)*

Ingredient—*n.* component, factor, constituent, element, module, section. *(refuse, counter-agent, non-ingredient, incongruity, residuum.)*

Inherent—*adj.* congenial, ingrained, intrinsic, inbred, essential, innate, immanent, inborn, natural. *(ascititious, separable, foreign, extraneous, superficial, temporary.)*

Initiative—*n.* leadership, start, example, independence, commencement, enterprise. *(termination, wake, prosecution, rear.)*

Injunction—*n.* order, exhortation, requirement, mandate, precept, command. *(insubordination, infraction, nonobservance, non-compliance, disobedience.)*

injurious—*adj.* deleterious, noxious, baleful, wrongful, damaging, abusive, baneful, hurtful, prejudicial, detrimental, pernicious, mischievous. *(advantageous, helpful, constructive, healing, beneficial.)*

innocence—*n.* inoffensiveness, guiltlessness, purity, sinlessness, innocuousness, guilelessness, simplicity, harmlessness. *(offensiveness, guilt, corruption, sinfulness, reprehensibility, hurtfullness, guile, contamination, impurity.)*

innocent—*adj.* blameless, pure, spotless, harmless, sinless, guiltless, naive, unsophisticated, unwordly, ingenuous, honest, chaste, virginal. *(sinful, guilty, corrupt, impure, wily, evil, culpable, immoral, nefarious, tainted, dishonest.)*

innocuous—*adj.* harmless, moderate, wholesome, bland, inoffensive. *(deleterious, obnoxious, insidious, hurtful, pernicious.)*

inquiry—*n.* question, investigation, examination, scrutiny, probe, exploration, interrogation, asking, search, research, analysis. *(supposition, hypothesis, guess, theory, conjecture, intuition, assumption.)*

insatiable—*adj.* unappeasable, ravenous, greedy, unlimited, voracious, omnivorous, rapacious. *(delicate, dainty, appeasable, moderate, fastidious, squeamish, limited.)*

insidious—*adj.* treacherous, dangerous, sly, artful, wily, underhanded, designing, deceitful, crafty. *(undesigning, straightforward, innocuous, overt, sincere, frank.)*

insincere—*adj.* false, deceitful, fraudulent, hollow, perfidious, hypocritical, dishonest, guileful, double-dealing, devious. *(earnest, honest, sincere, direct, truthful, genuine, candid, straightforward.)*

insinuate—*v.* insert, ingratiate, suggest, hint, convey, introduce, worm, intimate, infuse. *(retract, extract, withdraw, remove, alienate.)*

insipid—*adj.* vapid, uninteresting, flavorless, pointless, prosy, monotonous, stupid, tasteless, characterless, flat, lifeless, dull. *(savory, tasty, flavorful, delicious, pungent, stimulating, piquant, lively, provocative, spirited.)*

Insist—v. demand, contend, persist, urge, vouch, stand, maintain, persevere, assert. *(waive, yield, plead, abandon, forego, concede, surrender.)*

insolent—*adj.* overbearing, abusive, impertinent, offensive, surly, outrageous, rude, insulting, haughty, contemptuous, saucy, opprobrious, pert, scurrilous. *(courteous, civil, polite, obedient, deferential, respectful.)*

insolvent—*adj.* ruined, penniless, overextended, beggared, bankrupt. *(flourishing, solid, thriving, flush, monied, sound.)*

inspire—v. inspirit, imbue, encourage, enliven, breathe in, exhilarate, influence, animate, inflame, impel, inhale, cheer, infuse. *(dispirit, deter, discourage, stifle, depress, squelch.)*

inspiring—*adj.* encouraging, inspirational, moving, eloquent, lofty, motivating, heartening, stimulating, uplifting. *(depressing, dull, boring, uninspiring, dispiriting, discouraging.)*

instance—*n.* request, persuasion, solicitation, illustration, entreaty, occurrence, precedence, specimen, prompting, example, case, ex-emplification, point. *(warning, statement, misexemplification, breach, dissuassion, rule, depreciation, principle.)*

instill—v. infuse, import, insinuate, indoctrinate, pour, inculcate, introduce, implant. *(strain, eradicate, remove, discard, drain, extract, extirpation, eliminate.)*

instinctive—*adj.* voluntary, intuitive, innate, impulsive, natural, spontaneous. *(forced, willed, rationalistic, premeditated, cultivated, reasoning.)*

instruction—*n.* education, counsel, direction, command, guidance, teaching, information, advice, order. *(misinformation, misdirection, obedience, pupilage, misteaching, misguidance, misinstruction.)*

insufferable—*adj.* unpermissible, unendurable, outrageous, unbearable, unallowable, intolerable. *(allowable, supportable, bearable, tolerable, endurable.)*

insupportable—*adj.* intolerable, unendurable, obnoxious, unbearable, insufferable. *(comfortable, to be borne, tolerable, endurable.)*

integrity—*n.* honor, probity, candor, conscientiousness, rectitude, parity, virtue, uprightness, honesty, truthfulness, single-mindedness, entireness, completeness. *(sleight, meanness, duplicity, roguery, immorality, rascality, unfairness, underhandedness, chicanery, fraud.)*

Intellectual—*adj.* metaphysical, inventive, cultured, mental, psychological, learned, knowledgeable. *(unlearned, unintellectual, illiterate, unmetaphysical.)*

Intelligence—*n.* apprenhension, conception, report, tidings, information, rumor, intellectual, capacity, knowledge, news, notice, intellect, perception, publication, understanding, comphrension, mind, announcement, advice, instruction. *(misinformation, stupidy, suppression, darkness, silence, misguidance, misrepart, dullness, ineptitude, misapprehension, misunderstanding, misconception, ignorance, concealment, nonpublication, misintelligence.)*

Intensity—*n.* force, strain, energy, eagerness, strength, tension, concentration, attention, ardor. *(debility, languor, coolness, diminution, decrease, laxity, relaxative, indifference, coolness, hebetude.)*

Intentional—*adj.* designed, intended, contemplated, studied, planned, purposed, deliberate, done on purpose, premeditated. *(casual, accidental, haphazard, undersigned, unintentional, fortuitous.)*

Intercourse—*n.* dealing, intimacy, commerce, conversation, connection, correspondence, intercommunication. *(suspension, disconnection, interpellation, restraint, reticence, cessation, interception.)*

Interest—*n.* business, profit, share, curiosity, cause, consequence, concern, advantage, attention, behalf. *(disconnection, disadvantage, inattention, loss, indifference, boredom, unconcern, repudiation, incuriosity.)*

Interior—*adj.* inside, inner, proximal, enclosed, internal, encapsulated, remote, inland. *(exterior, outer, external, outside,exposed, distal, surface.)*

Intermediate—*adj.* included, comprised, moderate, transitional, interjacent, intervening, interposed, middle. *(surrounding, embracing, extreme, exclusive, advanced, circumjacent, enclosing, outside, excluded.)*

Interpret—v. render, explain, expone, declare, elucidate, solve, unravel, translate, construe, expound, represent, understand, decipher. *(misunderstand, misconceive, distort, misrepresent, confuse, misinterpret, mistake, falsify, misdeclare.)*

Interrupt—v. disconnect, obstruct, intersect, stop, hinder, break, discontinue, distrub. *(prosecute, resume, expedite, continue.)*

Interval—n. meantime, gap, interspace, space between, pause, season, interim, period, intermission, cessation. *(perpetuity, uninterruptedness, continuity, simultaneousness.)*

Intimate—v. communicate, declare, suggest, insinuate, allude, mention briefly, impart, announce, tell, hint. *(repress, withhold, proclaim, reserve, conceal.)*

Intoxication—n. poison, bewilderment, hallucination, ecstasy, alcoholism, drunkenness, venom, obfuscation, delirium, ravishment, inebriation, inebriety. *(clarification, sanity, melancholy, antidote, temperance, depression, sobriety, ebriety.)*

Intricate—adj. involved, labyrenthine, tortuous, perplexing, complicated, mazy, entangled. *(uninvolved, direct, plain, unadorned, obvious, simple.)*

Introduction—n. importation, taking, insertion, preliminary, initiative, vestibule, gate, prelude, conducting, induction, leading, presentation, commencement, preface, portico, entrance, preamble. *(extraction, elimination, estrangement, completion, egress, withdrawal, education, exportation, ejection, conclusion, end.)*

Introductory—adj. initatory, precursary, preparatory, beginning, prefatory, commendatory, preliminary. *(final, alienative, terminal, ultimate, valedictory, completive, conclusive, supplemental.)*

Intuition—n. apprehension, insight, clairvoyance, instinct, recognition. *(learning, elaboration, induction, reasoning, information, instruction, acquirement, experience.)*

Invalid—adj. sick, frail, incapacitated, infirm, wealthy, feeble. *(healthy, strong, hearty, well, vigorous.)*

Invent—v. contrive, imagine, conceive, devise, originate, frame, feign, create, discover, concoct, elaborate, design, fabricate, find out, forge. *(copy, reproduce, simulate, imitate, execute.)*

Invincible—*adj.* immovable, unsubduable, indomitable, insupirable, impregnable, unyielding, inexpugnable, irresistible, unconquerable, insurmountable. *(spiritless, weak, puny, vulnerable, effortless, powerless.)*

invisible—*adj.* ultimate, minute, concealed, atomic, mysterious. *(separable, obvious, divisible, discerptible, visible.)*

involve—*v.* confound, envelop, include, entangle, contain, implicate, mingle, compromise, complicate. *(extricate, liberate, disconnect, separate.)*

irreligious—*adj.* ungodly, profane, blasphemous, impious, godless, undevout. *(godly, reverential, devout, worshipful, religious, reverent, pious.)*

irrepressible—*adj.* ungovernable, insuppressible, unconfined, vibrant, excitable, unrepressible, uncontrollable, free. *(governable, calm, depressed, bound down, repressible, controllable.)*

irresponsible—*adj.* unencumbered, not answerable, lawless, despotic, unreliable.

(obligatory, imperative, under obligation, legal, trustworthy, legitimate, responsible, binding, chargeable on, lawful.)

irritate—*v.* annoy, exasperate, anger, provoke, agitate, irk, trouble, pester, offend. *(calm, soothe, appease, please, placate, pacify, comfort.)*

isolate—*v.* segregate, insulate, quarantine, sequester, detach, separate, exile, set apart. *(unite, mix, join, combine, blend, merge, coordinate.)*

J

jealous—*adj.* self-anxious, invidious, resentful, suspicious, envious, covetous. *(liberal, self-denying, unjealous, tolerant, unenvious, genial, indifferent.)*

jejune—*adj.* deficient, inadequate, lacking, wanting, inane, dull, insubstantial, insipid, prosaic. *(invigorating, vital, nourishing, solubrious, exciting, mature, inspired.)*

jeopardy—*n.* danger, exposure, risk, hazard, peril, insecurity, precariousness, liability. *(safety, security, certainty.)*

jingle—n. tinkle, jangle, ring, clink, rattle. *(harmony, melody, euphony, consonance, chord.)*

jocular—*adj.* humorous, witty, funny, whimsical, droll, jovial, frolicsome, amusing, jolly, comical. *(solemn, earnest, grave, sober, serious, sedate, humorless.)*

join—v. adhere, add, connect, annex, combine, accompany, splice, confederate, unite, link, adjoin, couple, associate, append. *(disjoin, disconnect, sever, separate, subtract, deviate, quit, disassociate.)*

jollification—n. festivity, fun, merry-making, jubilation, revelry, conviviality, carnival. *(tediousness, tedium, weariness, monotony, soberness, redundance.)*

jolly—*adj.* joyful, mirthful, jovial, robust, plump, gay, cheerful, merry, gladsome, genial, jubilant, lively. *(mournful, cheerless, lugubrious, gloomy, saturnine, lean, sad, joyless, unmirthful, morose.)*

jostle—n. push, jog, hustle, thrust, shake, tremor, jolt, collison. *(lead, guidance, convoy, escort, squire, pilot.)*

jovial—*adj.* gay, gleeful, blithe, cheerful, jocular, delightful, humorous, merry, animated, buoyant. *(dour, gloomy, melancholy, saturnine, somber, pensive, sober, cheerless, morose.)*

joy—n. pleasure, happiness, transport, ecstasy, bliss, mirth, festivity, charm, delight, blessedness, gladness, elation, exultation, felicity, rapture, gaiety, merriment, hilarity. *(pain, misery, grief, tears, despondency, distress, despair, sorrow, trouble, melancholy, affliction, depression.)*

jubilant—*adj.* triumphant, glad, congratulatory, joyous, exultant, elated, festive, ecstatic, radiant. *(mournful, wailing, penitential, remorseful, dejected, doleful, sorrowful, penitent, lugubrious, forlorn.)*

judgement—n. determination, sagacity, judiciousness, intellect, estimation, verdict, discernment, intelligence, award, arbitration, condemnation, decision, adjudication, penetration, sense, belief, opinion, sentence, discrimination, prudence. *(consideration, inquiry, speculation, investigation, insagacity, evidence, obtuseness, pronunciation, argument, proposition, pleading, injudiciousness.)*

judicious—*adj.* sagacious, wise, sensible, discreet, well-advised, discerning, cautious, thoughtful, expedient, prudent, well-judged, polite. *(unwise, foolish, imprudent, ill-judged, silly, impolitic, rash, injurious, unreasonable, indiscreet, ill-advised, inexpedient, blind.)*

juggle—*v.* cheat, shuffle, beguile, swindle, mystify, manipulate, mislead, conjure, bamboozle, trick, circumvent, overreach. *(correct, guide, undeceive, detect, direct, expose, enlighten, lead, disillusionize.)*

junior—*adj.* secondary, younger, subordinate, minor, inferior, youthful, immature, juvenile, adolescent. *(superior, older, advanced, elder, senior, primary, mature, adult.)*

just—*adj.* fitting, fair, harmonious, reasonable, honorable, impartial, upright, orderly, right, proper, decent, exact, true, proportioned, honest, sound, normal, equitable, regular, lawful, righteous. *(misfitted, ill-proportioned, inharmonious, unreasonable, biased, dishonorable, unequitable, irregular, disorderly, inexact, disproportioned, untrue, un-*

fair, unsound, partial, unjust, abnormal.)

justice—*n.* impartiality, right, propriety, desert, virtue, integrity, equity, fairness, reasonableness, uprightness. *(wrong, unfairness, unlawfulness, dishonor, inadequateness, injustice, partiality, unreasonableness.)*

justify—*v.* defend, vindicate, excuse, exonerate, acquit, warrant, advocate, plead for, varnish, clear. *(incriminate, tax, accuse, blame, censure, denounce, indict, implicate, condemn.)*

juvenile—*adj.* young, boyish, early, adolescent, childish, unsophisticated, puerile, youthful, infantine, girlish, immature, pubescent. *(later, womanly, aged, anile, adult, developed, superannuated, mature, manly, elderly, senile.)*

K

keen—*adj.* vehement, piercing, acute, biting, sarcastic, ardent, shrewd, knife-like, eager, sharp, penetrating, cutting, severe, satirical, prompt. *(languid, dull, flat, obtuse, blind, indifferent.)*

keep—*v.* restrain, detain, guard, suppress, conceal,

support, tend, conduct, obey, observe, celebrate, adhere to, hinder, possess, hold, retain, preserve, repress, maintain, continue, haunt, frequent, sustain, protect, practice. *(acquit, send, betray, divulge, abandon, disobey, transgress, desert, ignore, release, liberate, dismiss, neglect, discard, intermit, disregard, obviate, forsake.)*

key—*adj.* crucial, salient, decisive, vital, essential, basic, chief, fundamental, indispensable, material. *(immaterial, secondary, insignificant, minor, peripheral.)*

kind—*n.* character, designation, genus, sort, nature, breed, progeny, style, description, denomination, species, class, set. *(dissimilarity, unlikeness,variety.)*

kind—*adj.* benign, indulgent, clement, compassionate, good, forbearing, charitable, benevolent, tender, humane, lenient, gentle, gracious, kind-hearted. *(harsh, cruel, illiberal, bitter, unkind, severe, hard, ruthless.)*

kindle—*v.* light, ignite, provoke, inflame, arouse, excite, stir, enkindle, awaken, set fire to. *(douse, smother, quench, stifle, extinguish.)*

kindness—*n.* goodness, benevolence, philanthropy, humanity, tolerance, compassion, tenderness, mercy, generosity, goodwill, charity. *(meanness, cruelty, inhumanity, coldness, severity, unkindness, malevolence.)*

kindred—*adj.* akin, fraternal, familial, allied, harmonious, congenial, related, united, germane. *(uncongenial, dissimilar, different, unlike, alien, unrelated.)*

king—*n.* sovereign, lord, czar, tycoon, master, potentate, leader, monarch, chief. *(subject, slave, serf, follower, dependent, vassal, servant.)*

knack—*n.* skill, ability, gift, genius, aptitude, facility, flair, dexterity, cleverness. *(ineptitude, gaucherie, clumsiness, awkwardness, disability.)*

knit—*v.* join, fasten, affix, link, attach, connect, unite, secure, weave, bind. *(part, divide, separate, split.)*

knot—*n.* bond, difficulty, twist, cluster, band, protuberance, joint, tie, intricacy, perplexity, collection, group. *(unfastening, solution, unraveling, multitude, untie, indentation, smoothness, cavity, loosening, dissolution, crowd, explication, dispersion, evenness.)*

knotty—*adj.* gnarled, bumpy, knotted, rough, lumpy, uneven, nodular, coarse, rugged. *(flat, level, smooth, plane, obvious, clear.)*

knowing—*adj.* astute, sharp, sagacious, proficient, acute, intelligent, well-informed, perceptive, accomplished, shrewd, discerning, penetrating, skillful, experienced. *(dull, gullible, stolid, unwise, silly, simple, innocent, undiscerning.)*

knowledge—*n.* comprehension, understanding, experience, familiarity, notice, instruction, enlightenment, attainments, erudition, apprehension, recognition, conversance, acquaintance, cognizance, information, learning, scholarship, ability, wisdom. *(inobservance, deception, misunderstanding, inconversance, ignorance, incognizance, rudeness, uneducatedness, illiterateness, incapacity, misapprehension, incomprehension, misconception, inexperience, unfamiliarity, misinformation, misinstruction, untutoredness.)*

L

laborious—*adj.* diligent, indefatigable, burdensome, wearisome, hard-working, difficult, tedious, strenuous, assiduous, painstaking, arduous, toilsome, industrious, active. *(indiligent, easy, indolent, facile, simple, idle, dainty, lazy, light, feasible.)*

lack—*n.* deficiency, absence, shortcoming, want, gap, failure, insufficiency, dearth, omission. *(surplus, extra, excess, sufficiency, plethora, adequacy, amplitude.)*

laconic—*adj.* curt, epigrammatic, concise, terse, concentrated, summary. *(wordy, prosy, circumlocutory, prolix, tedious, talkative, garrulous, laquacious.)*

laggardly—*adv.* tardily, slowly, belatedly, dilatorily, hesitantly, languidly, sluggishly, slackly, backwardly. *(quickly, speedily, willingly, smartly, readily, briskly.)*

lame—*adj.* faltering, hesitating, impotent, halt, imperfect, crippled, weak, hobbling, ineffective, deformed, defective. *(agile, efficient, cogent, telling, nimble, robust, potent, satisfactory, convincing, effective.)*

language—*n.* talk, dialect, tongue, phraseology, accents, expression, verbalization, speech, conversation, discourse, diction, articulation, vernacular. *(jabber, babel, cry, bark, roar, dumbness, jargon, inarticulateness, chatter, gabble, speechlessness, gibberish, whine, howl, obmutescence, muteness.)*

languid—*adj.* weary, unnerved, pining, enervated, flagging, apathetic, spiritless, faint, feeble, unbraced, drooping, exhausted. *(healthy, strong, vigorous, braced, fatigued, robust, active.)*

large—*adj.* bulky, abundant, ample, comprehensive, catholic, vast, substantial, wide, big, extensive, capacious, liberal, enlightened, great. *(mean, circumscribed, scanty, niggardly, petty, minute, sordid, small, narrow, contracted, illiberal, bigoted.)*

last—*v.* remain, endure, live, persevere, continue, hold, abide. *(fail, fly, depart, terminate, expire, cease, fade, wane, disappear.)*

last—*adj.* ending, concluding, past, lowest, ultimate, terminal, latest, final, hindmost, extreme, remotest. *(introductory, opening, ensuing, minor, nearest, temporary, first, initiatory, foremost, highest, next.)*

latent—*adj.* hidden, potential, dormant, quiescent, suspended, inactive, smoldering, passive, concealed, covert. *(evident, active, apparent, manifest, kinetic, patent, activated, developed.)*

laud—*v.* extol, glorify, honor, applaud, esteem, compliment, approve, acclaim, praise. *(denigrate, belittle, decry, censure, disparage, minimize.)*

laughter—*n.* glee, ridicule, contempt, mocking, merriment, derision, cachinnation. *(tears, sorrow, veneration, whimper, wailing, weeping, mourning, admiration, respect, whine.)*

law—*n.* edict, decree, order, enactment, method, principle, legislation, jurisdiction, ordinance, jurisprudence, rule, regulation, command, statute, mode, sequence, code, adjudication. *(disorder, rebellion, hazard, irregularity, casualty, chaos, accident, misrule, anarchy, insubordination, chance, caprice.)*

lawful—*adj.* permissible, right, fair, rightful, permitted, legitimate, legal, orderly, allowable, constitutional. *(impermissible, wrong, unfair, prohibited, illegal, unlawful, lawless.)*

lay—*v.* establish, allay, arrange, put, set down, repose, place, deposit, prostrate, dispose, spread. *(raise, excite, disorder, abrade, elevate, erect, lift, disarrange, scrape.)*

lead—*v.* guide, induce, pass, inaugurate, persuade, conduct, influence, accompany, precede, spend, commence, convoy, direct. *(mislead, dissuade, leave, depart, misguide, misconduct, follow, abandon.)*

lead—*n.* prominence, guidance, direction, control, priority. *(inferiority, followership, submission, subordination.)*

lean—*v.* rest, tend, depend, repose, slope, slant, incline, support, bend, hang, confide. *(re-erect, rise, reject, straighten, stabilitate, erect, raise.)*

lean—*adj.* lank, emaciated, bony, scraggy, slender, skeletal, scanty, meagre, tabid, shrivelled, thin, skinny. *(brawny, fleshy, well- conditioned, fat, plump.)*

learned—*adj.* erudite, skilled, literary, well-informed, profound, versed, conversant, read, scholarly, knowing. *(illiterate, unlearned, uneducated, unscholarly, inconversant, ignorant.)*

learning—*n.* erudition, lore, acquirements, scholarship, tuition, wisdom, knowledge, literature, letters, attainments, education, culture, skill. *(boorishness, emptiness, intuition, inspiration, nescience, ignorance, sciolism, illiterateness, revelation.)*

leave—*n.* permission, concession, sanction, liberty, license. *(prohibition, veto, inhibition, refusal, restriction, prevention.)*

leery—*adj.* wary, suspicious, cautious, dubious, skeptical, unsure, uncertain, shy, distrustful. *(credulous, gullible, confident, trustful, secure, assured.)*

legal—*adj.* legitimate, lawful, licit, rightful, legalistic, judiciary, statutory, juristic, permissible, legislative. *(illegal, unlawful, illicit, extrajudicial, invalid, illegitimate.)*

legend—*n.* fable, story, saga, myth, marvelous, fiction. *(fact, occurrence, event, history, actual.)*

lengthy—*adj.* prolix, long-drawn, diffuse, verbase, interminable, tedious, elongated. *(compendious, short, laconic, condensed, fleeting, suc-*

cinct, concise, curt, brief, compact.)

leniency—*n.* indulgence, patience, mercifulness, softness, pity, charity, benevolence, compassion, mildness, mercy, gentleness. *(roughness, severity, sternness, harshness, mercilessness, implacability.)*

lesson—*n.* warning, lecture, information, exercise, precept, instruction, homily. *(misguidance, misinstruction, deception, misinformation.)*

lethargic—*adj.* apathetic, lazy, sluggish, drowsy, languid, dull, comatose, slow, sleepy, slothful, indolent, idle. *(vigorous, vital, energetic, alert, animated, lively, strenuous, spirited.)*

level—*n.* surface, equality, plane, platform, coordinateness, floor, position, horizontalness, aim, ground. *(acclivity, inequality, verticality, elevation, declivity, unevenness, uncoordinateness.)*

level—*v.* smooth, flatten, raze, align, plane, roll, equalize. *(furrow, graduate, engrave, roughen, disequalize.)*

level—*adj.* plain, even, flat, uniform, smooth, horizontal. *(uneven, rolling, sloping, broken, rough.)*

libel—*n.* detraction, calumny, defamatory, lampoon, innuendo, defamation, traducement, slander, publication. *(vindication, eulogy, puff, encomium, retraction, cancellation, apology, panegyric, advocacy.)*

liberal—*adj.* gentle, polished, free, bountiful, enlarged, ample, large, munificent, noble-minded, tolerant, lavish, plentiful, refined, generous, catholic, capious, profuse, handsome, abundant, bounteous. *(low, boorish, illiberal, niggardly, greedy, narrow-minded, prejudiced, scanty, bigoted, mean, inadequate, churlish, ungenerous, grasping, avaricious, gainful, conservative, contracted.)*

liberty—*n.* leave, permission, license, immunity, impropriety, voluntariness, audacity, exemption, freedom, independence, privilege, franchise, insult, volition. *(servitude, constraint, dependence, compulsion, respect, necessity, predestination, bondage, slavery, restraint, submission, obligation, deference, considerateness, fatality.)*

licentious—*adj.* dissolute, lax, debauched, loose, libertine, unbridled, voluptuous, rakish, self-indulgent, profligate. *(strict, self-controlled, self-denying, rigid, puritanical, temperate, sober, ascetic.)*

lie—*n.* untruth, subterfuge, fib, falsity, deception, falsehood, fabrication, evasion, fiction. *(veracity, truth, reality, fact.)*

lie—*v.* repose, remain, lounge, be, rest. *(stir, change, rise, move.)*

life—*n.* duration, condition, spirit, animation, personality, society, history, vitality, career, existence, vigor, state, morals, activity, conduct, vivacity. *(decease, non-existence, torpor, lethargy, extinction, lifelessness, mortality, death, dullness, portraiture.)*

lift—*v.* elevate, upheave, hoist, erect, heighten, raise, upraise, exalt, elate. *(sink, crush, overwhelm, plunge, lower, depress, hurl, degrade, cast, dash.)*

light—*n.* radiance, gleam, scintillation, flash, brilliancy, splendor, candle, lantern, instruction, understanding, day, luster, life, luminosity, beam, phosphorescence, coruscation, brightness, effulgence, blaze, lamp, explanation, illumination, interpretation. *(dimness, shade, night,*

gloom, misinterpretation, dusk, misunderstanding, death, tenebrosity, mystification, extinguish, darkness, obscurity, duskiness, extinction, ignorance, confusion.)*

light—*adj.* portable, buoyant, easy, scanty, unencumbered, slight, unsteady, vain, characterless, unthoughtful, inadequate, unsubstantial, not difficult, bright, trifling, sparse, imponderous, unweighty, volatile, digestible, active, empty, gentle, capricious, frivolous, thoughtless, unconsidered, incompact, inconsiderable, whitish. *(dark-colored, heavy, weighty, leaden, hard, full, encumbered, oppressed, loaded, ballasted, serious, violent, firm, cautious, reliable, sensible, thoughtful, adequate, compact, ponderous, immovable, solid, indigestible, lazy, burdened, weighed, laden, grave, important, steady, principled, reflective, liable, earnest, well-considered, stiff, dark, substantial.)*

likeness—*n.* resemblance, similitude, copy, portrait, image, carte de visite, appearance, picture, similarity, correspondence, parity, imitation, representation, effigy. *(dissimilitude, inequality, original, difference, dissimilarity, disparity, unlikeness.)*

line—*n.* thread, outline, direction, course, succession, continuity, filament, cord, length, row, verse, method, sequence. *(contents, divergency, fluctuation, interruption, discontinuance, constancy, breath, space, deviation, variation, solution.)*

link—*v.* couple, combine, merge, attack, join, consolidate, fuse, fasten, splice, connect. *(untie, sever, divide, disconnect, part, detach, divorce, disengage, uncouple.)*

liquid—*adj.* liquescent, running, fluent, mellifluous, flowing, smooth, moist, fluid, melting, watery, soft, limpid, clear. *(solidified, congealed, dry, insoluble, discordant, hard, cohesive, solid, concrete, harsh, indissolvable.)*

listen—*v.* attend, incline, heed, eavesdrop, hear, hearken, give ear, overhear. *(ignore, repudiate, neglect, disregard, refuse.)*

literal—*adj.* grammatical, close, positive, plain, precise, exact, verbal, real, actual. *(substantial, free, allegorical, spiritual, general, metaphorical.)*

literary—*adj.* scholarly, bookish, studious, erudite, poetic. *(unstudious, untutored, unscholarly, illiterate.)*

literature—*n.* erudition, study, attainment, literary works, writings, lore, reading, learning, scholarship. *(genius, inspiration, creation, intuition.)*

little—*adj.* tiny, diminutive, brief, unimportant, slight, inconsiderable, illiberal, petty, dirty, dwarf, miniature, small, pigmy, short, scanty, insignificant, weak, trivial, mean, paltry, shabby. *(bulky, enormous, long, monstrous, big, developed, large, important, serious, liberal, huge, noble, handsome, magnanimous, full, full-sized, much, grave, momentous, generous, highminded.)*

live—*v.* grow, continue, dwell, act, subsist, exist, prevail, vegetate, survive, abide, last, behave, breathe. *(perish, demise, vanish, fall, depart, decrease, expire, die, wither, migrate, fade, languish, drop.)*

live—*adj.* vital, animate, energetic. *(defunct, inert, inanimate.)*

load—*n.* lading, oppression, drag, encumbrance,

burden, weight, cargo, incubus. *(support, alleviation, lightness, consolation, solace, refreshment, emptiness.)*

load—*v.* charge, cargo, oppress, weight, burden, lade, cumber. *(unload, lighten, belleve, liberate, disburden, disencumber, alleviate.)*

loan—*n.* mortgage, hypothecation, accommodation, advance, credit. *(foreclosure, recall, return, resumption.)*

loathsome—*adj.* detestable, evil, repulsive, abominable, obnoxious, disgusting, horrible, revolting, contemptible, nasty. *(delightful, sweet, beautiful, lovely, charming, engaging, alluring, attractive.)*

locate—*v.* establish, fix, lodge, detect, place, settle, dispose, discover, pinpoint. *(disestablish, remove, leave, displace, dislodge, conceal.)*

lofty—*adj.* towering, dignified, stately, majestic, tall, sublime, elevated, high, eminent, haughty, airy. *(low, undignified, unstately, unimposing, affable, dwarfed, depressed, stunted, ordinary, mean, unassuming.)*

logical—*adj.* argumentative, close, rational, sound, cogent. *(fallacious, inconclusive, confused, illogical.)*

lonesome—*adj.* dreary, wild, desolate, isolate, lonely, forlorn, forsaken, solitary. *(befriended, frequented, gay, bustling, cheerful, happy, festive, populous, animated.)*

long—*adj.* produced, lengthy, prolix, diffuse, interminable, protracted, dilatory, tedious, extensive, far-reaching. *(curt, brief, quick, condensed, small, short, curtailed, speedy, concise.)*

loose—*v.* unfasten, let go, free, untie. *(fasten, retain, hold, secure, tie.)*

loose—*adj.* detached, scattered, incompact, inexact, dissoluted, released, licentious, unbound, flowing, sparse, vague, rambling. *(tied, tight, lashed, thick, dense, pointed, exact, strict, conscientious, precise, bound, fastened, moored, close, secured, compact, accurate, consecutive, logical, scientific.)*

loquacious—*adj.* chatty, wordy, talkative, garrulous, verbose, vociferous, voluble, gushy, profuse. *(reticent, silent, reserved, taciturn, terse, quiet.)*

lose—*v.* drop, forfeit, vanish, miss, mislay, misplace, waste, flounder, fail. *(retain, recover, earn,* *treasure, utilize, abandon, reject, vanquish, keep, find, locate, guard, economize, preserve, discard.)*

loss—*n.* dropping, missing, waste, damage, depletion, mislaying, forfeiture, privation, detriment. *(recovery, satisfaction, economy, advantage, preservation, gain, profit, earning, restoration, augmentation.)*

lot—*n.* fortune, hazard, doom, destiny, chance, fate, ballot, heritage. *(provision, disposal, purpose, portion, grant, law, allotment, arrangement, design, plan.)*

loud—*adj.* sonorous, noisy, vociferous, obstreperous, tumultuous, sounding, resonant, audible, clamorous. *(gentle, whispering, murmuring, pattering, dulcet, quiet, peaceful, soft, subdued, rustling, babbling, tinkling, inaudible.)*

love—*n.* attachment, devotion, charity, fondness, kindness, affection, passion, benevolence. *(dislike, alienation, bitterness, indifference, infidelity, unkindness, uncharitableness, loathing, hatred, disaffection, estrangement, coldness, repugnance, desertion, malice.)*

lovely—*adj.* lovable, beautiful, delightful, gracious, charming, amiable, enchanting, pleasing. *(unamiable, hateful, plain, unattractive, distasteful, unlovely, unlovable, hideous, homely.)*

lover—*n.* wooer, swain, fiance, beau, suitor, sweetheart. *(wife, spouse, mate, husband.)*

low—*adj.* sunk, stunted, deep, inaudible, gentle, degraded, poor, abject, unworthy, feeble, frugal, subdued, insignificant, humble, abated, depressed, declining, cheap, subsided, dejected, mean, base, lowly, moderate, repressed, reduced. *(lofty, ascending, high, violent, excited, eminent, strong, influential, honorable, intensified, wealthy, ample, rich, elevated, tall, rising, exorbitant, loud, elated, considerable, high-minded, proud, aggravated, raised.)*

lower—*v.* decrease, bate, drop, sink, humble, submerge, diminish, depress, reduce, abate, humiliate, debase. *(raise, exalt, superior, aggrandize, elevate, hoist, heighten, increase.)*

lower—*adj.* secondary, inferior, subordinate. *(superior, elevate, higher.)*

loyal—*adj.* obedient, allegiant, true, constant,

staunch, submissive, faithful. *(insurgent, rebellious, unfaithful, untrue, disaffected, treacherous, insubmissive, malcontent, disobedient, unallegiant, inconstant.)*

lucid—*adj.* understandable, plain, transparent, pellucid, distinct, evident, comprehensible, clear, bright. *(dark, fuzzy, vague, confusing, unintelligible, gloomy, opaque, turgid.)*

lucky—*adj.* auspicious, successful, blessed, favorable, fortunate, prosperous. *(unfortunate, unprosperous, ill-fated, luckless, unpromising, unlucky, inauspicious, adverse, disastrous.)*

ludicrous—*adj.* farcical, comic, funny, preposterous, comical, ridiculous, laughable, droll. *(momentous, sad, mournful, lugubrious, sombre, solemn, doleful, serious, grave, sorrowful, tragic, melancholy.)*

lugubrious—*adj.* mournful, dismal, sad, doleful, melancholy, gloomy, woeful, depressed, downcast, sorrowful. *(happy, content, joyous, cheerful.)*

lunatic—*n.* maniac, psychopath, madman, schizophrenic. *(philosopher, genius, solon, luminary, rational.)*

lurid—*adj.* lowering, dismal, sensational, gloomy, murky, wan. *(luminous, bright, sunny.)*

luscious—*adj.* delicious, honied, toothsome, delectable, sweet, sugary, delightful, savory. *(sharp, bitter, unpalatable, sour, tart.)*

luxurious—*adj.* self- indulgent, sensual, voluptuous, epicurean, pampered, pleasurable. *(painful, ascetic, austere, hardy, hard, spartan, self-denying.)*

luxury—*n.* epicurism, wantonness, softness, delicacy, profuseness, wealth, effeminacy, voluptuousness, self-indulgence, animalism, dainty. *(asceticism, self-denial, penury, hardness, stoicism, hardship, need.)*

lying—*adj.* false, untruthful, deceit, mendacious, untrue. *(veracious, honesty, true.)*

M

macabre—*adj.* ghastly, gruesome, horrible, weird, grim, eerie, dreadful, deathly, horrid. *(lovely, delightful, appealing, pleasant, beautiful, inviting.)*

mad—*adj.* demented, lunatic, crazy, frantic, wild, unbalanced, distracted, insane, furious, infuriated, maniacal, rabid. *(sound, quiet, lucid, unexcited, sane, sober, sensible, composed.)*

madden—*v.* enrage, inflame, provoke, infuriate, exasperate. *(pacify, mesmerize, soothe, lay, calm, assuage.)*

magnanimous—*adj.* high-minded, high-souled, lofty, chivalrous, honorable, noble, exalted, liberal. *(petty, mean, selfish, vindictive.)*

magnetic—*adj.* captivating, alluring, tantalizing, entrancing, hypnotic, enthralling, fascinating, intriguing, dynamic. *(repulsive, offensive, repellent, forbidding, antimagnetic.)*

magnificent—*adj.* magnanimous, splendid, august, gorgeous, grand, majestic, sublime, exalted, noble, pompous, superb, imposing, stately, dignified. *(mean, paltry, beggarly, ordinary, unimposing, unpretentious, petty, little, flat, humble, tawdry, tame.)*

maid—*n.* girl, lass, virgin, maiden, damsel, miss. *(married woman, matron, dowager, matriarch.)*

maintain—*v.* carry on, protract, preserve, perpetuate, continue, extend, overhaul, fix, mend, secure. *(discontinue, refrain, cease, ruin, demolish, quit, wreck.)*

majority—*n.* predominance, priority, preponderance, bulk, minority, superiority, seniority, lion's share. *(juniority, childhood, minority, inferiority, little.)*

make—*v.* produce, frame, create, construct, do, execute, gain, find, establish, reach, shape, bring about, fashion, fabricate, effect, perform, compel, constitute, mould, form. *(unmake, dismember, destroy, miss, mar, dismantle, disestablish, annihilate, undo, disintegrate, defeat, lose.)*

malaise—*n.* disquiet, alienation, uneasiness, anxiety, apprehension, nervousness, discontent, qualm, exhaustion, fatigue. *(serenity, well-being, vim, contentment, restfulness, vigor, hardiness.)*

malevolent—*adj.* vicious, spiteful, hostile, pernicious, malign, mean, malignant, evil, hateful, antagonistic. *(kind, friendly, amicable, benevolent, cordial, compassionate.)*

manage—*v.* manipulate, conduct, mould, contrive,

husband, wield, operate, handle, control, administer, regulate, train, direct. *(impracticable, unmanageable, refractory, spoil, follow, difficult, impossible, intractable.)*

manageable—*adj.* feasible, docile, practicable, submissive, easy, possible, tractable. *(impracticable, unmanageable, refractory, contrary, difficult, impossible, intractable, unwieldy.)*

management—*n.* conduct, government, skill, skillful treatment, operation, treatment, administration, address, superintendence. *(misconduct, misgovernment, maladroitness, maltreatment, maladministration, mismanage.)*

manifest—*adj.* obvious, conspicuous, clear, plain, apparent, evident, open, candid, visible, distinct, indubitable, patent. *(dubious, indistinct, vague, invisible, inconspicuous.)*

manly—*adj.* courageous, open, frank, noble, fine, masculine, fearless, vigorous, manful, virile, dignified, bold, generous, chivalrous, firm, stately, mature, brave, hardy, manlike. *(childish, unmanly, weak, ungrown, cowardly, womanish, timid, dastardly, puny, boyish.)*

manner—*n.* method, form, kind, carriage, deportment, sort, practice, mode, style, fashion, behavior, habit. *(project, performance, action, appearance, creation, being, work, design, life, proceeding.)*

manners—*n.* behavior, courtesy, intercourse, refinement, demeanor, deportment, carriage, politeness. *(misbehavior, coarseness, unmannerliness, misdemeanor.)*

manufacture—*v.* production, make, composition, manipulation, devise, molding, fabrication, construction. *(employment, wear, destroy, use, consumption.)*

many—*adj.* abundant, manifold, sundry, myriad, multifarious, numerous, frequent, divers. *(scarce, infrequent, several, few, rare.)*

marginal—*adj.* insignificant, minor, unimportant, slight, trivial, expendable, borderline, indifferent replaceable. *(principal, capital, sovereign, crucial, primary, compelling.)*

mark—*n.* token, symptom, vestige, note, score, trace, sign, impression, indication. *(obliteration, plainness,* *erasure, deletion, effacement, unindicativeness.)*

mark—*v.* label, indicate, brand, signalize, observe, heed, specialize, identify, stamp, sign, decorate, stigmatize, note, regard, specify. *(overlook, mislabel, misindicate, misspecify, omit, obliterate, ignore, mismark, misobserve.)*

martial—*adj.* brave, warlike, belligerent, military. *(unmilitary, peaceful, conciliatory, unmartial.)*

marvel—*n.* prodigy, portent, wonder, astonishment, phenomenon, miracle, spectacle, admiration, amazement. *(unconcern, trifle, bagatelle, cipher, imposture, incuriosity, joke, farce, moonshine, drug.)*

masculine—*adj.* manly, hardy, virile, sturdy, male, manful, courageous. *(feminine, weak, womanly, effeminate, female, womanish.)*

mask—*n.* screen, ruse, hypocrisy, camouflage, pretext, pretense, cover. *(nakedness, exposure, verity, candor, unfolding, truth, detection, unmasking, openness.)*

mask—*v.* screen, cloak, shroud, disguise, hide, blink. *(unmask, divulge, detect, expose.)*

master—*n.* ruler, owner, proprietor, professor, chief, controller, adept, lord, governor, possessor, teacher. *(slave, property, tyro, pupil, subordinate, learner, servant, subject.)*

master—*v.* overcome, overpower, dominate, conquer, subdue. *(fail, succumb, capitulate to, yield, surrender.)*

masterful—*adj.* skillful, virtuoso, sharp, accomplished, commanding, able, authoritative, canny, wise, superb, deft. *(amateurish, inept, unable, incompetent, clumsy, unskillful, meek, spineless.)*

match—*n.* mate, contest, tally, pair, duplicate, equal, companion, competition, equality. *(inferior, oddity, inequality, unequal, superior, mismatched, disparity.)*

match—*v.* compare, pit, sort, mate, unite, equal, oppose, adapt, suit. *(exceed, surpass, dissociate, misfit, missort, divide, fail, predominate, mismatch, separate, misadapt.)*

matchless—*adj.* incomparable, surpassing, unrivaled, peerless, inimitable, consummate. *(ordinary, commonplace, undistinguished, common, every-day.)*

matter—*n.* stuff, body, material, substance, object, essence, gist, theme, content, sense. *(mind, intellect, moral, soul, ego, vision, thought, spirit.)*

mature—*adj.* grown, mellow, developed, full-grown, ripe, enriched, capable, complex, detailed, practiced. *(unripe, unfledged, raw, immature, tender, green, embryonic, young.)*

meagre—*adj.* lean, scanty, dry, paltry, thin, lank, barren, tame, sparse. *(fat, abundant, copious, generous, stout, brawny, fertile.)*

mean—*adj.* low, spiritless, contemptible, beggarly, vulgar, vile, intermediate, miserable, average, common, base, dishonorable, despicable, sordid, niggardly, middle. *(exalted, spirited, lordly, munificent, generous, excessive, superior, high, eminent, honorable, princely, liberal, extreme, exorbitant, deluxe.)*

mean—*n.* moderation, average, balance, medium, compromise, norm, rule. *(excess, disproportion, shortcoming, ultimate, inadequacy, extreme, preponderance, deficiency.)*

mean—*v.* purpose, signify, indicate, suggest, aim, intend, design, denote, hint.

(state, execute, declare, perform, say, enunciate, do.)

means—*n.* instrument, media, resources, funds. *(object, end, purpose, point.)*

mechanical—*adj.* automatic, spontaneous, unimpassioned, routine, habitual, unreflective, effortless. *(self-conscious, forced, appreciative, lively, impassioned, manual, labored, feeling, spirited, lifelike, animated.)*

meddlesome—*adj.* obtrusive, officious, interfering, impertinent, intrusive. *(reserved, inobtrusive, unofficious, aloof.)*

mediocrity—*n.* commonplace, average, inferiority, sufficiency, mean, medium. *(superiority, rarity, distinction, brilliance, uniqueness, excellence.)*

meek—*adj.* gentle, modest, docile, unassuming, mild, submissive, yielding. *(arrogant, irritable, high-spirited, domineering, bold, self-asserting, proud.)*

melancholy—*adj.* sad, disconsolate, moody, cast down, unhappy, gloomy, dejected, dismal, hypochondriac. *(sprightly, merry, gleesome, happy, gamesome, vivacious, lively, gladsome, blithesome, cheerful, mirthful.)*

mellifluous—*adj.* harmonious, sweet, mellow, soft, smooth, full-toned, resonant, musical, dulcet, mellifluent, sweet-sounding. *(discordant, jarring, unmusical, grating, harsh, raucous, hoarse.)*

mellow—*adj.* rich, jovial, soft, velvety, ripe, full-flavored, mature. *(harsh, acid, crabbed, dry, gruff, unripe, sour, acrid, sober.)*

memorable—*adj.* striking, conspicuous, noticeable, extraordinary, eminent, distinguished, great, remarkable, prominent, illustrious, famous. *(trifling, trivial, insignificant, slight, ordinary, petty, prosaic, unnoticeable, mediocre.)*

memory—*n.* reminiscence, tribute, recollection, retrospect, fame, remembrance, perpetuation, retention. *(oblivion, amnesia, forgetfulness, blank.)*

mend—*v.* restore, promote, rectify, amend, better, recondition, repair, correct, improve, reform, ameliorate. *(impair, retard, falsify, corrupt, injure, damage, pervert, deteriorate, spoil.)*

mendacious—*adj.* dishonest, false, guileful, deceitful, untruthful, fraudulent, deceptive, double-dealing, ly-ing, tricky. *(honest, true, creditable, sincere, veracious, truthful.)*

menial—*adj.* attendant, servile, lackey, drudge, domestic, dependent. *(sovereign, lordly, uncontrolled, dignified, autocratic, paramount, supreme, independent.)*

mental—*adj.* subjective, psychical, conscious, intellectual, psychological, metaphysical. *(objective, bodily, unconscious, corporal, physical.)*

mention—*n.* notice, observation, hint, indication, communication, declaration, announcement, remark. *(suppression, omission, disregard, silence, forgetfulness.)*

mercantile—*adj.* interchangeable, retail, business, marketable, commercial, wholesale. *(unmercantile, unmarketable, stagnant, inactive.)*

merchant—*n.* dealer, tradesman, trader, importer, shopkeeper, vendor. *(salesman, huckster, chandler, costermonger, shopman, hawker, peddler.)*

merciful—*adj.* kindhearted, gracious, humane, kind, compassionate, clement. *(unrelenting, inex-*

orable, callous, pitiless, re-morseless.)

mercurial—*adj.* flighty, volatile, capricious, fickle, unstable, changeable, erratic, impulsive, fluctuating, impetuous. *(steadfast, stable, predictable, constant, fixed, phlegmatic, callous.)*

mere—*adj.* unmixed, uninfluenced, unaffected, mundane, simple, pure, absolute, unadulterated. *(compound, biased, mixed, blended, impure.)*

merit—*n.* worth, desert, integrity, excellence, goodness, worthiness, virtue, ability. *(demerit, worthlessness, imperfection, defect, failing, dishonor, badness, unworthiness, weakness, error, fault.)*

meteoric—*adj.* phosphorescent, flashing, coruscant, brilliant, volcanic, momentary, displosive, pyrotechnic. *(beaming, steady, enduring, inconspicuous, permanent, burning, persistent.)*

method—*n.* system, way, mode, process, arrangement, technique, order, rule, manner, course, regularity, procedure. *(conjecture, empiricism, assumption, chaos, guess-work, disorder, quackery, experimentation.)*

methodical—*adj.* orderly, systematic, irregular, efficient, methodic, organized, disciplined. *(haphazard, irregular, disorderly, random, unsystematical.)*

meticulous—*adj.* scrupulous, fastidious, finicky, careful, perfectionist, exacting, nice, punctilious. *(careless, inexact, negligent, slovenly, perfunctory, sloppy.)*

middling—*adj.* average, well enough, mediocre, not bad, ordinary, moderate. *(first-rate, fine, good, glowing, splendid, excellent.)*

midst—*n.* center, throng, core, heart, middle, thick, nucleus, interior. *(confine, limit, purlieu, periphery, outskirt, edge, margin, extreme.)*

might—*n.* force, ability, potency, strength, power. *(infirmity, frailty, feebleness, weakness.)*

migrate—*v.* journey, emigrate, relocate, move, travel, resettle. *(bide, alight, settle, sojourn, remain, alight.)*

mild—*adj.* lenient, gentle, calm, tempered, meek, placid, genial, amiable, moderate, soft, tender. *(wild, savage, severe, harsh, balmy, bitter, violent, fierce, strong, merciless.)*

mind—*n.* spirit, memory, understanding, will, sentiment, belief, inclination, purpose, impetus, conception, remembrance, recollection, soul, liking, opinion, judgement, choice, desire, intellect. *(organization, proceeding, object, coolness, forgetfulness, body, action, conduct, resist, obviousness, indifference, aversion, ignore.)*

mindful—*adj.* attentive, careful, cautious, recollective, regardful, thoughtful. *(inattentive, oblivious, thoughtless, regardless, mindless.)*

mingle—*v.* compound, confound, intermingle, amalgamate, coalesce, mix, blend, confuse, associate. *(segregate, sort, discompound, classify, avoid, divide, separate, sift, analyze, eliminate, unravel.)*

minimize—*v.* little, diminutive, small, dwarf, microscopic, petite, tiny, minute, mini, wee. *(enlarge, expand, exaggerate, increase, maximize, stress, emphasize, magnify.)*

minister—*n.* officer, official, subordinate, clergyman, parson, preacher, shepherd, curate, religious, vicar, servant, delegate, ambassador, ecclesiastic, priest, divine, pastor, reverend. *(government, superior, head, fold, congregation, secular, monarch, master, principal, layman, flock.)*

minute—*adj.* microscopic, miniature, exact, specific, diminutive, tiny, searching, detailed, petite. *(enormous, tremendous, general, comprehensive, huge, monstrous, superficial, broad, momentous.)*

mischief—*n.* hurt, disservice, injury, damage, devilment, harm, damage, detriment, annoyance, ill-turn. *(good-turn, favor, advantage, gratification, benefit, compensation.)*

mischievous—*adj.* injurious, wanton, annoying, detrimental, spiteful. *(advantageous, conservative, protective, orderly, beneficial, reparatory, careful.)*

miscreant—*adj.* evil, corrupt, villainous, wicked, infamous, depraved, degenerate. *(moral, noble, ethical, virtuous, righteous, good.)*

miser—*n.* churl, curmudgeon, scrimp, cheapskate, hoarder, niggard, skinflint, screw. *(spendthrift, wastrel, rake, prodigal.)*

miserable—*adj.* forlorn, wretched, despicable, pathetic, disconsolate, abject, pitiable, worthless. *(happy, worthy, comfortable, joyous, respectable, contented.)*

misery—*n.* heartache, unhappiness, anguish, wretchedness, woe. *(glee, cheerfulness, joy, happiness.)*

misguided—*adj.* illadvised, misled, mistaken, unwarranted, foolish, indiscreet, misdirected, unwise, erroneous. *(wise, sound, judicious, sagacious, prudent.)*

mitigate—*v.* alleviate, extenuate, relieve, temper, soothe, placate, mollify, allay, moderate, ameliorate. *(aggravate, intensify, increase, harden, magnify, augment, enhance.)*

mock—*v.* ridicule, mimic, ape, deceive, taunt, imitate, jeer, flout, insult, deride. *(welcome, admire, esteem, salute, respect, compliment, praise.)*

model—*n.* pattern, type, design, facsimile, standard, kind, example, mold. *(copy, execution, work, imitation, deformity, distortion.)*

moderate—*v.* soften, regulate, govern, abate, temper, control, allay, repress. *(disorganize, misconduct, aggravate, disturb, excite.)*

moderate—*adj.* temperate, sober, dispassionate, abstinent, steady, typical, ordinary, limited, calm, sparing. *(intemperate, excessive, extraordinary, drastic, extravagant, rigorous, violent.)*

modern—*adj.* existent, new-fangled, recent, novel, contemporary, later, present, new, new-fashioned, late. *(bygone, olden, old-fashioned, obsolete, archaic, past, former, ancient, antiquated.)*

modesty—*n.* diffidence, humility, simplicity, puremindedness, sobriety, bashfulness, reserve, shyness. *(conceit, self-admiration, coxcombry, shamelessness, pride, effrontery, vanity, selfsufficiency, foppery, wantonness.)*

moisture—*n.* dampness, wet, damp, humidity, dew, evaporation, vapor, mist, drizzle, perspiration. *(aridity, dryness, dehumidification, drought, barrenness, dehydration.)*

moment—*n.* second, twinkling, weight, gravity, avail, jiffy, instant, importance, trice, force, consequence. *(period, generation, insignificance, unimportance, unconcern, inefficacy, age, century, triviality, worthlessness.)*

monopoly—*n*. engrossment, trust, exclusiveness, impropriation, privilege, appropriation, cartel, preoccupancy. *(partnership, competition, accessory, freetrade, participation, community.)*

monotonous—*adj*. unvaried, humdrum, tedious, repetitious, uniform, dull, undiversified. *(changing, diversified, varying.)*

monstrous—*adj*. portentous, deformed, hideous, intolerable, grotesque, prodigious, marvelous, abnormal, preposterous. *(familiar, fair, shapely, natural, just, typical, ordinary, unnoticeable, comely, regular, reasonable.)*

moody—*adj*. sullen, temperamental, unstable, melancholy, erratic, morose, petulant, dismal, pessimistic, lugubrious, unhappy. *(cheerful, amiable, happy, stable, phlegmatic, stoic, calm, compatible.)*

moral—*adj*. ideal, spiritual, probable, presumptive, virtuous, scrupulous, mental, intellectual, ethical, inferential, analogous, well-conducted, honest. *(material, demonstrative, immoral, unethical, vicious, physical, practical, mathematical, unprincipled.)*

mortal—*adj*. ephemeral, short-lived, fatal, destructive, corporeal, human, sublunary, deadly, perishable. *(immortal, life-giving, eternal, divine, celestial, venial, imperishable.)*

motive—*n*. purpose, prompting, reason, incitement, motivation, inducement, design, stimulus, impulse. *(action, deed, project, deterent, maneuver, execution, dissuasive, effort, attempt, preventive.)*

move—*v*. go, stir, agitate, impel, advance, instigate, migrate, provoke, change, progress, affect, actuate, propose, propel. *(stop, rest, allay, prevent, withdraw, remain, stand, lie, stay, deter, arrest.)*

movement—*n*. move, change of place, progress, motion, action. *(rest, stillness, inertia, quietness, pause, stop.)*

much—*adj*. plenteous, abundantly, considerable, ample, abundant, greatly, far, substantial. *(scant, shortly, near, sparse, little, slightly, short.)*

muddle—*v*. waste, confuse, misarrange, entangle, fail, fritter away, derange. *(manage, classify, organize, clarify, economize, arrange, simplify.)*

muggy—*adj.* misty, damp, dim, cloudy, humid, foggy, dank, murky, vaporous. *(bright, vaporless, airy, pleasant, clear.)*

multitude—*n.* swarm, throng, number, mob, horde, rabble, crowd, accumulation, assemblage, host. *(scantiness, paucity, sprinkling, minority, nothing.)*

munificent—*adj.* princely, generous, lavish, liberal, bounteous, philanthropic. *(beggarly, stingy, niggardly, penurious.)*

murmur—*v.* whisper, grumble, mutter, complain, drone, repine, purr. *(vociferate, clamor, bawl.)*

muscular—*adj.* brawny, sinewy, stalwart, lusty, husky, sturdy, powerful, robust, strong, athletic. *(flabby, lanky, frail, debile, feeble, soft.)*

musical—*adj.* harmonious, concordant, tuneful, euphonious, mellifluous, melodious, dulcet, rythmical. *(inharmonious, discordant, unmelodious, harsh, dissonant.)*

musty—*adj.* rank, frowzy, sour, mildewed, decaying, fusty, moldy, stale, fetid. *(fresh, aromatic, refreshing, odorous, fragrant, balmy.)*

mutter—*v.* mumble, sputter, murmur, grunt, grumble.

(exclaim, vociferate, enunciate, pronounce, articulate.)

mysterious—*adj.* obscure, unexplained, reserved, hidden, incomprehensible, inexplicable, cryptic, dim, veiled, unrevealed, unaccountable, secret, mystic. *(plain, explained, easy, simple, communicative, apparent, clear, obvious, understood, explainable, frank.)*

mystery—*n.* puzzle, secrecy, shrowd, quandry, arcanum, enigma, obscurity, veil. *(solution, truism, answer, publication, matter-of-fact, commonplace.)*

mystify—*v.* bamboozle, puzzle, mislead, perplex, confuse, hoodwink, confound, obfuscate, elude. *(enlighten, guide, interpret, illumine, inform, disclose.)*

mythical—*adj.* fictitious, unreal, fantastic, imaginary, legendary, fabricated, invented, fanciful, nonexistent. *(actual, true, factual, palpable, real.)*

N

nadir—*n.* foundation, floor, zero, base, root, rock bottom, nothing, minimum, bedrock. *(acme, summit, apex, zenith, peak, pinnacle.)*

naked—*adj.* bare, denuded, defenseless, unqualified, nude, unvarnished, simple, stripped, unclothed, undraped, destitute, uncolored, mere. *(robed, muffled, qualified, shrouded, varnished, embellished, dressed, draped, protected, veiled, colored.)*

name—*n.* cognomenation, title, reputation, appointment, fame, representation, nomenclature, designation, appelation, stead, authority. *(anonymousness, alias, pseudonym, ingloriousness, individuality, namelessness, misnomer, obscurity, disrepute, person.)*

name—*v.* designate, indicate, label, specify, call, nominate, title. *(miscall, misindicate, suggest, adumbrate, mention, misname, misdesignate, hint, shadow.)*

narrate—*v.* recite, tell, rehearse, describe, portray, relate, reveal, recapitulate, enumerate, paint. *(cover, withhold, veil, screen, smother, hide, conceal, shade.)*

narrow—*adj.* straightened, thin, contracted, cramped, scant, slender, scrutinizing, bigoted, tight, straight, confined, spare, near, limited, pinched, close, niggardly. *(broad, thick, easy, spacious, liberal, wide, ample, expanded.)*

nasty—*adj.* offensive, disagreeable, impure, unclean, loathsome, obscene, fowl, odious, indelicate, gross. *(pleasant, savory, agreeable, kind, pure, nice, sweet, admirable.)*

natural—*adj.* essential, normal, true, consistent, artless, inherent, original, intrinsic, regular, cosmical, probable, spontaneous. *(adventitious, monstrous, fictitious, affected, unsupposable, artful, ascetitious, incidental, abnormal, unnatural, improbable, forced.)*

nature—*n.* creation, structure, truth, kind, character, affection, attributes, naturalness, essence, constitution, disposition, sort, regularity, species. *(object, man, creature, unnaturalness, fiction, thing, invention, subject, being, art, monstrosity, romance, soul.)*

near—*adj.* close, neighboring, adjoining, nigh, adjacent. *(distant, remote, past, far.)*

neat—*adj.* immaculate, tidy, orderly, methodical, clean, shipshape, uncluttered, trim. *(disorderly, slovenly, unkempt, messy, disorganized.)*

necessary—*adj.* inevitable, certain, requisite, compulsory, expedient, unavoidable, indispensable, essential, needful. *(casual, free, discretional, unessential, optional, contingent, unnecessary, unrequired.)*

necessity—*n.* inevitableness, need, indigence, want, destiny, essential, indispensableness, requirement, fate. *(uncertainty, uselessness, affluence, contingency, choice, abundance, dispensableness, superfluity, competence, casualty, freedom.)*

nefarious—*adj.* atrocious, evil, despicable, odious, foul, vile, heinous, wicked, detestable, horrendous. *(honest, virtuous, noble, exalted, just, laudable, praiseworthy.)*

neglect—*v.* overlook, disregard, despise, omit, fail, slight, abandon, forget. *(respect, observe, esteem, attend, study, care for, consider, notice, regard, tend faster.)*

neglect—*n.* disregard, failure, slight, remissness, oversight, negligence, omission, default, carelessness. *(consideration, notice, esteem, care, attention, respect, regard.)*

nerve—*n.* firmness, boldness, resolution, endurance, strength. *(forceless,*

weak, impotent, cowardice, nerveless, feeble, enfeebled, palsied, bashfulness.)

neutral—*adj.* impartial, remote, uninvolved, unbiased, indifferent, withdrawn, aloof, peaceful, pacifist. *(partisan, prejudiced, committed, biased, definite, active, belligerent.)*

new—*adj.* recent, modern, unused, current, novel, fresh, original. *(ancient, antiquated, passe, used, obsolete, old, antique.)*

nice—*adj.* scrupulous, neat, dainty, agreeable, fine, exact, particular, delightful, fastidious, accurate, discerning, pleasant, finished. *(unscrupulous, rude, undiscriminating, nauseous, miserable, coarse, disagreeable, inaccurate, rough, nasty.)*

niggardly—*adj.* penurious, miserly, cheap, parsimonious, small, mercenary, frugal, stingy, thrifty, avaricious. *(liberal, generous, munificent, lavish, charitable, bountiful, profuse, ample.)*

nobility—*n.* dignity, peerage, loftiness, rank, grandeur, aristocracy, distinction, lordship, generosity. *(meanness, serfdom, contemptibleness, simplicity,* plebeianism, obscurity, commonalty, paltriness.)

noble—*adj.* aristocratic, illustrious, worthy, dignified, lofty-minded, fine, patrician, grand, generous, exalted, excellent, magnanimous, honorable. (plebeian, paltry, humble, mean, ignoble, despicable.)

noisome—*adj.* harmful, odorous, pestilential, hurtful, nocuous. (salutary, beneficial, curative, wholesome, salubrious.)

noisy—*adj.* clamorous, loud, stunning, riotous, uproarious, hectic, deafening. (soft, whispering, musical, harmonious, subdued, noiseless, peaceful, still, inaudible, soothing, melodious, tuneful, gentle.)

nominal—*adj.* suppositious, professed, formal, trivial, trifling, ostensible, pretended. (deep, important, substantial, intrinsic, essential, genuine, real, serious, grave, actual, veritable.)

nondescript—*adj.* indefinite, colorless, commonplace, vague, unclassifiable, indistinct, characterless, stereotyped. (unusual, distinctive, definite, vivid, unique, extraordinary.)

nonsense—*n.* trash, pretense, balderdash, foolishness, absurdity, folly, jest. (wisdom, fact, philosophy, reason, reality, sense, truth, gravity, science.)

notice—*n.* cognizance, advice, consideration, mark, attention, note, observation, heed, news, visitation. (disregard, mistidings, slight, ignorance, heedlessness, omission, misjudge, oversight, misinformation, neglect, amnesty, connivance, incognizance.)

notion—*n.* idea, judgment, belief, sentiment, thought, apprehension, conception, opinion, expectation. (falsification, misjudgment, misconception, misunderstanding, misapprenhension, misbelief, frustration.)

notorious—*adj.* undisputed, allowed, scandalous, known, recognized. (reputed, suspected, decent, reported.)

nude—*adj.* bare, naked, stark, undressed, denuded, disrobed, unadorned, exposed. (covered, clad, dressed, robed, appareled, clothed.)

nuisance—*n.* annoyance, pest, vexation, trouble, offense, plague. (delight, *gratification, pleasure, benefit, blessing, joy.)*

nullify—*v.* veto, cancel, repeal, abolish, revoke, rescind, annul, invalidate, obliterate, abrogate. *(decree, ratify, establish, power, existence, viability.)*

O

oasis—*n.* retreat, shelter, haven, sanctum, refuge, sanctuary, asylum, island. *(desert, jungle, crossroads, thick, mainstream.)*

obedience—*n.* compliance, meekness, subservience, submission. *(rebellion, obstinate, transgression, disobedience, resistance, violation, antagonism.)*

obese—*adj.* corpulent, fleshy, fat, stout, heavy, rotund, portly, plump, gross, overweight. *(thin, emaciated, gaunt, lean, slender, angular, lanky, skinny.)*

obey—*v.* comply, concur, yield, submit. *(disobey, refuse, transgress, resist.)*

object—*n.* sight, end, motive, view, goal, target, appearance, design, aim, intent. *(notion, fancy, idea, proposal, effect, illusion, conception, subject, purpose.)*

object—*v.* contravene, demur to, gainsay, protest, oppose, obstruct, disapprove, complain. *(approve of, applaud, agree, justify.)*

oblige—*v.* coerce, force, favor, gratify, constrain, please, compel, necessitate, benefit, accommodate, bind. *(acquit, persuade, disoblige, inconvience, release, induce, annoy.)*

obliging—*adj.* considerate, kind, complaisant, accommodating, amiable, compliant. *(rude, perverse, disobliging, hostile, discourteous, inconsiderate, unaccommodating.)*

obliterate—*v.* eradicate, raze, destroy, ruin, pulverize, crush, extinguish, annihilate, level, abolish. *(create, reconstruct, rehabilitate, restore, preserve, build.)*

oblivious—*adj.* distracted, heedless, unconscious, careless, forgetful, unaware, inattentive, disregardful. *(aware, alert, careful, watchful, mindful, cognizant, concerned, worried.)*

obscene—*adj.* immodest, lewd, indelicate, disgusting, vulgar, foul-mouthed, impure, foul, indecent, filthy. *(modest, pure, decent, innocent, respectable.)*

obscure—*adj.* dim, indistinct, uncertain, unascertained, unintelligible, cloudy, dark, mean, lowering, enigmatical, doubtful, humble. *(luminous, lucid, plain spoken, unambiguous, eminent, resplendent, prominent, bright, distinct, plain, intelligible, ascertained.)*

observance—*n.* fulfilment, rule, celebration, ceremony, form, practice, adherence, attention, respect, performance, custom. *(inattention, disuse, disrespect, desuetude, omission, nonperformance, unceremoniousness, evasion, inobservance, breach, disregard, informality.)*

observant—*adj.* attentive, obedient, heedful, perceptive, regardful, mindful, watchful. *(neglectful, heedless, disobedient, indifferent, oblivious, disregardful, unmindful.)*

observation—*n.* study, attention, comment, watching, contemplation, remark, notice. *(oversight, inattention, ignorance, apathy, disregard, inadvertence, silence.)*

obsolete—*adj.* archaic, outmoded, old-fashioned, passé, ancient, antiquated, out-of-date, old, extinct. *(up-to-date, modern, current, prevalent, new, present-day.)*

obstacle—*n.* obstructive, objection, difficulty, hurdle, check, bar, impediment, hindrance. *(proceeding, course, advancement, support, career.)*

obstinate—*adj.* stubborn, self-willed, obdurate, intractable, determined, headstrong, refractory, pertinacious, perverse. *(complaisant, docile, characterless, wavering, flexible, amenable, yeilding, ductile, irresolute.)*

obvious—*adj.* self-evident, explicit, open, perceptible, patent, plain, manifest, apparent. *(obscure, involved, vague, latent, remote, farfetched.)*

occasion—*n.* opportunity, cause, event, necessity, ground, happening, conjuncture, occurrence, need, reason, opening. *(unseasonableness, frustration, untimeliness.)*

occult—*adj.* hidden, mysterious, dark, mystic, unknown, latent, unrevealed, secret, supernatural. *(plain, clear, exposed, aware, open, developed, patent, familiar.)*

occupation—*n.* avocation, usurpation, tenure, pursuit, business, career, holding, employment, possession, encroachment, calling, trade.

(vacancy, abandonment, resignation, loafing, idleness, leisure, vacation.)

odd—*adj.* sole, remaining, alone, fragmentary, singular, queer, fantastical, nondescript, unique, unmatched, over, uneven, peculiar, quaint, uncommon. *(consociate, balanced, integrant, common, regular, systematic, normal, aggregate, matched, squared, even, usual.)*

odious—*adj.* offensive, abominable, repugnant, hated, hateful, detestable. *(grateful, acceptable, agreeable, delectable, pleasant, delightful.)*

odorous—*adj.* redolent, scented, fragrant, odoriferous, aromatic, heady, perfumed, spicy, ambrosial. *(smelly, noesome, rancid, noxious, malodorous, fetid.)*

offense—*n.* sin, umbrage, misdeed, wrong, outrage, trespass, vice, misdemeanor, attack, crime, transgression, injury, affront, insult, indignity. *(innocence, virtue, guiltlessness, defense, honor.)*

offensive—*adj.* obnoxious, displeasing, fetid, repugnant, unsavory, aggressive, distasteful, foul. *(grateful, pleasant, amiable, savory, defensive.)*

offer—*v.* exhibit, present, extend, volunteer, donate, propose, proffer, tender, adduce. *(withdraw, retain, divert, deny, withhold, retract, alienate.)*

office—*n.* duty, function, station, post, incumbency, service, appointment, employment, business. *(vacancy, sinecure, loafing, resignation, leisure.)*

officious—*adj.* interfering, forward, intermeddling, snooping, meddling, pushing, intrusive. *(negligent, unofficious, modest, reticent, backward, remiss, retiring.)*

often—*adv.* repeatedly, habitually, frequently. *(seldom, infrequently, scarcely.)*

old—*adj.* pristine, ancient, antiquated, senile, sedate, antique, aged, long-standing, preceding, obsolete. *(young, fresh, immature, subsequent, current, youthful, recent, modern, new-fashioned.)*

ominous—*adj.* suggestive, foreboding, unpropitious, sinister, portentous, threatening, premonitory. *(propitious, encouraging, promising, auspicious.)*

oncoming—*adj.* impending, imminent, approaching, looming, immediate, arriving, growing, successive, developing. *(retiring, distant, subsiding, retreating, receding, remote.)*

ongoing—*adj.* progressing, growing, continuing, advancing, prosperous, successful, viable, evolving, proceeding, unfolding. *(declining, flagging, terminating, abortive, concluding, regressive, deteriorating.)*

onslaught—*n.* assult, foray, raid, invasion, charge, offense, encounter, coup, aggression. *(retreat, stampede, recession, flight, counterattack, defense.)*

opaque—*adj.* murky, dense, clouded, obscure, impervious, hazy, muddy, nontranslucent. *(transparent, shiny, clear, lucid, limpid, translucent, pellucid.)*

open—*v.* lay-open, expose, disclose, begin, unfasten, commence, unclose, lay bare, explain, initiate. *(shut up, inclose, misinterpret, cover, seal, close, conceal, mystify, conclude.)*

open—*adj.* free, unshut, public, unrestricted, unaffected, accessible, barefaced, above-board, available, unclosed, frank, unsettled, unbarred, undetermined, genuine, liberal, candid, ingenuous, unfolded, unre-

served, undisguised. *(closed, unavailable, close, reserved, determined, blocked, inaccessible, barred, shut, secretive, settled.)*

opening—*n.* gap, space, chasm, initiation, inauguration, start, fissure, beginning, aperture, hole, opportunity, commencement, chink. *(obstruction, end, unreasonableness, inopportuneness, termination, conclusion, close, blockage, occlusion, stopgap, contretemps, enclosure.)*

operation—*n.* action, production, performance, manipulation, agency, exercise, influence, functioning *(inaction, cessation, inoperativeness, inefficiency, powerlessness, rest, inefficacy, misoperation, repose.)*

opinion—*n.* view, notion, idea, impression, theory, sentiment, conviction, judgment, estimation. *(actuality, fact, act, certainty, reality, happening, deed.)*

opportune—*adj.* auspicious, apt, favorable, timely, seasonable, convenient, fortunate, appropriate, suitable, proper. *(untimely, unfortunate, inopportune, unseasonable, inconvenient, unsuitable.)*

opposition—*n.* hostility, obstruction, antagonism, resistance, obstacle, rejection, aversion. *(cooperation, attraction, collaboration, combination, synergism, approval.)*

opposite—*adj.* adverse, opposed, inconsistent, contrary, counter, facing, repugnant, irreconcilable, antagonistic, contradictory. *(coincident, similar, identical, consentaneous, agreeing.)*

oppressive—*adj.* overpowering, galling, grinding, tyrannical, heavy, unjust, extortionate. *(just, lenient, compassionate, light.)*

oratorical—*adj.* eloquent, rhetorical, sermonizing, declamatory, orotund, elecutionary, bombastic. *(intimate, chatty, conversational, informal.)*

order—*n.* condition, direction, grade, decree, series, injunction, command, system, arrangement, sequence, rank, class, method, succession, precept. *(mess, jumble, chaos, disorder, anarchy.)*

order—*v.* dispose, adjust, command, ordain, appoint, mandate, manage, arrange, regulate, direct, classify, enjoin, prescribe. *(confusion, inversion, disorder, scramble,* disarrangement, unsettlement, execution.)*

ordinary—*adj.* wonted, plain, commonplace, matter of fact, habitual, settled, conventional, inferior, humdrum. *(unusual, rare, superior, extraordinary, uncommon.)*

organization—*n.* form, method, construction, structure. *(disorder, disorganization, confusion.)*

origin—*n.* commencement, cause, rise, inception, beginning, source, spring, derivation. *(conclusion, extinction, finish, termination.)*

original—*adj.* initiatory, peculiar, ancient, first, fundamental, primary, primordial, pristine, former. *(terminal, later, ultimate, derivative, subsequent, modern.)*

ostentatious—*adj.* showy, flashy, pretentious, flamboyant, immodest, garish, grandiose, overdone, gaudy. *(modest, plain, inconspicuous, reserved, somber, sedate, unpretentious.)*

ostracize—*v.* avoid, banish, expel, isolate, boycott, blackball, reject, shun, exclude, blacklist. *(accept, invite, include, welcome, embrace, acknowledge.)*

oust—*v.* dispossess, evict, dislodge, banish, remove,

eject, deprive. *(reinstate, restore, induct, install, readmit.)*

outbreak—*n.* epidemic, invasion, eruption, outburst, explosion, display, demonstration. *(recession, decline, waning, decrease, subsidence, tranquillity, quiet.)*

outcast—*n.* reprobate, vagabond, fugitive, exile, castaway, vagrant. *(hero, saint, leader, philanthropist, gentleman, queen, angel.)*

outlandish—*adj.* queer, foreign, barbarous, bizarre, rude, strange, grotesque, rustic. *(modish, ordinary, native, fashionable, commonplace.)*

outline—*n.* sketch, draft, plan, diagram, delineation, contour. *(substance, object, field, bulk, core, space, form, figure, subject, ground.)*

outrage—*n.* offense, mischief, ebullition, indignity, insult, cruelty, outbreak, wantonness, abuse, violence, affront. *(self-control, soothe, subsidence, calmness, moderation, self-restraint, coolness.)*

outrageous—*adj.* unwarrantable, wanton, nefarious, violent, diabolical, excessive, flagrant, unjustifiable, atro-

cious. *(reasonable, equitable, moderate, justifiable.)*

outset—*n.* start, exordium, opening, inauguration, inception, preface, commencement, beginning. *(termination, peroration, finale, close, conclusion.)*

outward—*adj.* apparent, sensible, ostensible, extrinsic, perceptible, extraneous, external, visible, superficial, forthcoming. *(intrinsic, inner, inapparent, interior, inward, internal, withdrawn.)*

overcome—*v.* conquer, exhaust, overwhelm, vanquish, defeat, surmount. *(capitulate to, give up, admit defeat, surrender to, give in to.)*

overflow—*v.* exuberance, deluge, surge, inundation, redundancy, superabundance. *(subsidence, dearth, deficiency, exhaustion.)*

overlook—*v.* connive, oversee, inspect, review, pardon, neglect, slight, condone, disregard, supervise, survey, excuse, forgive. *(scrutinize, mark, remember, visit, investigate.)*

oversight—*n.* omission, neglect, inadvertence, superintendence, heedless, error, mistake, slip, inspection. *(correction, attention, notice,* diligence, scruting, emendation, mark.)

overthrow—v. subvert, overturn, demolish, rout, discomfit, overset, capsize, reverse, destroy, upset, ruin, defeat, overcome, invert. *(reinstate, regenerate, revive, conserve, re-edify, restore, construct, reintegrate.)*

overwhelm—v. quell, drawn, swamp, inundate, crush, extinguish, subdue. *(reinvigorate, reestablish, extricate, capitulate, raise, reinstate, rescue.)*

owing—adj. imputable, overdue, attributable, due, ascribable. *(perchance, by accident, settled, casualty, by chance, paid.)*

own—v. hold, acknowledge, admit, maintain, confess, possess, have, avow. *(forfeit, disclaim, disinherit, abjure, deprive, alienate, lose, disavow, abandon, disown.)*

P

pacify—v. conciliate, still, quiet, placate, tranquilize, appease, calm, soothe. *(agitate, irritate, provoke, aggravate, exasperate, excite, rouse.)*

pack—v. compact, cook, cram, stow, compress. *(unsettle, displace, dissipate, un-*

load, neutralize, unpack, jumble, misarrange.)

pack—n. bundle, lot, load, weight, burden, package, parcel.

pain—n. suffering, uneasiness, labor, anguish, agony, torment, penalty, distress, grief, effort, torture. *(remuneration, delight, gratification, pleasure, relief, enjoyment, gladness, reward, ease, joy, felicity, alleviation.)*

pain—v. grieve, torment, hurt, agonize, torture, annoy, harass, distress, afflict, rack, trouble, aggrieve. *(please, rejoice, relieve, refresh, comfort, gratify, delight, charm, ease.)*

painful—adj. distressful, grievous, hurting, agonizing, afflicting, grieving, excruciating. *(soothing, painless, comforting, pleasing, enjoyable, delightful.)*

painstaking—adj. attentive, laborious, meticulous, careful, diligent. *(negligent, careless, sloppy, haphazard.)*

palatable—adj. savory, delicious, delectable, toothsome, tasteful, appetizing. *(unsavory, bitter, nauseating, distasteful, repugnant.)*

palatial—adj. splendid, glorious, superb, grand, imposing, luxurious, majestic, stately, grandiose. *(humble, mean, unpretentious, ramshackle.)*

pale—*adj.* wan, dim, etiolated, cadaverous, ashen, pallid, faint, undefined, sallow. *(high-colored, deep, florid, ruddy, conspicuous.)*

palliate—*v.* extenuate, minimize, excuse, soften, apologize for, mitigate, varnish, alleviate. *(inflame, intensify, magnify, exaggerate, aggravate.)*

palmy—*adj.* glorious, victorious, enjoyable, flourishing, prosperous, distinguished. *(inglorious, gloomy, unflourishing, depressed, undistinguished.)*

paltry—*adj.* shabby, trifling, shifty, pitiable, worthless, trashy, niggardly, mean, vile, shuffling, prevaricating, contemptible, beggarly. *(honorable, conscientious, straightforward, admirable, magnificent, weighty, noble, candid, determined, estimable, worthy.)*

pamper—*v.* indulge, cater to, cosset, spoil, cherish, please, satisfy, flatter, fondle, humor. *(mistreat, domineer, oppress, abuse, maltreat, bully, intimidate, chastise.)*

pang—*n.* throe, convulsion, anguish, twinge, discomfort, paroxysm, agony, smart, pain. *(enjoyment, delight, fascination, solace, refreshment, pleasure, gratification, delectation.)*

panicky—*adj.* alarmed, shocked, panic-stricken, stunned, fearful, stupefied, aghast, immobilized, speechless. *(imperturbable, cool, unruffled, steady, composed.)*

paradox—*n.* enigma, absurdity, dilemma, ambiguity, contradiction, mystery. *(proposition, truism, proverb, postulate, precept, axiom.)*

parallel—*adj.* congruous, abreast, analogous, equidistant, correspondent, correlative, concurrent. *(opposed, irrelative, divergent, distinct, different, contrariant, incongruous, unanalogous.)*

paralyze—*v.* benumb, enervate, enfeeble, stupefy, deaden, prostrate, debilitate. *(strengthen, lift up, sustain, restore, give life, nerve.)*

paramount—*adj.* principal, main, leading, dominant, superior, greatest, supreme, cardinal, primary, utmost, essential. *(minimum, immaterial, least, minor, slightest, secondary, subordinate, inconsequential.)*

pardon—*v.* condone, acquit, excuse, discharge, overlook, forgive, absolve, remit. *(visit, accuse, condemn, punish, incriminate.)*

parsimonious—*adj.* close, frugal, illiberal, miserly, stingy, sparing, penurious, niggardly. *(unsparing, extravagant, lavish, liberal, profuse.)*

part—*n.* piece, fraction, member, element, share, concern, lot, participation, party, faction, duty, ingredient, portion, side, fragment, division, constituent, ingredient, interest, behalf, item. *(completeness, integrity, mass, body, transaction, unite, affair, whole, entirety, totality, bulk, compound.)*

partake—*v.* participate, derive, share, accept, sample, enjoy. *(relinquish, cede, afford, abstain, forfeit, forego, yield.)*

partial—*adj.* local, specific, inequitable, biased, peculiar, fragmentary, restricted, favoring, unfair, particular. *(total, general, equitable, fair, thorough, unbiased, unrestricted, universal, impartial, just.)*

particular—*adj.* specific, detail, special, minute, careful, exact, precise, nice, unique, local, subordinate, partial, fastidious, scrupulous, accurate, delicate, circumstantial. *(general, uncareful, comprehensive, inexact, coarse, undiscriminating, abundant, universal, unspecial, inaccurate, unscrupulous, rough, indiscriminate.)*

partisan—*n.* follower, henchman, supporter, promoter, disciple, adherent, party man, clansman. *(renegade, apostate, maverick, independent.)*

partition—*n.* division, compartment, separation, allotment, severance, screen, barrier, enclosure, demarcation, distribution. *(non-distinction, inclusion, combination, juncture, union, incorporation, generalization, collection, non-partition, non-separation, comprehension, coalition, amalgamation, concatenation.)*

partner—*n.* sharer, colleague, confederate, partaker, spouse, collaborator, associate, coadjutor, participator, accomplice, companion. *(opponent, alien, counter-agent, rival, enemy, competitor.)*

passable—*adj.* navigable, admissible, ordinary, mediocre, traversable, tolerable, penetrable. *(impervious, inadmissible, superior, excellent, impassable, impenetrable).*

passage—*n.* thoroughfare, course, route, clause, sentence, corridor, paragraph, journey, road, avenue, channel, phrase. *(book, chapter, part, clause.)*

passionate—*adj.* fiery, emotional, excitable, avid, impassioned, eager, enthusiastic, zestful, ardent. *(apathetic, unresponsive, phlegmatic, unconcerned, serene, placid.)*

passive—*adj.* inert, unresisting, negative, patient, apathetic, inactive, quiescent, unquestioning, enduring. *(alert, positive, malcontent, impatient, aggressive, active, resistant, insubmissive, vehement.)*

pastime—*n.* entertainment, diversion, sport, relaxation, recreation, amusement, play. *(study, task, work, profession, business, labor, occupation.)*

patent—*adj.* evident, plain, apparent, obvious, indisputable. *(questionable, cryptic, ambiguous, dubious.)*

pathetic—*adj.* moving, tender, poignant, meeting, affecting, emotional. *(unimpassioned, unaffecting, humorous, ludicrous, farcical.)*

patience—*n.* resignation, perseverance, sufferance, endurance, submission. *(insubmissiveness, rebellion, impatience, resistance, exasperation, repining, inconsistency.)*

pattern—*n.* sample, exemplar, shape, mold, prototype, model, archetype, specimen, precedent, design. *(caricature, mockery, misrepresentation, perversion, monstrosity.)*

pause—*n.* cessation, halt, rest, interlude, stop, suspension, intermission. *(advancement, perseverance, continuance, furtherance.)*

pause—*v.* suspend, forbear, wait, demur, desist, cease, delay, intermit, stay, hesitate, stop. *(proceed, persist, maintain, perserve, advance, continue.)*

peace—*n.* tranquility, repose, order, reconciliation, concord, amity, quiet, calm, pacification, calmness, harmony. *(disturbance, agitation, disorder, war, variance, conflict, strife, noise, tumult, hostility, embroilment, discord.)*

peaceable—*adj.* inoffensive, peaceful, mild, serene, orderly, placid, unwarlike, quiet, innocuous, unquarrelsome. *(warlike, fierce, quarrelsome, violent, restless, chaotic, pugnacious, litigious, savage, hostile, bellicose.)*

peculiar—*adj.* personal, special, exceptional, particular, singular, strange, odd, eccentric, private, character-istic, exclusive, specific, unusual, uncommon, rare. *(common, universal, ordinary, conventional, public, general, unspecial.)*

peculiarity—*n.* individuality, idiosyncrasy, uniqueness, speciality, distinctiveness. *(universality, uniformity, homogeneity, normalcy, generality, community, homology.)*

peevish—*adj.* testy, crabby, irritable, grouchy, touchy, petulant, querulous, sullen. *(amiable, genial, complaisant, jovial, good-natured, affable.)*

penetrating—*adj.* piercing, acid, sharp, severe, pungent, caustic, biting, shrill, harsh, deafening. *(dull, muted, bland, blunt, soft, mild, shallow, apathetic, dense.)*

pensive—*adj.* dreaming, sad, wistful, melancholy, somber, serious, solemn, thoughtful, reflective. *(happy, gay, jovial, carefree, frivolous, joyous, cheerful.)*

people—*n.* community, mob, herd, vulgar, mass, inhabitants, fellow-creatures, race, society, group, nation, populace, crowd, persons, commonalty, tribe. *(nobility, ruler, gentry, oligarchy, aristocracy, government, blue bloods.)*

perceive—*v.* distinguish, observe, touch, recognize, know, detect, discern, descry, feel, see, understand. *(misobserve, misunderstand, misperceive, miss, ignore, overlook, misconceive.)*

perception—*n.* apprehension, sight, understanding, vision, discernment, cognizance. *(ignorance, misapprehension, unawareness, incognizance, misunderstanding, imperception.)*

peremptory—*adj.* express, absolute, dictatorial, imperious, positive, categorical, decisive, authoritative, dogmatic, despotic. *(entreative, mild, postulatory, untenable, docile, flexible, suggestive.)*

perfect—*adj.* complete, indeficient, absolute, impeccable, unblemished, unexceptionable, ripe, flawless, pure, consummate, full, mature, immaculate, faultless, infallible, blameless. *(meagre, scant, deficient, imperfect, fallible, marred, defective, spoilt, incomplete, faulty, short, defective, blemished, inept.)*

perfectly—*adv.* wholly, completely, exactly, impeccably, fully, accurately, entirely, totally. *(incompletely, inaccurately, defectively, imperfectly, partially.)*

perform—*v.* do, transact, enact, execute, fulfil, complete, perpetrate, accomplish, act, achieve, discharge, effect, consumate. *(mar, misexecute, misenact, spoil, neglect, miss, misperform, botch, misconduct.)*

perhaps—*adv.* peradventure, maybe, probably, possibly, perchance. *(inevitably, certainly, positively.)*

perilous—*adj.* dangerous, risky, insecure, hazardous, tricky. *(secure, certain, guarded, safe.)*

period—*n.* date, era, duration, limit, end, determination, interval, time, epoch, age, continuance, bound, conclusion. *(datelessness, infinity, illimitability, indefiniteness, beginning, indeterminateness, eternity, immemoriality, perpetuity, endlessness.)*

periodic—*adj.* recurrent, stated, systematic, alternate, calculable, regular. *(eccentric, incalculable, fitful, incessant, indeterminate, irregular, spasmodic.)*

peripheral—*adj.* borderline, marginal, surrounding, outlying, tangential, incidental, exterior, outer, surface. *(primary, basic, intrinsic, proximal, central, inner, essential.)*

permanence—*n.* endurance, stability, survival, permanency, continuance, duration, perpetuity. *(mortality, brevity, transience, evanescence.)*

pernicious—*adj.* deadly, malignant, hurtful, damaging, lethal, destructive, ruinous, fatal, harmful. *(beneficial, tonic, healthful, salubrious, innocuous, invigorating.)*

perpetual—*adj.* unceasing, eternal, unfailing, continual, incessant, infinite, constant, uninterrupted, endless, everlasting, perennial, enduring. *(periodic, temporary, falling, occasional, casual, unstable, inconstant, recurrent, transient, exhaustible, momentary.)*

perplex—*v.* puzzle, involve, complicate, bewilder, harass, nonplus, entangle, embarrass, entangle, encumber, confuse, mystify. *(enlighten, disentangle, elucidate, explain, disencumber, clear, explicate, simplify.)*

perseverance—*n.* steadfastness, indefatigability, tenacity, endurance, persistence, constancy, resolution, stamina. *(unsteadfastness, caprice, vacillation, indecision, levity, hesitation, volatility, inconstancy, fit-*

fulness, *irresoluteness, wavering, variableness.)*

persuade—*v.* influence, convince, urge, incite, cajole, induce, incline, dispose, allure. *(disincline, compel, mispersuade, coerce, discourage, deter, indispose, misinduce.)*

pertinent—*adj.* applicable, material, apropos, suited, relevant, apt, germane, significant, fitting, appropriate. *(foreign, irrelevant, unrelated, alien, unsuitable, extraneous, impertinent.)*

perverse—*adj.* untoward, fractious, unmanageable, crochety, forward, eccentric, stubborn, wayward, intractable. *(ductile, governable, accommodating, obliging, normal, docile, amenable, complacent, pleasant.)*

pet—*adj.* favorite, darling, dear, cherished, precious, beloved, dearest. *(despised, unloved, detested, scorned, disliked.)*

petite—*adj.* dainty, little, diminutive, small, wee, undersized, slight. *(large, big, gross, ample.)*

petition—*n.* entreaty, application, salutation, request, invocation, instance, supplication, craving, appeal, prayer. *(expostulation, com-*

mand, claim, requirement, dictation, censure, deprecation, protest, injunction, demand, exaction.)

petty—*adj.* mean, ignoble, narrow, contemptible, insignificant, small, paltry, trifling, trivial. *(large, chivalrous, broad, magnificent, great, magnanimous, liberal, noble, generous.)*

philanthropy—*n.* generosity, charity, munificence, benevolence, humanity, charitableness, beneficence. *(stinginess, cynicism, misanthropy, ill will, selfishness, hostility.)*

philosopher—*n.* savant, master, thinker, schoolman, doctor, teacher. *(sciolist, tyro, foal, dunce, simpleton, ignoramus, freshman, greenhorn, apprentice.)*

philosophical—*adj.* sound, calm, scientific, enlightened, tranquil, unprejudiced, wise, conclusive, rational, accurate. *(crude, loose, popular, sciolistic, emotional, unphilosophical, unsound, vague, inaccurate, unscientific.)*

physical—*adj.* material, tangible, corporeal, concrete, natural, visible, substantial, objective, real. *(moral, immaterial, intangible, supernatural, psychic, mental,* *intellectual, hyperphysical, invisible, unsubstantial, spiritual.)*

picture—*n.* resemblance, painting, image, photograph, engraving, likeness, drawing, representation. *(mirror, original, pattern.)*

picturesque—*adj.* seemly, scenic, pictorial, photogenic, graphic, comely, graceful, artistic. *(uncouth, dead, unpicturesque, flat, monotonous, unseemly, banal, rude, ugly, tame.)*

piece—*n.* element, fragment, portion, section, share, unit, swatch, quantity, amount, bit, division. *(whole, sum, entirety, assemblage, set, total, zero, none.)*

pinion—*v.* restrain, manacle, shackle, fetter, fashion, bind, tether, fasten, strap. *(free, release, unloose, liberate, loosen, unshackle.)*

piquant—*adj.* sharp, racy, biting, smart, keen, tart, savory, pungent, lively, severe, cutting, stimulating, stinging. *(dull, characterless, bland, insipid, tame, flat.)*

pithy—*adj.* forceful, expressive, spongy, succinct, terse, laconic, concise. *(characterless, weak, pointless, vapid, redundant, diluted, flat.)*

pity—*n.* compassion, commiseration, sympathy, empathy, condolence, mercy, tenderness, ruth. *(hardheartedness, scorn, pitilessness, apathy, rancor, ruthlessness, cruelty, rage, relentlessness.)*

place—*v.* assign, establish, attribute, put, situate, set, locate, fix, settle, deposit. *(remove, unsettle, disestablish, misattribute, uproot, extirpate, transport, detach, disturb, disarrange, misplace, misassign, transplant, eradicate.)*

plain—*adj.* even, smooth, clear, unobstructed, manifest, obvious, simple, natural, homely, open, unembellished, artless, lucid, level, feat, unencumbered, uninterrupted, evident, unmistakable, easy, unaffected, unvarnished, unsophisticated, unreserved. *(undulating, rough, abrupt, confused, obstructed, questionable, dubious, enigmatical, obtruse, fair, sophisticated, varnished, complicated, embellished, uneven, rugged, broken, encumbered, uncertain, interrupted, ambiguous, hard, affected, beautiful, artful.)*

plan—*n.* drawing, sketch, scheme, project, stratagem,

system, design, draft, contrivance, device.

plan—*v.* devise, design, picture, contrive, sketch out, hatch, illustrate. *(confuse, twist, distort, falsify, obscure, perplex.)*

platonic—*adj.* intellectual, cold, mental, ecstatic, philosophical, unsensual. *(animal, sexual, passionate, intense, ardent, sensual.)*

plausible—*adj.* superficial, unctuous, pretentious, right, colorable, probable, credible, specious, passable, fairspoken, ostensible, apparent, feasible. *(sterling, absurd, unlikely, profound, genuine, unmistakable.)*

playful—*adj.* sportive, frolicsome, vivacious, frisky, sprightly, lively, jocund, gay. *(dull, somber, sedate, earnest, grave.)*

plea—*n.* vindication, ground, apology, request, appeal, excuse, justification, defense, entreaty. *(accusation, action, charge, impeachment, indictment.)*

pleasant—*adj.* agreeable, pleasurable, gratifying, enlivening, delicious, jocular, exquisite, congenial, merry, grateful, acceptable, desirable, cheerful, sportive, delectable, satisfactory. *(un-grateful, obnoxious, offensive, lugubrious, ill-humored, distasteful, unpleasant, disagreeable, dull, unacceptable, unlively.)*

pleasure—*n.* gratification, choice, self-indulgence, will, purpose, favor, indulgence, entertainment, enjoyment, sensuality, voluptuousness, preference, inclination, determination, satisfaction. *(suffering, trouble, self-denial, disinclination, indisposition, refusal, elation, pain, affliction, asceticism, abstinence, aversion, denial.)*

plebian—*adj.* vulgar, lowbred, ignoble, crude, low, lowborn, coarse. *(noble, refined, high-bred, elite, patrician, aristocratic, high-born.)*

pliable—*adj.* limber, plastic, supple, lithe, docile, flexible, pliant. *(stiff, firm, rigid, hard, stubborn.)*

plot—*n.* plan, combination, machination, scheme, intrigue, stratagem, conspiracy.

plot—*v.* concoct, contrive, hatch, scheme, devise, conspire, frame, plan.

plump—*adj.* bloated, distended, fat, chubby, massive, swollen, portly, rotund, corpulent. *(lean, emaciated, angular, slender, skinny, thin, bony, lank, weazen.)*

plunge—*v.* dive, duck, sink, immerse, thrust under, spurt, pitch headlong, dip, douse, submerge, precipitate, overwhelm. *(issue, raise, rescue, rise, emerge, soar, extricate.)*

plural—*adj.* many, manifold, multiple, several, numerous, multiplex. *(singular, unique, solitary, lone, single, sole.)*

poetic—*adj.* lyric, creative, imaginative, inspired, metrical, dreaming, rhythmic, lilting. *(prosaic, literal, stolid, unimaginative, routine, matter-of-fact.)*

poisonous—*adj.* infectant, toxic, corruptive, noxious, malignant, peccant, pestiferous, deleterious, venomous, vicious, vitiative, baneful, morbific, virulent, mephitic. *(genial, sanative, healthful, restorative, hygeian, salubrious, wholesome, beneficial, invigorative, innoxious, remedial.)*

polite—*adj.* refined, courteous, complaisant, courtly, genteel, gracious, accomplished, elegant, well-bred, obliging, civil, polished. *(rude, ill-bred, boorish, disobliging, insolent, awkward, uncouth, discourteous, clownish.)*

politic—*adj.* wise, provident, judicious, wary, discreet, tactful, prudent, sagacious, diplomatic, cunning, well, devised. *(unwise, undiplomatic, blundering, impolitic, imprudent, improvident.)*

pompous—*adj.* gorgeous, showy, ostentatious, lofty, bombastic, stiff, pretentious, assuming, arrogant, magnificent, splendid, sumptuous, stately, grand, turgid, inflated, coxcombical. *(unobtrusive, unassuming, humbleminded, retiring, unpretending, modest, plain-mannered.)*

ponderous—*adj.* bulky, heavy, massive, cumbersome, hefty, big, weighty, enormous, awkward. *(flimsy, airy, fragile, delicate, light, small, dainty.)*

poor—*adj.* moneyless, penniless, meager, deficient, unsatisfactory, thin, bold, destitute, indigent, impecunious, weak, insufficient, faulty, inconsiderable, scanty. *(wealthy, affluent, liberal, ample, sufficient, considerable, prosperous, rich, copious, abundant, large, moneyed, satisfactory.)*

popular—*adj.* current, public, received, beloved, approved, liked, prevalent, common, vulgar, general, favorite, prevailing, wide-spread. *(restricted, detested, esoteric,* *odious, disliked, exclusive, scientific, unpopular.)*

portentous—*adj.* menacing, fateful, impending, alarming, sinister, ominous, inauspicious, prophetic. *(auspicious, cheering, comforting, encouraging, propitious.)*

positive—*adj.* actual, absolute, real, unconditional, explicit, settled, indisputable, express, assured, direct, overbearing, decisive, dogmatical, substantial, fixed, independent, unequivocal, definitive, conclusive, enacted, confident, dogmatic. *(insubstantial, fictitious, relative, dependent, implied, questionable, uncertain, indirect, suspicious, doubtful, negative, unreal, imaginary, contingent, conditional, dubious, moral, fallacious, occasional.)*

possess—*v.* enjoy, hold, own, inherit, occupy, have, entertain. *(renounce, resign, surrender, forfeit, abandon, abjure, lose, submit.)*

possible—*adj.* feasible, potential, conceivable, practicable, likely. *(impossible, impracticable, absurd, unfeasible.)*

postpone—*v.* delay, procrastinate, suspend, defer, prorogue. *(accelerate, sustain, dispatch, expedite.)*

posterity—*n.* progeny, children, issue, heirs, descendents, offspring, scions. *(forbears, ancestors, progenitors, forefathers.)*

potent—*adj.* effective, stiff, strong, powerful, compelling, powerful, impressive, serious, cogent, vigorous, solid. *(feeble, weak, mild, impotent, ineffectual, dubious, frail, inefficient.)*

poverty—*n.* need, destitution, penury, want, indigence. *(wealth, affluence, prosperity.)*

power—*n.* capacity, potentiality, strength, might, susceptibility, dominion, command, agency, rule, effectiveness, strength, faculty, capability, ability, force, energy, influence, sway, government, authority, jurisdiction. *(incapability, inability, imbecility, insusceptibility, powerlessness, subservience, feebleness, incapacity, impotence, weakness, inertness, subjection, obedience, ineffectiveness.)*

powerful—*adj.* potent, energetic, masterful, mighty, strong, puissant. *(poor, weak, feeble, fragile.)*

practice—*n.* habit, experience, action, manner, routine, performance, usage, exercise, exercitation, custom.

(dishabituation, theory, nonperformance, disuse, inexperience, speculation, abolition.)

practice—*v.* exercise, carry on, perform, deal in.

praise—*v.* laud, honor, puff, compliment, applaud, flatter, panegyrize, eulogize, commend, glorify, celebrate, extol. *(censure, reprove, disparage, blame, discommend.)*

prayer—*n.* supplication, orison, suit, worship, request, petition, entreaty, benediction. *(expostulation, restriction, disrespect, irreverence, mockery.)*

precaution—*n.* provision, anticipation, care, prudence, providence, forethought, premonition, pre-arrangement. *(improvidence, thoughtlessness, carelessness, negligence.)*

precede—*v.* forego, lead, preface, introduce, herald, usher, anticipate, head, pave the way, forerun. *(follow, result, ensue, succeed, postdate.)*

precious—*adj.* valuable, cherished, beloved, of great value, dear, priceless, costly, treasured, estimable. *(valueless, unvalued, unappreciated, useless, vile, cheap, worthless, disesteemed.)*

precise—*adj.* exact, pointed, correct, formal, scrupulous, punctilious, formal, explicit, definite, nice, accurate, particular, specific, terse, ceremonious. *(vague, rough, loose, ambiguous, informal, casual, unceremonious, indefinite, inexact, inaccurate, circumlocutory, tortuous.)*

predict—*v.* foretell, prognosticate, foreshadow, anticipate, prophesy, forecast, forebode.)*

prediction—*n.* prognostication, fore-announcement, foretelling, presage, foreshowing, augury, anticipation, prophecy, vaticination, premonstration, forebodement. *(relation, account, report, narration, history, description.)*

preface—*n.* proem, prologue, premiss, preliminary, introduction, prelude, preamble. *(sequel, epilogue, supplement, postscript, peroration, appendix.)*

prefer—*v.* elect, fancy, advance, favor, further, choose, select, promote. *(postpone, withhold, depress, exclude, reject, defer, degrade.)*

prejudice—*n.* prejudgment, bias, injury, impairment, partiality, damage, preconception, prepossession, predisposition, unfairness, harm, detriment, disadvantage. *(fairness, judgment, advantage, detachment, impartiality.)*

premature—*adj.* crude, untimely, precipitate, rash, inopportune, unseasonable, hasty, precocious, unauthenticated, too early. *(timely, opportune, mature, ripe, seasonable.)*

premium—*n.* guerdon, douceur, bribe, bonus, bounty, reward, remuneration, encouragement, enhancement, recompense, prize. *(fine, mulct, penalty, amercement, forfeit.)*

preparation—*n.* readiness, provision, development, apprenticeship. *(without, provision, unpreparedness, unawareness.)*

prepare—*v.* adapt, adjust, fit, arrange, lay, equip, ready, qualify, groom, provide, order, plan, furnish. *(misadapt, derange, demolish, disconcert, confuse, misfit, misprovide, disarrange, subvert.)*

prepossessing—*adj.* alluring, winning, engaging, personable, attractive, charming, taking. *(sinister, repulsive, unpleasant, unattractive.)*

preposterous—*adj.* exorbitant, absurd, foolish, fantastic, ridiculous, monstrous, unreasonable, irrational. *(due, sound, reasonable, right,* orderly, sensible, just, fair, moderate, judicious.)*

presence—*n.* Influence, closeness, attendance, nearness, intercourse. *(absence, distance, remoteness, separation, distraction.)*

preserve—*v.* guard, keep safe, protect, rescue, shield, spare, defend, save, uphold, maintain. *(destroy, damage, ruin, dilapidate.)*

president—*n.* moderator, chairman, superintendent, commander-in-chief, principal. *(subordinate, corporation, ward, component, institution, member, constituent, society.)*

press—*v.* crowd, force, squeeze, compress, constrain, instigate, impress, encroach, harass, palpate, urge, compel, crush, express, hurry, inculcate, throng. *(inhibit, entice, solicit, skim, free, ease, relieve, touch, relax, persuade, allure, graze, liberate, avoid, manipulate.)*

presume—*v.* anticipate, venture, conjecture, deem, surmise, assume, suppose, apprehend, take for granted, believe. *(deduce, argue, withdraw, distrust, conclude, infer, prove, retire, hesitate.)*

pretend—*v.* simulate, allege, propound, profess, imitate, feign, offer, exhibit, affect. *(unmask, test, refute, verify, detect, substantiate, corroborate.)*

pretense—*n.* pretext, simulation, mask, show, plea, make believe, pretension, mimicry, excuse, fabrication, cloak, color, garb, assumption, hoax. *(reality, simplicity, guilelessness, veritableness, fact, frankness, verity, truth, candor, openness, actuality.)*

pretty—*adj.* attractive, trim, pleasing, fine, delicate, comely, handsome, neat, tasteful, beautiful. *(grotesque, homely, ugly, ungainly, plain.)*

prevailing—*adj.* ruling, operative, prevalent, ascendant, most, common, current, controlling, influential, predominant, rife, most general. *(diminishing, powerless, uneffectual, mitigated, subordinate.)*

prevent—*v.* obstruct, neutralize, thwart, anticipate, frustrate, checkmate, preclude, hinder, bar, nullify, intercept, forefend, obviate. *(aid, expedite, instigate, advance, induce, produce, promote, facilitate, encourage, accelerate, cause.)*

price—*n.* figure, compensation, appraisement, expenditure, worth, cost, charge, expense, value. *(discount, remit-*

tance, reduction, abatement, donation, allowance.)

pride—*n.* haughtiness, self-exaltation, conceit, vanity, loftiness, lordliness, arrogance, gratification. *(meekness, self-distrust, humility, lowliness, modesty.)*

priggish—*adj.* dandified, affected, conceited, pedantic, coxcombical, foppish, prim. *(sensible, simple-minded, casual, plain, unaffected, informal.)*

prim—*adj.* precise, starched, self-conscious, priggish, puritanical, formal, demure, stiff, unbending. *(easy, unaffected, free, libertine, naive, unformal, genial, natural.)*

primary—*adj.* original, elementary, chief, important, primitive, first, embryonic, pristine, earliest, main, principal, leading. *(subordinate, unimportant, subsequent, later, following, secondary, posterior, inferior.)*

primitive—*adj.* primeval, pristine, simple, archaic, aboriginal, old-fashioned, quaint, unsophisticated. *(new-fangled, modish, civilized, modern, sophisticated.)*

princely—*adj.* munificent, superb, regal, supreme, distinguished, imperial, august, magnificent, royal. *(mean, ig-*

noble, beggarly, niggardly, vulgar.)

principal—*adj.* first, leading, primary, pre-eminent, main, paramount, prominent, highest, chief, foremost. *(subordinate, minor, supplemental, auxiliary, peripheral, inferior, secondary subject.)*

principle—*n.* origin, cause, substance, power, truth, law, axiom, rule, postulate, ethics, source, motive, energy, element, faculty, tenet, doctrine, maxim. *(manifestation, action, development, exercise, formation, dishonesty, exhibition, application, issue, operation.)*

private—*adj.* peculiar, secret, retired, secluded, privy, special, individual, not public. *(public, unconcealed, general, open, available.)*

privilege—*n.* immunity, right, advantage, exemption, priority, prerogative, franchise, liberty, claim. *(disqualification, prohibition, subordination, inhibition, disfranchisement, exclusion.)*

prize—*n.* spoil, prey, trophy, guerdon, honors, palm, award, booty, plunder, forage, laurels, premium, ovation. *(forfeiture, penalty, sacrifice, failure, stigma, mulct, taint, loss, fine,*

amercement, disappointment, brand, infamy.)

probability—*n.* presumption, chance, expectation, verisimilitude, appearance, likelihood. *(improbability, inconceivableness, unlikelihood, impossibility, doubtfulness.)*

probable—*adj.* presumable, reasonable, anticipated, likely, credible. *(incredible, unlikely, unreasonable, implausible.)*

problem—*n.* question, dilemma, puzzle, conundrum, query, riddle, difficulty, predicament, paradox, mystery. *(answer, solution, response, discovery, finding out, deciphering.)*

proceed—*v.* pass, progress, issue, flow, initiate, arise, move, advance, continue, emanate. *(deviate, stand, stop, stay, discontinue, retire, ebb, regress, recede, retreat, desist.)*

procession—*n.* march, file, train, cavalcade, parade, retinue, caravan, cortege. *(herd, rush, mob, rout, rabble, disorder, confusion, disarray.)*

prodigal—*adj.* profuse, reckless, squandering, profligate, improvident, lavish, extravagent, wasteful. *(saving, economical, miserly, close-*

fisted, cautious, frugal, hoarding, niggardly, close.)

prodigious—*adj.* portentous, vast, astounding, monstrous, huge, surprising, extraordinary, marvelous, wonderful, gigantic, enormous, amazing, remarkable. *(common-place, usual, moderate, picayune, ordinary, every-day, familiar.)*

produce—*n.* yield, profit, effect, consequence, amount, product, agricultural products, fruit, result.

produce—*v.* bear, afford, create, yield, prolong, render, cause, furbish, lengthen, exhibit, originate, extend. *(retain, withhold, destroy, curtail, contract, stifle, withdraw, neutralize, annihilate, shorten, reduce, subvert.)*

product—*n.* result, consequence, emanation, generate, work, fruit, issue, effect. *(principle, motive, operation, tendency, cause, law, power, energy, action, force.)*

production—*n.* evolution, genesis, manufacture, creation, growth, origination, formation, product. *(consumption, use.)*

profane—*v.* secular, unsanctified, irreligious, ungodly, godless, blasphemous, pervert, temporal, unconsecrated, unholy, irreverent, wicked, impious. *(consecrated, spiritual, reverent, godly, devout, glorify, holy, sacred, sanctified, religious, pious.)*

profess—*v.* avow, own, pretend, lay claim to, certify, declare, acknowledge, confess, proclaim. *(suppress, disavow, renounce, rebuff, abjure, conceal, disown, repudiate.)*

profit—*n.* emolument, avail, benefit, use, value, gain, advantage, acquisition, service, improvement. *(detriment, disadvantage, harm, waste, loss, damage.)*

profitable—*adj.* advantageous, beneficial, productive, gainful, lucrative, worthwhile, desirable, useful, remunerative. *(disadvantageous, detrimental, unprofitable, vain, unproductive, damaging, useless, unremunerative, unprofitable, undesirable, unbeneficial, fruitless.)*

program—*n.* notice, catalogue, performance, calendar, plan, advertisement, schedule. *(rehearsal, resume, précis, recital, review, analysis, repetition.)*

progress—*n.* advance, proceeding, journey, speed, progression, growth, advancement, movement, way, proficiency. *(stoppage, stay, delay, failure, relapse, retardation, retreat, retrogression.)*

project—*n.* purpose, scheme, device, undertaking, venture, plan, design, contrivance. *(chance, hazard, peril.)*

prominent—*adj.* protuberant, embossed, manifest, eminent, main, leading, distinctive, jutting, protrusive, relieved, extended, conspicuous, distinguished, important, characteristic. *(concave, indented, engraved, withdrawn, minor, unimportant, undistinguishable, secondary, subordinate, receding, rebated, hallowed, entailed, average, inconspicuous, indistinctive.)*

promiscuous—*adj.* confused, unselected, undistributed, common, casual, unordered, heterogeneous, mingled, undistinguished, unarranged, unassorted, unreserved, disorderly. *(select, arranged, reserved, exclusive, homogeneous, nice, sorted, orderly, distributed, assorted.)*

promise—*v.* engage, covenant, stipulate, guarantee, pledge, assure, warrant.

promise—*n.* assurance, pledge, covenant, stipulation, engagement, word, oath.

promote—*v.* further, excite, raise, prefer, encourage, aid, advance, exalt, elevate. *(repress, check, depress, dishonor, disable, discourage, hinder, allay, degrade.)*

prompt—*v.* alert, active, brisk, unhesitating, incite, ready, responsive, quick, apt. *(sluggish, inactive, deter, unready, irresponsive.)*

pronounce—*v.* utter, propound, express, assert, enunciate, proclaim, articulate, declare, affirm, deliver. *(mispropound, suppress, silence, swallow, mumble, subdue, mispronounce, misaffirm, stifle, choke, gabble.)*

proof—*n.* trial, criterion, test, establishment, demonstration, testimony, verification, essay, examination, comprobation, evidence, scrutiny, authentication. *(failure, short-coming, undemonstrativeness, error, reprobation, disproof, invalidity, fallacy.)*

proper—*adj.* appertinent, own, special, adapted, suitable, just, equitable, decent, fit, applicable, peculiar, personal, constitutional, befitting, suited, appropriate, fair, right, becoming. *(inappertinent, universal, unbefitting, unsuited, indecent, inappropriate, improper, common, in-*

congruous, alien, non-special, unadopted, unsuitable, wrong, unbecoming, unorthodox.)

property—*n.* attribute, nature, possessions, wealth, gear, ownership, acquisitions, quality, peculiarity, characteristic, goods, estate, resources.

proportion—*n.* relation, distribution, symmetry, uniformity, harmony, correlation, adaptation, rate, adjustment, interrelationship. *(misadjustment, disparity, disorder, disproportion, irregularity, misproportion, incongruity, disharmony, irrelation.)*

propose—*v.* tender, bring forward, intend, propound, design, move, suggest, offer, proffer, purpose, mean. *(denounce, deprecate, dispute, discount, deny, protest, contradict.)*

prosaic—*adj.* matter-of-fact, prolix, unimaginative, dull, tedious. *(animated, lively, eloquent, provocative, graphic, poetic, interesting, fervid.)*

prospect—*n.* vision, landscape, anticipation, assurance, view, field, hope, probability, promise. *(dimness, darkness, veiling, hopelessness, shadow, improbability, viewlessness, obscurity, cloud, occultation.)*

prospectus—*n.* plan, announcement, scheme, brochure, synopsis, program, catalogue, bill, compendium. *(proceeding, subject, transaction, enactment.)*

prosperity—*n.* weal, good fortune, good luck, affluence, success, welfare, well-being. *(woe, failure, depression, reverse, unsuccess, adversity.)*

protect—*v.* fortify, shield, cover, save, screen, vindicate, defend, guard, preserve, secure. *(endanger, abandon, forsake, expose, betray, imperil.)*

prototype—*n.* original, first, norm, example, precedent, sample, absolute, pattern, model. *(imitation, rerun, facsimile, reproduction, copy.)*

protracted—*adj.* prolonged, lengthy, extensive, extended, diffuse, rambling, interminable. *(short, concise, brief, abbreviated, limited.)*

proud—*adj.* haughty, supercilious, boastful, vain, elated, lofty, magnificent, appreciative, self-conscious, arrogant, imperious, presumptuous, prideful, imposing, ostentatious, self-satisfied. *(humble, unpresuming, lowly, unimposing, humiliated,* deferential, affable, meek, mean, ashamed.)

prove—*n.* assay, establish, ascertain, show, examine, validate, attest to, verify, try, test, demonstrate, argue, confirm, substantiate. *(pretermit, misindicate, disprove, disestablish, invalidate, pass, misdemonstrate, refute, contradict, neutralize.)*

proverbial—*adj.* current, customary, unquestioned, notorious, acknowledged. *(unfounded, suspected, unfamiliar, dubious, questionable, suspicious.)*

provide—*v.* arrange, afford, cater, contribute, get, produce, stipulate, donate, prepare, procure, supply, yield, furnish, agree, collect. *(neglect, withhold, appropriate, deny, divert, retain, mismanage, disallow, overlook, misprovide, refuse, alienate, misemploy.)*

province—*n.* region, section, domain, precinct, territory, tract, department, sphere. *(capital, metropolis, center, center of government.)*

provision, provisions—*n.* arrangement, supply, food, victuals, eatables, rations, preparations, produce, anticipation, supplies, edibles. *(pittance, misprovision, thoughtlessness, destitution, dearth,*

dole, neglect, scantiness, forgetfulness, want, oversight, starvation.)

provoke—*v.* summon, irritate, challenge, impel, exasperate, tantalize, infuriate, educe, rouse, excite, vex, offend, anger. *(relegate, soothe, propitiate, conciliate, allay, pacify.)*

proxy—*n.* substitution, agent, representative, commissioner, delegate, deputy, agency, representation, substitute, surrogate, lieutenant. *(personality, person, deputer, principalship, principal, authority, superior.)*

prudent—*adj.* wary, circumspect, careful, vigilant, judicious, wise, cautious, discreet. *(unwary, indiscreet, uncircumspect, imprudent, reckless, foolish, incautious, rash, audacious, silly, liberal.)*

prudish—*adj.* over-modest, squeamish, demure, puritanical, coy, over-nice, reserved. *(promiscuous, free, uninhibited.)*

public—*adj.* notorious, social, open, exoteric, generally known, universal, common, national, general. *(secret, domestic, close, solitary, individual, parochial, private, secluded, personal.)*

pull—v. drag, extract, haul, tug, magnetize, pluck, draw, adduce. *(eject, propel, thrust, push, extrude.)*

punch—v. pierce, pommel, bore, strike, perforate, poke, puncture. *(plug, bung, stop, seal, snap.)*

punish—v. castigate, correct, discipline, scourge, penalize, chastise, chasten, whip. *(recompense, indemnify, exonerate, reward, remunerate.)*

pupil—n. learner, tyro, ward, disciple, scholar, student, novice. *(master, adept, tutor, guardian, teacher, proficient.)*

puppy—n. fop, prig, coxcomb, youth, dude. *(clown, lout, boor, bumpkin.)*

pure—adj. unmixed, genuine, mere, quietless, unadulterated, unsullied, chaste, clean, immaculate, unspotted, sheer, innocent, unpolluted, clear, simple, absolute, uncorrupted, unblemished, real, spotless, undefiled, guileless. *(turbid, adulterated, corrupt, stained, defiled, guilty, faulty, foul, impure, mixed.)*

purpose—n. design, meaning, object, end, point, objective, resolve, intention, mind, view, aim, scope. *(fortune, accident, lot, lottery, incident, hit, chance, fate, hazard, casualty.)*

purpose—v. determine, resolve, propose, persist, intend, design, mean. *(risk, revoke, venture, jeopardize, stake, chance, hazard, miscalculate.)*

push—v. drive, shove, press against, butt, urge, accelerate, jostle, reduce, press, impel, propel, thrust, expedite. *(draw, adduce, pull, drag, haul.)*

put—v. lay, propose, situate, place, set. *(raise, transfer, dislodge, withdraw, remove, displace.)*

putrid—adj. rancid, decaying, spoiled, moldering, moldy, rotten, contaminated, decomposed, bad. *(pure, fresh, wholesome, healthy, untainted.)*

puzzle—n. bewilderment, confusion, intricacy, enigma, embarrassment, doubt, conundrum, labyrinth, quandary. *(solution, extrication, lucidity, clue, disentanglement, explanation.)*

puzzle—v. perplex, bewilder, mystify, complicate, confuse, pose, embarrass, confound. *(instruct, clarify, illumine, enlighten.)*

Q

quack—*n.* mountebank, impostor, humbug, fraud, empiric, charlatan, pretender. *(gull, victim, dupe, prey.)*

quaint—*adj.* recondite, elegant, odd, affected, archaic, singular, charming, old-fashioned, curious, abstruse, nice, whimsical, antique, fanciful. *(ordinary, coarse, modern, fashionable, current, dowdy, commonplace, usual, common, modish.)*

qualified—*adj.* adapted, suitable, eligible, fitted, competent. *(unable, deficient, impotent, inept.)*

quality—*n.* character, attribute, disposition, sort, description, power, nature, stature, tendency, condition, property, peculiarity, temper, kind, capacity, virtue. *(heterogeneousness, incapacity, indistinctiveness, disqualification, disability, mediocrity, anomalousness, nondescript, weakness, triviality, ineffectiveness, negation.)*

qualm—*n.* scruple, uneasiness, regret, pang, twinge, fear, compunction, apprehension, uncertainty. *(security, comfort, firmness, confidence, invulnerability, easiness.)*

quandry—*n.* dilemma, perplexity, entanglement, impasse, crisis, plight, predicament, fix, doubt. *(relief, assurance, ease, certainty, plain sailing.)*

quantity—*n.* amount, size, measure, portion, magnitude, share, volume, division, bulk, sum, aggregate, part. *(deficiency, want, scantiness, loss, diminution, wear, dearth, margin, waste, deduction, inadequacy, leakage, insufficiency, deterioration.)*

quarrel—*n.* altercation, squabble, tumult, wrangle, disagreement, hostility, embroilment, broil, controversy, brawl, affray, feud, dispute, variance, misunderstanding, quarreling, bickering. *(conversation, pleasantry, friendliness, amity, agreement, goodwill, confabulation, chat, conciliation, peace.)*

quarrelsome—*adj.* irascible, litigious, brawling, hot-tempered, choleric, irritable, argumentative, petulant, pugnacious, fiery, contentious. *(amenable, mild, unquarrelsome, conciliatory, bland, meek, suave, accommodating, peaceable, genial, inoffensive.)*

quarter—*n.* district, territory, forbearance, source, pity, region, locality, mercy.

*(mercilessness, cruelty, piti-
lessness, extermination, ruthlessness, unsparingness.)*

queasy—*adj.* sick,
nauseated, edgy, squeamish,
restless, upset, giddy. *(relaxed, content, comfortable,
easy, untroubled.)*

queer—*adj.* whimsical,
cross, crochety, eccentric,
weird, odd, quaint, strange,
singular. *(common, familiar,
orthodox, customary, ordinary, usual.)*

quell—*v.* quiet, subdue,
reduce, disperse, scatter, vanquish, pacify, tranquillize,
curb. *(excite, stimulate, kindle, incite, spur, irritate,
enrage.)*

question—*v.* inquire,
doubt, ask, dubitate, dispute,
catechize, interrogate, investigate, controvert. *(state,
pronounce, concede, affirm,
allow, answer, dictate, assert,
enunciate, grant, endorse.)*

question—*n.* interrogation,
inquiry, scrutiny, topic, investigation, doubt, debate.
*(response, answer, admis-
sion, retort, concession, reply, solution, explanation.)*

questionable—*adj.* dubious, suspicious, disputable,
uncertain, hypothetical,
doubtful, problematical, debatable. *(evident, obvious,*

*unequivocal, indisputable,
certain, self-evident.)*

quick—*adj.* rapid, expeditious, hasty, ready, sharp,
adroit, keen, active, nimble,
agile, sprightly, fast, intelligent, precipitous, irasible,
speedy, swift, prompt, clever,
shrewd, fleet, brisk, lively,
alert, transient. *(tardy, inert,
dull, gradual, insensitive,
slow, sluggish, inactive.)*

quiet—*n.* repose, calm,
rest, pacification, peace,
stillness, tranquillity, appeasement, silence. *(motion,
agitation, disturbance, tumult, uproar, unrest, noise, excitement, turmoil.)*

quiet—*v.* appease, pacify,
lull, soothe, silence, calm,
allay, still, hush, tranquilize.
*(excite, agitate, urge, blare,
goad, rouse, disturb, stir.)*

quit—*v.* resign, relinquish,
cease, release, give up, forsake, leave, abandon, discharge, surrender, depart
from. *(occupy, bind, haunt,
continue, enter, seek, invade,
enforce.)*

quite—*adv.* entirely, wholly, altogether, fully, totally,
perfectly, completely, truly.
*(imperfectly, scarcely, insuffi-
ciently, partially, hardly, barely.)*

quixotic—*adj.* impractical,
idealistic, romantic, lofty, fan-

tastic, chivalrous, visionary. *(practical, prosaic, pragmatic, realistic, hardheaded.)*

quote—*v.* name, plead, note, cite, repeat, paraphrase, adduce, allege. *(refute, oppose, traverse, misadduce, deny, rebut, disprove, retort, contradict, misquote.)*

R

rabid—*adj.* zealous, dedicated, fanatical, bigoted, unreasonable, deranged, frantic, maniacal, frenzied. *(reasonable, normal, moderate, sound, sober, lucid, rational, sane, steady.)*

racy—*adj.* fresh, piquant, spicy, smart, vivacious, animated, rich, fine-flavored, pungent, spirited, lively. *(stupid, flavorless, languid, dull, morose.)*

radiant—*adj.* luminous, bright, lustrous, sparkling, shining, brilliant, ecstatic, beaming, elated, merry. *(dull, murky, dim, gloomy, downcast, somber, sad, blurred.)*

radical—*adj.* fundamental, natural, unsparing, entire, immanent, underived, profound, deep-seated, original, thorough-going, extreme, innate, essential, ingrained. *(ascititious, partial, superficial, con-servative, derived, traditional, acquired, adventitious, extraneous, moderate.)*

rage—*n.* rabidity, indignation, fury, anger, dudgeon, passion, ferocity, wrath, choler, frenzy, ire, mania, madness. *(moderation, temperateness, quiescence, assuagement, mildness, serenity, softness, reason, gentleness, calmness, mitigation.)*

rage—*v.* storm, be furious, rave, seethe, be violent, fume. *(be peaceful, be calm, mollify, be composed, lull.)*

raise—*v.* heave, exalt, promote, lift, enhance, rouse, call forth, rear, collect, erect, propagate, intensify, elevate, advance, heighten, awaken, excite, cultivate, produce, summon, originate. *(cast, degrade, dishonor, depreciate, compose, calm, destroy, disband, hush, neutralize, curtail, confute, lay, depress, retard, lull, lower, quiet, blight, disperse, stifle, silence.)*

rampant—*adj.* wild, flagrant, excessive, unrestrained, prevalent, menacing, boisterous, ungovernable, comprehensive, universal. *(bland, mild, calm, decorous, local, moderate, contained, dispassionate.)*

range—*n.* dispose, place, collocate, concatenate, stroll, scope, rove, rank, class, order, file, ramble. *(disconnection, derangement, disturbance.)*

rank—*n.* line, order, grade, series, dignity, row, tier, degree. *(disorder, incontinuity, intermission, plebianism, commonalty, breach, hiatus, disconnection, solution, meanness.)*

rank—*adj.* exuberant, excessive, proliferating, luxuriant, rampant, extreme. *(sparse, fragrant, scanty, pure, wholesome.)*

rankle—*v.* smoulder, irritate, disquiet, embitter, fester, burn, gall. *(cool, calm, compose, improve, heal, close, quiet.)*

rapid—*adj.* swift, accelerated, instantaneous, flying, quick, speedy. *(tardy, cumbrous, deliberate, slow, lazy, retarded.)*

rapture—*n.* delight, exultation, joy, ecstasy, felicity, bliss, passion, rejoicing, transport. *(misery, revulsion, disgust, distress, discontent, affliction.)*

rare—*adj.* choice, excellent, volatile, exceptional, unusual, uncommon, extraordinary, dispersed, precious, sporadic, scarce, infrequent, few, sparse, singular, incomparable, unique, valuable, thin. *(frequent, numerous, ordinary, regular, dense, common, worthless, valueless, mediocre, abundant, mean, usual, crowded, vulgar, cheap.)*

rash—*adj.* audacious, precipitate, foolhardy, adventurous, indiscreet, overventuresome, unwary, impulsive, headstrong, hasty, reckless, careless, thoughtless, venturesome, heedless, incautious. *(cautious, discreet, dubitating, reluctant, prudent, timid, wary, calculating, unventuresome, hesitating.)*

rate—*n.* impost, duty, allowance, quota, price, status, tax, assessment, standard, ratio, worth, value. *(rebate, discount, allowance, percentage.)*

rate—*v.* calculate, value, abuse, evaluate, appraise, compute, estimate, scold. *(repose, be quiescent, loaf.)*

rational—*adj.* sound, reasoning, judicious, sensible, equitable, fair, logical, sane, intelligent, reasonable, sober, probable, moderate. *(unsound, silly, absurd, fanciful, preposterous, unreasonable, exorbitant, emotional, insane, weak, unintelligent,* *injudicious, extravagant, un-reasoning, irrational.)*

ravel—*v.* undo, unwind, fray, disentangle, separate, untwist. *(complicate, confuse, mend, entangle, conglomerate.)*

ravish—*v.* transport, enrapture, violate, debauch, captivate, entrance, enchant, charm, outrage. *(disgust, pique, rile, displease, provoke, harass.)*

raw—*adj.* unprepared, unripe, unseasoned, fresh, unpracticed, bare, exposed, chill, piercing, crude, uncooked, unfinished, bleak, inexperienced, green, untried, bald, galled, unrefined. *(dressed, finished, cooked, mature, seasoned, expert, healed, habituated, practiced, tried, genial, processed, prepared, ripe, mellow, experienced, adept, familiar, trained, covered, balmy.)*

reach—*v.* thrust, obtain, attain, grasp, strain, lengthen, aim, extend, stretch, arrive at, gain, penetrate. *(stop, revert, miss, drop, recoil, fail, cease, rebate.)*

read—*v.* interpret, unravel, recognize, comprehend, learn, persue, decipher, discover. *(misinterpret, misobserve, misunderstand, overlook.)*

ready—*adj.* responsive, alert, speedy, dexterous, skillful, expert, easy, fitted, disposed, free, compliant, quick, accessible, prompt, expeditious, unhesitating, apt, handy, facile, opportune, prepared, willing, cheerful. *(tardy, hesitating, dubitating, unhandy, remote, unavailable, unsuited, unwilling, unprepared, grudging, incompliant, difficult, unready, slow, reluctant, awkward, clumsy, inaccessible, inopportune, unfitted, indisposed, constrained, unaccommodating, irresponsive, doubtful.)*

real—*adj.* veritable, authentic, true, developed, tangible, actual, existent, legitimate, genuine. *(imaginary, non-existent, false, adulterated, pretended, possible, counterfeit, fictitious, unreal, untrue, artificial, assumed, potential.)*

really—*adv.* truly, unquestionably, indubitably, veritably, indeed. *(possibly, falsely, fictitiously, doubtfully, questionably, perhaps, untruly.)*

reason—*n.* account, explanation, proof, understanding, rationality, propriety, order, sake, target, purpose, ground, cause, motive, apology, reasoning, right, justice, object. *(pretense, falsifica-*

tion, disproof, absurdity, irrationality, unreason, unfairness, aimlessness, nonsense, unaccountableness, pretext, misinterpretation, misconception, unreasonableness, fallacy, wrong, impropriety, folly.)

reason—v. discuss, infer, deduce, conclude, cogitate, debate, argue. (back up, comply, abet, encourage, agree.)

reassure—v. restore, inspirit, countenance, bolster, rally, encourage, animate. (cow, intimidate, unnerve, discountenance, discourage, brow-beat.)

rebuff—v. repel, check, oppose, reject, rebuke, repulse, snub. (encourage, welcome, abet, accept, support.)

rebuff—n. discouragement, check, refusal, rebuke, repulsion. (encouragement, spur, acceptance, welcome.)

rebuke—v. chide, reprimand, berate, censure, reprove, rebuff. (encourage, applaud, extol, incite, approve, eulogize.)

receipt—n. reception, acknowledgement, acquisition, voucher, custody. (rejection, exclusion, emission, expulsion.)

receive—v. accept, hold, assent to, acquire, take, ad-

mit, entertain. (impart, reject, emit, expend, give, afford, discharge.)

reception—n. admittance, acceptation, salutation, entertainment, admission, acceptance. (protest, rejection, dismissal, renunciation, abjuration, denial, repudiation, non-acceptance, discardment, adjournment.)

recess—n. nook, retirement, seclusion, vacation, depression, holiday, cavity, withdrawal, retreat, privacy. (protrusion, publicity, promontory, work time, projection, discharge.)

reckless—adj. heedless, foolhardy, rash, regardless, improvident, venturesome, careless, incautious, thoughtless, precipitate, inconsiderate. (heedful, timid, thoughtful, provident, wary, prudent, circumspect, careful, cautious, chary, calculating, considerate.)

reckon—v. calculate, regard, value, consider, infer, enumerate, judge, compute, count, estimate, account, argue. (miscalculate, misreckon, miscompute, misestimate, miscount.)

reclusive—adj. solitary, recluse, secluded, isolated, cloistered, ascetic, withdrawn, eremitic. (sociable, *gregarious, convivial, companionable, wordly, accessible.)*

recognize—*v.* acknowledge, know, avow, allow, discern, identify, concede, own, recollect. *(overlook, repudiate, disown, scrutinize, disallow, ignore, misobserve, disavow.)*

recollect—*v.* recall, bethink, reminisce, think of, recreate, recover, remember, bring to mind. *(lose, forget, obliterate, overlook.)*

recommend—*v.* confide, applaud, advise, sanction, commend, praise, approve. *(disapprove, warn, dissuade, disparage, condemn, deter.)*

recompense—*v.* remunerate, indemnify, repay, compensate, repair, requite, reward, satisfy, reimburse. *(injure, spoil, dissatisfy, damnify, mar, misrequite.)*

recompense—*n.* indemnification, remuneration, requital, reward, amends, satisfaction.

reconcile—*v.* conciliate, pacify, adjust, suit, appease, reunite, unite, propitiate, harmonize, adapt. *(sever, estrange, derange, antagonize, separate, incite, disharmonize, alienate, conflict.)*

record—*n.* entry, list, inventory, catalogue, schedule, scroll, roll, instrument, remembrance, memorandum, chronicle, register, enrollment, index, registry, archive, enumerative, memento. *(oblivion, desuetude, immemorality, amnesty, disremembrance, obliteration, nonregistration, obsolescence.)*

recover—*v.* repossess, retrieve, save, heal, revive, reanimate, recapture, regain, resume, recruit, cure, restore. *(forfeit, sacrifice, impair, decline, succumb, relapse, lose, miss, deteriorate, decay.)*

recovery—*n.* regaining, vindication, restitution, retrieval, replacement, reanimation, revival, improvement, redemption, repossession, reinstatement, renovation, re-establishment, rectification, reanimation. *(forfeiture, deprival, loss, abandonment, retrogression, ruin, declension, defection, privation, sacrifice, relapse, decay, incurableness.)*

recreation—*n.* cheer, amusement, revival, sport, relaxation, regeneration, refreshment, holiday, reanimation, diversion, pastime. *(toil, labor, work, employ-*

ment, drudgery, weariness, lassitude, fatigue, assiduity.)

redeem—*v.* regain, make amends for, ransom, rescue, satisfy, liberate, discharge, reconvert, repurchase, retrieve, recompense, recover, fulfill. *(lose, abandon, surrender, rescind, sacrifice, pledge, forfeit, betray.)*

reduce—*v.* diminish, attenuate, narrow, weaken, subdue, bring, subject, curtail, convert, lessen, abridge, impoverish, contract, impair, subjugate, refer, classify. *(magnify, augment, exalt, extend, broaden, renovate, expand, restore, liberate, except, transform, enlarge, increase, produce, amplify, invigorate, repair, free, dissociate.)*

redundant—*adj.* expendable, extra, superfluous, marginal, wasteful, additional, dispensable, repetitious, unnecessary. *(essential, central, necessary, concise, brief, indispensable.)*

refer—*v.* associate, advert, relate, belong, apply, relegate, attribute, assign, connect, point, allude, appeal. *(dissociate, misappertain, misbeseem, disunite, disresemble, disconnect, misapply, alienate.)*

refinement—*n.* purification, sublimation, elegance, civilization, finesse, polish, clarification, filtration, delicacy, cultivation, subtility, sophistry, discernment. *(grossness, turbidity, coarseness, unrefinement, foulness, inelegance, broadness, vulgarity, bluntness, impurity, rudeness, boorishness, unsophisticatedness.)*

reflect—*v.* image, mirror, consider, cogitate, contemplate, muse, heed, animadvert, reverberate, return, exhibit, think, meditate, ponder, ruminate, advert. *(dissipate, dream, rove, wool-gather, disregard, absorb, overlook, divert, idle, wander, star-gaze, connive.)*

reform—*v.* ameliorate, rectify, reclaim, remodel, reorganize, regenerate, improve, amend, correct, better, rehabilitate, reconstitute. *(vitate, deteriorate, stabilitate, impair, stereotype, degenerate, corrupt, worsen, perpetuate, confirm, deform.)*

refresh—*v.* refrigerate, revive, renovate, renew, cheer, brace, revitalize, cool, invigorate, reanimate, recreate, restore, freshen. *(oppose, burden, annoy, fatigue, debilitate, relax, depress,* heat, weary, afflict, tire, exhaust, enervate.)

refuse—v. withhold, decline, veto, repudiate, deny, reject. (afford, concede, permit, acquiesce, grant, yield.)

refuse—n. scum, sediment, sweepings, offscourings, remains, waste, dross, offal, dregs, recrement, trash, debris. (pickings, flower, prime, merchandise, cream, firstfruits, chattels.)

regard—v. view, esteem, deem, respect, revere, conceive, notice, behold, mind, contemplate, consider, affect, reverence, value, heed, scrutinize. (overlook, despise, miss, contemn, loathe, misconceive, misjudge, reject, disregard, dislike, hate, misconsider, misestimate.)

regardless—adj. inconsiderate, unmindful, unobservant, indifferent, imprudent, heedless, despising, careless, inattentive, disregarding. (considerate, alert, attentive, cautious, scrupulous, careful, mindful, regardful, prudent, circumspect.)

regenerate—v. rehabilitate, improve, remedy, edify, reform, uplift, redeem, rejuvenate, reanimate, redo, recreate, convert, better, civilize. (debase, lower, corrupt, degenerate, defile, demolish, crush, deprove.)

regret—v. lament, miss, deplore, brood, grieve, repent, desiderate. (hail, abandon, forget, overlook, disregard, welcome, approve, abjure.)

regret—n. grief, remorse, concern, repentance, sorrow, lamentation, anguish. (contentment, tranquillity, peace of mind, comfort, solace.)

regular—adj. normal, orderly, stable, recurrent, systematic, established, formal, certain, customary, ordinary, stated, periodical, methodic, recognized, symmetrical. (exceptional, capricious, irregular, fitful, variable, erratic, abnormal, uncertain, unusual, habitual, rare, disordered, unsymmetrical, eccentric.)

regulation—n. law, disposal, rule, government, control, organization, arrangement, adjustment, method, order, statute. (disorder, misgovernment, disarrangement, caprice, insubjection, license, uncontrol, misrule, anarchy, maladministration, nonregulation, chaos.)

reject—v. renounce, cast away, repel, decline, refuse, ignore, exclude, throw out, repudiate, discard. (welcome, appropriate, hail, select, endorse, admit, accept, choose.)

rejoice—v. glory, joy, gladden, revel, cheer, enliven, jubilate, gratify, delight, exult, triumph, be glad, please. *(grieve, weep, repent, afflict, weary, disappoint, darken, pain, vex, mope, annoy, mourn, lament, sorrow, trouble, oppress, depress, burden, distress, sadden.)*

relation—v. aspect, narration, fitness, bearing, homogeneity, relevancy, ratio, agreement, kindred, reference, correlation, appurtenancy, connection, proportion, affinity, association, pertinency, harmony, relative, kinsman. *(disconnection, irrelevancy, disproportion, unfitness, heterogeneity, disagreement, isolation, alien, irrelation, dissociation, disharmony, impertinency, misproportion, independence, unsuitableness.)*

release—v. loose, discharge, acquit, extricate, indemnify, exempt, free, liberate, quit, parole, disengage. *(constrain, shackle, fetter, enslave, yoke, bind, confine.)*

relevant—adj. apt, contingent, pertinent, apropos, related, germane, suitable, appropriate, connected, applicable, on target. *(inappropriate, alien, unrelated, irrelevant, foreign, immaterial.)*

relief—n. support, extrication, respite, mitigation, help, remedy, exemption, refreshment, succor, comfort, release, alleviation, aid, assistance, redress, deliverance. *(aggravation, burdensomeness, exhaustion, discomfort, hamper, oppression, intensification, trouble, weariness.)*

religion—n. creed, belief, piety, godliness, denomination, holiness, faith, theology, profession, sanctity. *(irreligion, atheism, unbelief, sacrilege, blasphemy, profanity, sanctimoniousness, formalism, irreverence, reprobation, scoffing, skepticism, hypocrisy, pharisaism, godlessness, impiety.)*

religious—adj. godly, devotional, holy, reverent, sacred, pious, devout, divine. *(ungodly, sacrilegious, skeptical, agnostic, impious, profane, undevout, blasphemous.)*

relish—n. recommendation, flavor, gusto, appetite, sapidity, allure, zest, enhancement, savor, taste, piquancy. *(disflavor, nauseousness, insipidity, antipathy, unsavoriness, drawback, disrecommendation, disrelish.)*

remain—v. continue, stop, halt, rest, abide, endure, loiter, accrue, stay, wait, tarry, sojourn, dwell, last. *(vanish,* depart, hasten, flit, pass, transfer, fly, remove, speed, press, disappear.)

remarkable—*adj.* noticeable, unusual, striking, notable, famous, rare, prominent, eminent, singular, observable, extraordinary, noteworthy, distinguished, peculiar. *(unnoticeable, mean, every-day, inconspicuous, undistinguished, unremarkable, ordinary, commonplace.)*

remedy—*v.* restorative, reparation, relief, specific, rectify, cure, counteraction, redress, help. *(disease, infection, ill, deterioration, provocation, undermine, evil, hurt, plague, impairment, aggravation.)*

remember—*v.* recall, bear in mind, review, mind, recollect, retain. *(obliviate, overlook, forget, disregard, ignore.)*

remembrance—*n.* memory, token, memento, nostalgia, reminiscence, recollection, memorial, souvenir. *(oblivion, forgetfulness, obscurity.)*

remiss—*adj.* careless, inattentive, slow, idle, dilatory, remissful, delinquent, slack, negligent, wanting, slothful, lax, tardy. *(careful, active, alert, diligent, meticulous, strict, energetic, attentive, assiduous, painstaking.)*

remit—*v.* pardon, forego, surrender, resign, condone, relax, absolve, discontinue, forgive. *(intensity, exact, deteriorate, increase, enforce.)*

remorse—*n.* anguish, penitence, qualm, contrition, compunction, self-condemnation, regret. *(self-approval, pride, self-congratulation, complacency, satisfaction.)*

remote—*adj.* indirect, unrelated, alien, separate, inaccessible, contingent, distant, unconnected, foreign, heterogeneous. *(close, connected, actual, homogeneous, proximate, present, urgent, current, near, direct, related, immediate, essential, pressing.)*

remove—*v.* separate, transport, transfer, oust, suppress, depart, uproot, displace, abstract, carry, eject, dislodge, migrate, obliterate. *(conserve, perpetuate, reinstate, install, fasten, fix, stand, remain, abide, sustain, restore, stabilitate, establish, reinstall, dwell, stay.)*

render—*v.* present, restore, give, apportion, surrender, requite, submit, deliver, return, give up, assign, pay. *(retain, appropriate, misapportion, misrequite, refuse, keep,* *withhold, alienate, misappropriate.)*

renegade—*adj.* heretical, insurgent, rebellious, traitorous, dissident, mutinous, maverick, apostate, disloyal. *(faithful, obedient, loyal, steadfast, unswerving.)*

renew—*v.* restore, renovate, furbish, repeat, reissue, reform, modernize, transform, recreate, refresh, rejuvenate, recommence, reiterate, regenerate. *(wear, vitiate, discontinue, weaken, deprove, cancel, impair, deteriorate, exhaust, corrupt, defile.)*

renounce—*v.* abjure, disown, disavow, quit, abandon, resign, relinquish, reject, repudiate, disclaim, forego, deny, resign, recant. *(recognize, maintain, propound, vindicate, profess, retain, accept, defend, acknowledge, claim, assert, own, avow, hold.)*

renowned—*adj.* celebrated, famous, illustrious, prominent, wonderful. *(obscure, unknown, anonymous, unrecognized.)*

repay—*v.* reimburse, reward, requite, indemnify, refund, remunerate, recompense, retaliate. *(misappropriate, waste, extort, exact,* *circumvent, defraud, embezzle, alienate, confiscate.)*

repeal—*n.* rescission, annulment, termination, abrogation, recall, revocation. *(establishment, perpetuation, endurance, continuance.)*

repeal—*v.* revoke, cancel, recall, reverse, invalidate, abolish, rescind, annul, abrogate, discontinue, delete. *(establish, institute, enact, confirm, secure, continue, pass, sanction, perpetuate.)*

repeat—*v.* iterate, cite, relate, quote, recapitulate, reaffirm, reproduce, reiterate, renew, rehearse. *(drop, abandon, suppress, misquote, misrepresent, misconvey, discontinue, discard, ignore, misrepeat, misrecite, neglect, misinterpret.)*

repeatedly—*adv.* frequently, often, again and again, many times. *(rarely, seldom, occasionally.)*

repentance—*n.* contrition, regret, sorrow, self-condemnation, remorse, contrition, penitence, compunction, self-reproach. *(obduracy, hardness, self-approval, smugness, impenitence, recusancy, reprobation.)*

repetition—*n.* reiteration, iteration, diffuseness, relation, verbosity, recapitulation, dwelling upon. *(precedence, newness, freshness, singularity, uniqueness.)*

replace—*v.* supply, reinstate, re-establish, supersede, restore, substitute, rearrange. *(abstract, remove, move, deprive, deviate, withdraw, damage.)*

reply—*v.* answer, rejoin, rebut, replicate, respond. *(drop, pass, question, disregard, ignore, pretermit.)*

reply—*n.* rejoinder, replication, retaliation, answer, response. *(ignoring, pass by, stimulus.)*

report—*v.* relate, circulate, narrate, describe, communicate, divulge, declare, announce, tell, notify, recite, detail. *(hush, misreport, misrelate, expunge, falsify, silence, suppress, misrepresent.)*

report—*n.* announcement, narration, description, declaration, rumor, repute, reverberation, disclosure, tidings, relation, recital, news, communication, fame, noise. *(suppression, silence, fabrication, reticence, noiselessness, misannouncement.)*

represent—*v.* delineate, exhibit, state, indicate, enact, denote, dramatize, symbolize, resemble, portray, play, reproduce, personate, describe, embody, illustrate. *(misdelineate, falsify, misrepresent, misportray, distort, caricature, minimize.)*

representative—*n.* commissioner, agent, deputy, embodiment, delegate, proxy, vicigerent, soverign, emissary, constituency, substitute, personation, vicar, principal. *(dictator, autocrat, despot.)*

repress—*v.* control, inhibit, block, restrain, hinder, stifle, squelch, swallow, curb, quell, subdue. *(liberate, encourage, allow, permit, free, sanction, authorize.)*

reproach—*n.* censure, rebuke, blame, reprobate, lecture, taunt, reprove, upbraid. *(praise, approval, laud, glory, esteem.)*

reprobate—*n.* villain, miscreant, scalawag, degenerate, castaway, ruffian, rascal. *(pattern, model, paragon, example, mirror, saint.)*

repudiate—*v.* disown, abjure, disclaim, revoke, disavow, discard, divorce, renounce, contradict. *(own, assert, vaunt, profess, acknowledge, concede, accept, avow, vindicate, retain, claim, recognize.)*

repulsive—*adj.* deterrent, odious, unattractive, revolting, repugnant, forbidding, ungenial, ugly, disagreeable.

(agreeable, winning, fascinating, seductive, enchanting, pleasant, charming, attractive, captivating, alluring.)

reputable—*adj.* creditable, reliable, estimable, dependable, honorable, respectable. *(discreditable, disgraceful, unrespectable, dishonorable, disreputable, notorious.)*

rescue—*v.* recover, liberate, save, preserve, salvage, retake, recapture, extricate, deliver. *(imperil, surrender, expose, endanger, betray, abandon, impede.)*

resemblance—*n.* similarity, affinity, semblance, portrait, likeness, reflection, image, similitude, representation. *(dissimilarity, difference, contrast, contrariety, unlikeness, disresemblance.)*

resent—*v.* resist, recalcitrate, be indignant at, repel, rebel, take exception to. *(submit, pardon, approve, overlook, acquiesce, condone.)*

reserve—*n.* retention, accumulation, shyness, modesty, reservation, limitation, coldness, coyness, evasiveness. *(rashness, immodesty, spontaneity, boldness, recklessness.)*

residence—*n.* stay, home, domicile, dwelling, mansion, sojourn, abode, habitation.

resist—*v.* oppose, check, baffle, disappoint, frustrate, withstand, hinder, thwart. *(yield, surrender, comply, weaken, capitulate.)*

resolute—*adj.* decided, constant, steadfast, bold, unshaken, decisive, determined, fixed, steady, persevering, firm. *(infirm, cowardly, faltering, inconstant, weak, shy.)*

resource—*n.* means, expedients, riches, assets, material, supplies, wealth. *(exhaustion, drain, poverty, want, destitution, lack, nonplus.)*

respect—*v.* esteem, revere, appreciate, regard, honor, venerate. *(disrespect, deride, dishonor, scorn.)*

respond—*v.* rejoin, answer, reply, acknowledge, notice. *(disregard, neglect, ignore, overlook.)*

rest—*n.* relaxation, indolence, lassitude, idleness, leisure, retirement, siesta, repose, tranquillity, calm. *(work, activity, exertion, sweat, toil, turmoil, agitation.)*

restless—*adj.* uneasy, disquieted, agitated, unsettled, wandering, turbulent, unquiet, disturbed, sleepless, anxious, roving. *(settled, steady, calm, quiet, peaceful.)*

restrain—*v.* hinder, withhold, curb, coerce, abridge, confine, tether, check, stop, repress, suppress, restrict, limit. *(let go, free, liberty, give full rein to, release, flow.)*

result—*n.* consequence, inference, event, effect, conclusion, issue, aftermath. *(origin, beginning, cause, seed.)*

retain—*v.* restrain, keep, hold, withhold. *(give up, yield, abandon.)*

retire—*v.* leave, secede, abdicate, withdraw, deport, recede. *(continue, advance, proceed.)*

retort—*v.* answer, repartee, retaliate.

retreat—*n.* departure, seclusion, privacy, shelter, evacuation, refuge, retirement, withdrawment, solitude, asylum. *(forward march, progress, advance.)*

return—*v.* requite, recompense, remit, restore, repay, render, report, remember. *(question, assert, claim, displace, remove.)*

reveal—*v.* disclose, unveil, open, impart, announce, show, communicate, divulge, uncover, discover. *(withhold, conceal, disguise, hide, keep secret, cover.)*

revengeful—*adj.* resentful, spiteful, malicious, vindictive, merciless. *(ingenuous, hearty, kind, charitable, cordial, open, frank, generous.)*

revenue—*n.* returns, proceeds, result, wealth, dividends, receipts, income. *(outgo, expense, disbursements.)*

reverence—*n.* honor, adoration, esteem, veneration, awe. *(disdain, contempt, scorn, arrogance.)*

review—*n.* resurvey, survey, revise, revision, evaluation, re-examination, retrospect, reconsideration.

reward—*n.* compensation, pay, retribution, accolade, recompense, remuneration, requital. *(fine, punishment, penalty, damages.)*

rhetorical—*adj.* eloquent, articulate, fluent, pompous, expressive, pretentious. *(inarticulate, ill-spoken, tongue-tied, fumbling.)*

rich—*adj.* affluent, ample, abundant, costly, precious, luscious, lavish, wealthy, opulent, copious, fruitful, sumptuous, generous. *(weak, cheap, sordid, destitute, poor, straitened, scanty.)*

ridicule—*n.* wit, raillery, irony, mockery, satire, gibe, sneer, sarcasm, derision, banter, burlesque, travesty, jeer.

(praise, respect, honor, homage, deference.)

ripe—*adj.* mellow, finished, developed, mature, complete. *(young, unfinished, tender, green, incomplete.)*

rise—*v.* ascend, mount, climb, arise, scale, emanate. *(sink, decline, fall, slump.)*

risk—*n.* hazard, jeopardy, peril, vulnerability, exposure, danger. *(security, safeness, safety, protection.)*

rival—*n.* emulator, competitor, antagonist, opponent. *(colleague, associate, collaborator, ally, partner.)*

road—*n.* highway, lane, route, course, way, street, pathway, passage, thoroughfare.

robbery—*n.* depredation, despoliation, pillage, piracy, theft, steal, plunder, caper, looting.

romance—*n.* novel, tale, mystery, fable, fiction.

romantic—*adj.* fanciful, glamorous, extravagant, chimerical, wild, sentimental, fictitious. *(familiar, timorous, aloof, unromantic, frigid, cold.)*

room—*n.* compass, latitude, space, apartment, scope, chamber.

rotund—*adj.* rounded, spherical, circular, globular, plump, fat, corpulent, chubby, stout. *(slim, lean, trim, svelte, thin, slender.)*

round—*adj.* spherical, globose, orbed, full, rotund, curved, circular, globular, orbicular, cylindrical, plump. *(oblong, lean, slender, thin, square, angular.)*

rout—*v.* smite, conquer, defeat, vanquish. *(recede, retire, withdraw.)*

route—*n.* path, track, roadway, passage. *(drift, digression, twist, meander.)*

royal—*adj.* regal, imperial, noble, princely, majestic, splendid, magnanimous, aristocratic, kingly, monarchical, kinglike, august, superb, illustrious. *(low, humble, plebian, coarse, vulgar, tawdry, common.)*

ruin—*n.* downfall, fall, defeat, subversion, bane, mischief, destruction, perdition, overthrow, pest, collapse. *(construction, creation, improve, enhance, build.)*

rule—*n.* law, maxim, canon, method, control, sway, authority, empire, regulation, precept, guide, order, direction, government. *(misrule, violence, revolt, misgovernment, confusion, riot, rebellion, conflict.)*

rustic—*adj.* rude, inelegant, honest, awkward, coarse, unadorned, artless, uncouth, rural, plain, unpolished, untaught, rough, simple. *(stylish, elegant, sophisticated, blasé, chic.)*

ruthless—*adj.* pitiless, heartless, unfeeling, hardened, cold, cruel, brutal, relentless, merciless. *(tenderhearted, gentle, indulgent, compassionate, sympathetic.)*

S

sabotage—*v.* disable, sap, wreck, subvert, vandalize, hamper, damage, obstruct, incapacitate. *(enhance, strengthen, abet, assist, cooperate, reinforce.)*

sacred—*adj.* divine, consecrated, devoted, venerable, blessed, holy, hallowed, dedicated, religious, reverend, sanctified. *(secular, sinful, profane, violable, impious, temporal, unconsecrated.)*

sacrifice—*n.* slaughter, offering victim, martyr, scapegoat, oblation, homage, holocaust, corban, hecatomb. *(gain, seizure, usurpation, confiscation, appropriation, profit.)*

sad—*adj.* mournful, dejected, cheerless, sedate, grave, afflictive, sorrowful, despondent, calamitous, gloomy, depressed, downcast, serious, grievous. *(lively, spirited, jolly, seductive, cheerful, gay, happy, sprightly, fortunate.)*

safe—*adj.* unendangered, sure, protected, secure, unscathed. *(hazardous, dangerous, risky, exposed, in danger.)*

sagacious—*adj.* acute, keen, judicious, intelligent, shrewd, cunning, wise, rational, prudent, sensible, tactful. *(irrational, stupid, foolish, obtuse, silly, ignorance, fatuous.)*

salient—*adj.* outstanding, noticeable, striking, signal, conspicuous, prominent, obvious, palpable, manifest. *(depressed, minor, trifling, insignificant, trivial, unimportant.)*

salutary—*adj.* healthful, remedial, beneficial, advantageous, useful, wholesome, profitable, salubrious. *(tainted, unhealthy, detrimental, infectious.)*

sample—*n.* illustration, specimen, instance, example.

sanction—*v.* endorse, support, approve, ratify. *(disapprove, forbid, hinder, censure.)*

sarcasm—*n.* irony, ridicule, sneering, scorn, contempt, jeer, taunting, vitrial, bitterness. *(compliment, praise, flattery, admiration, eulogy, commendation, enthusiasm.)*

satire—*n.* sarcasm, ridicule, burlesque, humor, pasquinade, lampoon, irony, mockery, wit.

satisfaction—*n.* content, pleasure, compensation, remuneration, atonement, felicity, contentment, gratifiation, recompense, amends, indemnification. *(discomfort, want, displeasure, discontent, resentment, shame, unhappiness.)*

satisfy—*v.* content, gratify, fulfill, compensate, indemnify, satiate, please, recompense, remunerate. *(renege, fail, trouble, sadden, deplete, drain, vex.)*

saucy—*adj.* insolent, impudent, disrespectful, impertinent, rude. *(well-bred, demure, respectful, mannerly, amiable.)*

savage—*adj.* wild, untaught, feral, unpolished, brutish, heathenish, cruel, fierce, merciless, murderous, ferocious, uncultivated, rude, uncivilized, brutal, barbarous, inhuman, pitiless, unmerciful. *(refined, gentle, humane, domesticated, tame, cultured, kind, merciful, human.)*

save—*v.* rescue, protect, reserve, redeem, prevent, preserve, deliver, spare. *(expose, throw away, sacrifice, abandon, give up.)*

saying—*n.* speech, maxim, by-word, apothegm, proverb, utterance, declaration, adage, aphorism, saw.

scandal—*n.* detraction, calumny, reproach, disgrace, outrage, defamation, slander, opprobrium, shame. *(glory, respect, honor, esteem, praise.)*

scanty—*adj.* gaunt, scarce, deficient, meager, inadequate. *(plenty, full, ample, copious.)*

scarce—*adj.* infrequent, uncommon, rare, unique, deficient. *(general, frequent, common, usual, abundant.)*

scatter—*v.* dissipate, strew, diffuse, sprinkle, disperse, spread. *(keep together, preserve, assemble, gather, collect, unite.)*

scheme—*n.* project, contrivance, device, strategy, plot, plan, design, purpose.)*

scholar—*n.* intellectual, sage, pupil, disciple, professor, academician. *(ignoramus, illiterate, simpleton, dunce, dolt.)*

science—*n.* art, knowledge, literature, expertness, skill. *(illiteracy, ignorance, sciolism.)*

scoff—*v.* mock, jeer, ridicule, belittle, sneer, deride, taunt, revile. *(exalt, extol, value, praise, appreciate.)*

scorn—*n.* disdain, contumely, slight, contempt, disregard, derision, despite, dishonor. *(respect, admiration, approval, flattery, love, honor.)*

scrimp—*v.* save, stint, economize, hoard, grudge, scrape, withhold, be parsimonious. *(spend, pour, lavish, squander, waste.)*

scrupulous—*adj.* careful, hesitating, meticulous, cautious, ethical, conscientious. *(careless, daring, reckless, dishonest, negligent, unscrupulous, scatterbrained.)*

scurrilous—*adj.* abusive, low, insulting, offensive, vile, mean, foul-mouthed, scurrile, obscene, opprobrious, reproachful, insolent, gross, vulgar, foul, indecent. *(proper, delicate, polite, decent, refined, well-bred.)*

seasoned—*adj.* mature, knowing, ripe, weathered, experienced, veteran, practiced, hardened. *(immature, green, innocent, starry-eyed, untried.)*

secret—*adj.* concealed, unseen, private, recondite, covert, privy, confidential, hidden, secluded, unknown, obscure, latent, clandestine. *(free, public, revealed, known, open.)*

sectarian—*adj.* partisan, heretic, schismatic, fanatic, clannish. *(nonpartisan, broadminded, nonsectarian.)*

section—*n.* division, portion, segment, part, component. *(entirety, all, whole, totality.)*

security—*n.* defense, shelter, certainty, assurance, confidence, pledge, invulnerability, protection, guard, safety, ease, carelessness, surety. *(exposure, uncertainty, hazard, danger, doubt.)*

sedate—*adj.* demure, calm, quiet, settled, passive, unruffled, sober, serious, grave, serene. *(frolicsome, ruffled, disturbed, excitable, flighty, indiscreet, agitated.)*

seem—*v.* look, appear, manifest.

seemly—*adj.* fit, proper, congruous, decent, conventional, becomingly, suitable, appropriate, meet, decorous, polite. *(immodest, gross, outrageous, rude, improper, unconventional.)*

segregate—*v.* disconnect, seclude, isolate, sequester, exclude, quarantine, ghettoize, divorce, disunite. *(blend, integrate, unify, desegregate, mix.)*

seize—*v.* grasp, snatch, arrest, capture, embrace, catch, clutch, append, take. *(relinquish, liberate, free, let go, loose, let pass.)*

selective—*adj.* choosy, critical, discriminating, finicky, fastidious, percipient, exacting, cautious, careful. *(random, inclusive, promiscuous, careless, unselective, undemanding.)*

self-control—*n.* self-discipline, independence, self-restraint, equilibrium, stability, balance, fortitude, willpower. *(instability, weakness, hotheadedness, excitability.)*

selfish—*adj.* egotistic, self-centered, greedy, mean, tight, egotistical, self-interested, mercenary, rapacious, stingy. *(selfless, generous, altruistic, giving, magnanimous, charitable.)*

sense—*n.* reason, sensation, meaning, signification, opinion, reaction, judgment, understanding, perception, feeling, import, notion. *(anesthesia, atrophy, paralysis, numbness.)*

sensible—*adj.* wise, satisfied, astute, persuaded, intelligent, cognizant, logical. *(foolish, dense, obtuse, scatterbrained, impractical.)*

sentiment—*n.* opinion, sensibility, emotion, feeling, thought, notion.

sepulchral—*adj.* funereal, dismal, somber, dreary, morbid, ghastly, melancholy, cheerless, lugubrious. *(bright, vivacious, lively, inviting, cheerful.)*

serene—*adj.* fair, balmy, cool, peaceful, tranquil, placid, relaxed, dignified, nonchalant. *(agitated, anxious, excitable, stormy, turbulent, hectic.)*

serious—*adj.* solemn, weighty, pensive, grave, important, thoughtful. *(lively, light, happy, frivolous, gay, unimportant.)*

serve—*v.* minister to, promote, obey, help, benefit, officiate, succor, subserve, aid, assist, support. *(obstruct, dissatisfy, thwart, hinder, betray, deceive.)*

set—*v.* settle, decline, consolidate, establish, harden, sink, subside, compose. *(ascend, mount, agitate, run, melt, fuse, dislodge, flow, rise, soar, stir, loosen, soften, mollify.)*

set—*adj.* established, determined, formal, conventional, fixed, firm, regular. *(unorthodox, eccentric, unusual, unconventional.)*

settle—*v.* establish, arrange, adjust, decide, quiet, still, fall, lower, acquiesce, agree, stabilize, fix, regulate, compose, determine, allay, adjudicate, sink, subside, calm, abate. *(disestablish, derrange, aggravate, disturb, misdetermine, misplace, rise, move, increase, scramble, remove, misregulate, discompose, disorder, confuse, heighten, misarrange, unsettle, ascend, disagree.)*

settlement—*n.* dregs, precipitation, location, stabilization, colony, subsidence, residuum, colonization, arrangement. *(perturbation, fluctuation, disorder, turbidity, excitement.)*

several—*adj.* distinct, sundry, various, numerous, different, separate, diverse, divers. *(same, indistinguishable, united, integral, communal, one, identical, inseparable, total.)*

severe—*adj.* austere, grave, harsh, rigorous, afflictive, violent, exact, censorious, sarcastic, keen, cruel, serious, stern, strict, rigid, sharp, distressing, extreme, critical, caustic, cutting, better, demanding. *(smiling, relaxed, mild, jocund, indulgent, trivial, loose, inconsiderable, lenient, moderate, considerate, tender, compassionate, gentle, gay, genial, cheerful, jocose, joyous, light, trifling, inexact, uncritical, inextreme, kind, feeling.)*

shabby—*adj.* threadbare, beggarly, impoverished, ragged, contemptible, paltry, mangy. *(dapper, debonair, admirable, new, spendthrift.)*

shadowy—*adj.* cloudy, dark, gloomy, somber, mysterious, dim, obscure, murky. *(brilliant, sunny, bright, clear, sharp, dazzling.)*

shallow—*adj.* slight, trifling, superficial, trivial, unprofound, shoal, flimsy, simple. *(profound, deep, serious, meaningful.)*

sham—*n.* ghost, illusion, delusion, shadow, counterfeit, deception, phantom, mockery, pretense, unreality, affectation. *(reality, substantiality, authenticity, sincerity, verity, truth, substance.)*

shame—*n.* humiliation, decorum, shamefacedness, dishonor, contempt, discredit, remorse, dispraise, abashment, modesty, decency, reproach, ignominy, degradation. (barefacedness, impudence, indecorum, honor, exaltation, credit, shamelessness, glory, immodesty, indecency, impropriety, renown, pride.)

shameful—adj. degrading, outrageous, indecent, despicable, unbecoming, disgraceful, scandalous, dishonorable. (respectable, estimable, honorable, reputable.)

shape—v. mould, adapt, adjust, create, make, fashion, form, figure, delineate, contrive, execute. (distort, misdelineate, discompose, misproduce, destroy, pervert, misadapt, derange, miscontrive, caricature, ruin.)

shape—n. form, mould, pattern, model, silhouette, figure, outline, fashion, cost. (disorder, disarray, confusion.)

share—n. apportionment, division, allowance, contingent, segment, portion, lot, participation, quota, allotment, dividend. (mass, entirety, aggregate, whole, total.)

sharp—adj. fine, shrewd, clever, acute, aculeated, pungent, shrill, afflictive, harsh, cutting, active, sore, animated, perceptive, spirited, thin, keen, discerning, sarcastic, pointed, penetrating, acid, piercing, distressing, severe, eager, ardent, hard. (indifferent, blunt, obtuse, light, rounded, mellow, hollow, trivial, gentle, tender, sluggish, indifferent, spiritless, ambiguous, tame, thick, dull, knobbed, bluff, bass, deep, trifling, mild, soft, lenient, inactive.)

shatter—v. dissipate, derange, rend, shiver, disintegrate, burst, split, disrupt, break in pieces, demolish, dismember. (organize, fabricate, rear, strengthen, constitute, construct, collocate, compose.)

sheer—adj. mere, unqualified, absolute, unadulterated, gauzy, pure, unmixed, unmitigated, simple. (qualified, modified, partial, limited, adulterated.)

shelve—v. discard, stifle, postpone, dismiss, swamp, shift. (prosecute, revive, expedite, agitate, start, pursue.)

shift—v. alter, shelve, remove, rearrange, change, transfer, displace. (fasten, insert, plant, restrain, place, fix, locate, pitch.)

shift—n. expedient, pretext, change, device, resource, deviation, transference, contrivance, artifice, substitute, motive, evasion. (fixity, retention, gripe, permanence, miscontrivance, steadiness, location.)

shocking—*adj.* horrible, hateful, abominable, foul, astounding, sad, disgraceful, revolting, loathsome. *(honorable, delightful, edifying, attractive, enticing, comforting, pleasing, charming, creditable, exemplary, alluring.)*

short—*adj.* limited, inadequate, near, condensed, lacking, defective, weak, incomplete, inextensive, abrupt, brief, concise, abridged, scanty, insufficient, less, deficient, imperfect, soon, narrow, incomprehensive, blunt. *(protracted, unlimited, ample, adequate, exuberant, long, large, complete, deferred, strong, extensive, bland, inabrupt, diffuse, elongated, extended, plentiful, abundant, sufficient, liberal, copious, distant, wide, comprehensive, exceeding, courteous, expanded.)*

shortsighted—*adj.* imprudent, myopic, unthinking, unwise, reckless, impulsive, indiscreet, thoughtless, foolish. *(prudent, circumspect, cautious, thoughtful, sagacious.)*

show—*v.* present, unfold, teach, conduct, evince, prove, verify, explain, exhibit, demonstrate, reveal, inform, manifest. *(suppress, with-*

hold, mystify, misdemonstrate, contradict, deny, misinterpret, misexplain, screen, conceal, hide, obscure, wrap, misdeclare, refute, disprove, falsify.)*

show—*n.* exhibition, parade, illusion, semblance, pretext, pretense, pageantry, appearance, pomp, demonstration, likeness, profession. *(disappearance, suppression, disguise, unlikeness, reality, substance, deception, nonappearance, concealment, secrecy, sincerity, dissimilarity, ungenuineness.)*

showy—*adj.* gaudy, gorgeous, tinsel, garish, gay, high-colored, flashy. *(unnoticeable, quiet, subdued, dingy, inconspicuous.)*

shrewd—*adj.* penetrating, discriminating, discerning, perceptive, sagacious, astute, intelligent, acute, keen. *(undiscerning, dull, stupid, ignorant, stolid, unsagacious.)*

shrink—*v.* shrivel, retire, revolt, deflate, contract, withdraw, recoil. *(expand, venture, dare, dilate, amplify, stretch.)*

shrivel—*v.* dry up, wrinkle, decrease, degenerate, contract, wither, corrugate. *(flatten, unfold, dilate, rejuvenate, expand, develop, spread.)*

shuffle—*v.* interchange, intershift, derange, wade, equivocate, cavil, mystify, dissemble, jumble, confuse, shift, intermix, agitate, prevaricate, quibble, sophisticate, palter. *(distribute, arrange, reveal, confuse, declare, elucidate, deal, apportion, order, compose, propound, explain.)*

shy—*adj.* reserved, bashful, chary, shrinking, sheepish, timid, modest, suspicious. *(brazen-faced, audacious, aggressive, reckless, bold, impudent.)*

sick—*adj.* ill, distempered, weak, disgusted, feeble, nauseated, corrupt, valetudinarian, queasy, disordered, indisposed, ailing, morbid, impaired, diseased. *(well, sound, strong, salubrious, vigorous, whole, healthy, robust, well-conditioned.)*

sickly—*adj.* diseased, ailing, pining, morbid, vitiated, tainted, languishing, valetudinary, weak, disordered, feeble, drooping, unhealthy, delicate. *(healthy, flourishing, sound, rugged, robust, strong, vigorous, salubrious.)*

side—*n.* edge, border, face, plane, interest, policy, boundary, behalf, margin, verge, laterality, aspect, party, cause. *(body, interior, neutrality, severance, opposition, detachment, center, core, es-*sence, disconnection, secession.)*

sight—*n.* perception, vision, spectacle, inspection, representation, image, appearance, seeing, view, visibility, show, examination. *(invisibility, obscuration, oversight, undiscernment, blunder, non-perception, blindness, disappearance, non-appearance.)*

sign—*n.* indication, memorial, symbol, prefiguration, type, symptom, mark, presage, gesture, token, proof, expression, emblem, badge, premonition, prognostic, signal, wonder. *(misrepresentation, misleader, misindication, falsification.)*

signal—*adj.* conspicuous, extraordinary, memorable, important, distinguished, prominent, eminent, remarkable, notable, illustrious, salient. *(common, mediocre, unimportant, obscure, ordinary, unnoticeable, unmemorable.)*

signify—*v.* purport, mean, indicate, denote, declare, forebode, imply, presage, portend, prognosticate, represent, communicate, betaken, utter. *(suppress, misdenote, refute, preclude, obviate, conceal, misindicate, nullify, neutralize.)*

silence—*n.* stillness, peace, quiet, muteness, oblivion, tactiturnity, calm, hush, secrecy, lull. *(loquacity, chatter, brawl, clatter, babel, agitation, storm, roar, reverberation, fame, commotion, proclamation, celebrity, remembrance, effusiveness, garrulity, talkativeness, noise, clamor, din, tumult, restlessness, unrest, bruit, resonance, cackling, publicity, rumor, repute.)*

silly—*adj.* foolish, shallow, weak, unwise, imprudent, fatuous, absurd, simple, witless, indiscreet. *(intelligent, wise, discreet, sound, mature, rational, deep, sagacious, astute, prudent.)*

similar—*adj.* resembling, common, concordant, congruous, kindred, correspondent, alike, homogeneous, harmonious. *(unlike, alien, discordant, contrary, incongruous, different, dissimilar, heterogeneous.)*

simple—*adj.* incomplex, unblended, pure, mere, plain, unartificial, sincere, single-minded, silly, homely, unsophisticated, elementary, primal, transparent, rudimentary, single, uncompounded, isolated, unmixed, absolute, unadorned, artless, undesigning, unaffected, weak, humble, lowly, ultimate. *(complex, blended, fused, multigenerous, compound, eminent, subdivided, connected, complicated, artificial, designing, double-minded, self-conscious, sophisticated, complete, perfect, embellished, double, compounded, mixed, multi-form, various, articulated, organized, modified, elaborate, artful, insincere, affected, sagacious, great, illustrous, developed.)*

simultaneous—*adj.* concomitant, synchronous, contemporary, con-current, synchronic. *(separate, intermittent, diachronic, periodic, inconcurrent, apart.)*

sin—*n.* iniquity, ungodliness, evil, crime, immorality, wrongdoing, transgression, unrighteousness, wickedness, impurity. *(obedience, righteousness, godliness, virtue, goodness, sinlessness, holiness, purity.)*

sincere—*adj.* unmixed, unadulterated, honest, unvarnished, cordial, unfeigned, genuine, true, pure, heartfelt, hearty, unaffected, candid, frank. *(adulterated, insincere, feigned, false, duplicity, impure, dishonest, hypocritical, pretended.)*

single—*adj.* one, alone, individual, solitary, sole, uncombined, separate, unmarried, private, isolated, unaccompanied. *(many, united, frequent, conglomerate, plural, collective, numerous, married, blended.)*

singular—*adj.* individual, eminent, conspicuous, unusual, odd, quaint, unexampled, solitary, eccentric, exceptional, remarkable, queer, unparalleled, single, unique, extraordinary, consummate, uncommon, peculiar, whimsical, unprecedented, sole, fantastic, particular, curious. *(frequent, ordinary, unnoticeable, customary, regular, nondescript, common, numerous, usual, every-day, general.)*

sinister—*adj.* evil, pernicious, malevolent, noxious, ominous, corrupt, malign, disastrous, menacing. *(good, auspicious, benign, fortunate, promising.)*

situation—*n.* position, state, post, condition, aspect, office, plight, standing, dilemma, locality, birth, topography, seat, place, residence, footing, predicament. *(nonlocation, non-assignment, displacement, non-appearance, dislodgement, nonsituation, absence, unfixedness.)*

skeptical—*adj.* suspicious, cynical, doubtful, agnostic, dubious, questioning, quizzical, incredulous, unbelieving, unconvinced. *(credulous, certain, gullible, confident, believing, sure.)*

skillful—*adj.* skilled, polished, expert, proficient, adroit, deft, capable, clever, competent, versed. *(clumsy, awkward, inept, unskilled, bungling, unqualified.)*

slander—*v.* injure, malign, discredit, asperse, smear, defame, libel, vilify, denigrate. *(commend, defend, praise, eulogize, laud, extol.)*

slender—*adj.* narrow, slim, trivial, inadequate, feeble, meagre, superficial, spindly, thin, slight, small, spare, fragile, flimsy, inconsiderable. *(thick, robust, considerable, deep, pudgy, stout, broad, massive, ample.)*

sloppy—*adj.* messy, dirty, careless, tacky, slovenly, untidy, slipshod, substandard, frowzy. *(careful, trim, clear, immaculate, meticulous, tidy.)*

slow—*adj.* inactive, lazy, tardy, gradual, dull, lingering, inert, deliberate, sluggish, unready, slack, late, tedious, dilatory. *(quick, rapid, ready, early, immediate, punctual, active, fast, alert, prompt, sudden.)*

slur—*n.* smear, affront, insult, innuendo, detraction, disparagement, insinuation, reproach. *(commendation, honor, eulogy, compliment, praise, homage.)*

sly—*adj.* subtle, artful, underhanded, stealthy, covert, cunning, crafty, wily, astute. *(frank, undesigning, candid, open, artless.)*

small—*adj.* diminutive, minute, trivial, paltry, mean, slender, inferior, modest, little, slight, feeble, insignificant, narrow, weak, fine. *(large, considerable, extensive, spacious, strong, liberal, broad, weighty, great, big, bulky, ample, stout, important.)*

smart—*adj.* pungent, quick, sharp, active, brilliant, witty, spruce, fresh, showy, intelligent, keen, piercing, vigorous, severe, clever, vivacious, ready, brisk, dressy. *(heavy, slow, stupid, unready, unwitty, shabby, bland, clownish, dull, aching, inactive, sluggish, slow-minded, dowdy.)*

smooth—*adj.* plain, flat, glossy, soft, unobstructed, oily, silken, suave, even, level, polished, sleek, unruffled, bland. *(rough, abrupt, unpolished, blunt, abrasive, uneven, rugged, precipitous, harsh.)*

smother—*v.* stifle, gag, suppress, strangle, swallow, asphyxiate, suffocate, repress, conceal, choke, allay. *(ventilate, cherish, vent, publish, divulge, excite, fan, foster, nurture, promulgate, spread, purify.)*

smug—*adj.* complacent, cocky, serene, placid, self-satisfied, triumphant, conceited. *(apologetic, hesitant, sheepish, modest, diffident.)*

snappy—*adj.* energetic, curt, keen, animated, crisp, quick, fashionable, stylish, smart. *(slow, threadbare, dowdy, languid, lazy, shabby, seedy.)*

sneer—*n.* gibe, taunt, contempt, superciliousness, grimace, disdain, scoff, jeer, disparagement, scorn. *(eulogy, deference, laudation, complement, commendation.)*

snub—*n.* check, reprimand, insult, rebuke.

snug—*adj.* housed, compact, sheltered, cozy, close, compressed, comfortable. *(loose, uncompact, bare, uncovered, shivering, exposed, disordered, uncomfortable.)*

sober—*adj.* unintoxicated, calm, dispassionate, sound, serious, sedate, abstemious, rational, moderate, temperate, cool, reasonable, self-possessed, unexcited, grave, steady, deliberate, circumspect, lucid, staid, dignified, prim, severe, serious, somber. *(drunk, heated, extreme, impassioned, agitated, passionate, immoderate, erratic, befuddled, eccentric, intemperate, intoxicated, excited, unreasonable, furious, extravagant, exorbitant, flighty, besotted, crazed, gay, carefree, wanton, muddled.)*

society—*n.* polity, collection, fellowship, participation, sociality, intercourse, culture, sodality, community, company, association, companionship, connection, communion. *(personality, separation, unsociality, dissociation, privacy, individuality, segregation, solitariness, disconnection, seclusion.)*

soft—*adj.* pressible, smooth, fine, glossy, gentle, kind, flexible, sleek, luxurious, tender, undecided, mild, supple, yielding, impressible, delicate, balmy, feeling, effeminate, unmanly, irresolute. *(tough, unyielding, rigid, unimpressible, coarse, abrupt, rigorous, severe, unfeeling, austere, inflexible, self-denying, hard, determined, strident, stubborn, rough, harsh, ungentle, cut-*

ting, unkind, sharp, stern, ascetic, resolute.)

soften—*v.* palliate, mitigate, dulcify, yield, humanize, compose, moderate, enervate, mollify, assuage, lenify, macerate, abate. *(indurate, excite, harden, infuriate, toughen, aggravate, consolidate, intensify.)*

solace—*v.* alleviate, calm, soothe, comfort, cheer, bolster, mitigate, console, reassure, ameliorate. *(depress, aggravate, irritate, undermine.)*

solemn—*adj.* formal, reverential, ceremonial, religious, serious, awesome, sacred, devotional, ritual, impressive, grave. *(undevotional, light, trivial, informal, frivolous, profane, secular, gay, unceremonial, unsolemn, flippant.)*

solicitous—*adj.* regardful, nervous, apprehensive, fearful, vigilant, anxious, troubled, caring, avid, yearning. *(relaxed, carefree, nonchalant, cool, apathetic, indifferent, unenthusiastic.)*

solid—*adj.* firm, resistant, strong, substantial, just, impenetrable, cubic, solidified, hard, compact, dense, weighty, valid, sound, stable. *(hollow, frail, flimsy, resilient, impressible, liquid, soft, light,* weak, unsound, weakly, flexible, yielding, brittle, elastic, malleable, fluid, frivolous, trifling, invalid, fallacious.)

solitude—n. remoteness, retirement, wildness, barrenness, privacy, withdrawal, loneliness, seclusion, isolation, desertion, wilderness. (combination, continuity, conjunction, complication, union, mystification, integration, gregariousness, amalgamation, connection, entanglement, confusion, obscurity.)

somber—adj. funereal, grim, dark, melancholy, sepulchral, dreary, sad, doleful, gloomy. (festive, cheerful, gay, bright, joyous.)

sophisticated—adj. experienced, knowledgeable, aware, worldy, cosmopolitan, blase, intellectual, cultured. (simple, naive, primitive, provincial, unseasoned, ingenuous, sophomoric.)

sore—adj. irritated, excoriated, scarified, grievous, heavy, raw, abscessed, painful, susceptible, ulcerous, afflictive, burdensome, chafed. (sound, healthful, grateful, unbroken, light, unburdensome, untroublesome, delighted, painless, whole, healed, unsacrified, trivial, pleasant.)

sorry—adj. pained, afflicted, hurt, doleful, mortified, dejected, mean, shabby, apologetic, worthless, grieved, woe-be-gone, down-hearted, vexed, poor, vile. (rejoiced, pleased, fine, handsome, agreeable, glad, delighted, gratified, choice.)

sort—n. species, class, character, manner, condition, designation, category, genus, kind, nature, order, rank, quality, description. (solitariness, non-classification, heterogeneity, non-description, uniqueness, variegation.)

sound—adj. unbroken, perfect, well-grounded, unimpaired, firm, vigorous, solid, irrefutable, valid, correct, logical, substantial, entire, whole, unhurt, uninjured, healthy, strong, weighty, irrefragable, thorough, wholesome. (broken, impaired, frail, unsound, light, unfounded, weak, fallacious, unwholesome, risky, unsubstantial, partial, injured, unhealthy, fragile, trivial, hollow, imperfect, incorrect, invalid, feeble.)

sour—adj. rancid, turned, crusty, crabbed, morose, churlish, tart, acetous, peevish, fermented, coagulated, harsh, austere, pungent, acid, bitter, acrimonious. (wholesome, mellow,

203

kindly, affable, sweet, genial, untainted.)

sovereign—*adj.* enthroned, imperial, sanctioned, ruling, authoritative, almighty, free, dominant, paramount. *(dethroned, powerless, unauthorized, minor, subservient, secondary, petty.)*

spacious—*adj.* extensive, vast, large, roomy, voluminous, broad, expansive, ample, capacious, wide. *(restricted, narrow, cramped, inextensive, limited, uncomfortable, confined.)*

spare—*v.* afford, reserve, husband, retain, grudge, omit, withhold, abstain, liberate, save, grant, do without, economize, store, discard, forbear, refrain. *(squander, lavish, vent, expend, indulge, dissipate, spend, waste, scatter, pour.)*

spare—*adj.* unplentiful, meagre, chary, frugal, restricted, niggardly, thin, superfluous, available, additional, minimal, scanty, inabundant, economical, stinted, parsimonious, disposable, lean. *(plentiful, profuse, unrestricted, bountiful, ornate, unstinted, available, elaborate, ample, abundant, liberal, generous, unsparing, unbounded.)*

spasmodic—*adj.* irregular, fitful, erratic, occasional, transient, sudden, convulsive, changeable, transitory. *(continuous, lasting, regular, uninterrupted.)*

special—*adj.* specific, appropriate, distinctive, especial, unique, exceptional, particular, peculiar, proper, extraordinary. *(universal, generic, typical, general, common.)*

speculation—*n.* consideration, view, weighing, theory, hypothesis, assumption, conjecture, contemplation, thought, scheme. *(proof, verification, certainty, substantiation, fact, realization.)*

speed—*v.* expedite, urge, hasten, press, plunge, dispatch, accelerate, hurry. *(delay, obstruct, loiter, linger, stay, dawdle, retard, postpone, drag, creep, lag.)*

speed—*n.* swiftness, haste, promptness, nimbleness, rush, rapidity, agility, quickness. *(sluggishness, inertia, laziness, slowness, delay.)*

spend—*v.* waste, squander, lay out, disburse, dissipate, lavish, bestow, exhaust, expend, consume. *(save, accumulate, economize, conserve, retain, hoard, husband.)*

spirit—*n.* breath, soul, essential, ego, quality, immateriality, disembodiment, apparition, energy, enthusiasm, earnestness, zeal, temper, motive, courage, distillation, air, life, vital force, essence, intelligence, spectre, ghost, ardor, activity, courage, disposition, principle. *(body, materiality, deadness, organization, embodiment, dejection, listlessness, lifelessness, flesh, torpor, sluggishness, timidity, substance, corporeity, frame, spiritlessness, soullessness, dejection, slowness.)*

spirited—*adj.* lively, ardent, sprightly, enterprising, courageous, animated, vivacious, buoyant. *(dispirited, cowardly, inert, dull, depressed.)*

spiritual—*adj.* religious, ghostly, immaterial, intellectual, psychic, divine, holy, ethical, incorporeal. *(fleshly, gross, sensuous, secular, carnal, unspiritual, material.)*

spite—*n.* malevolence, pique, ill-will, rancor, bitterness, malice, spleen, grudge, hatred, vindictiveness. *(kindliness, benevolence, charity, good-will.)*

splendid—*adj.* showy, sumptuous, glorious, imposing, superb, heroic, signal, incredible, brilliant, magnifi-cent, gorgeous, pompous, illustrious, famous, grand. *(obscure, somber, beggarly, ordinary, inglorious, dreadful, dull, tame, poor, unimposing, ineffective.)*

split—*v.* separate, cleave, rive, splinter, rend, disagree, divide, disunite, fragment, crack, burst, sunder, secede. *(unite, coalesce, agree, consolidate, integrate, cohere, amalgamate, conform, splice.)*

spoil—*v.* strip, devastate, denude, vitiate, deteriorate, damage, mar, plunder, rob, pillage, corrupt. *(enrich, replenish, improve, ameliorate, preserve, repair, invest, endow, renovate, better, rectify.)*

spontaneous—*adj.* self-generated, self-evolved, unbidden, extemporaneous, gratuitous, voluntary, self-originated, willing. *(imposed, unwilling, premeditated, involuntary, compulsionary, necessitated, calculated.)*

sporadic—*adj.* occasional, rare, spasmodic, unexpected, irregular, unscheduled, isolated, infrequent. *(regular, continuous, epidemic, extensive, frequent, general, unlimited.)*

sport—*n.* frolic, joke, fun, merriment, recreation, pastime, entertainment, play, wantonness, diversion, gaiety, amusement, game. *(seriousness, earnestness, work, toil, business.)*

spread—*v.* stretch, open, divulge, publish, diffuse, distribute, circulate, ramify, inflate, extend, expand, unfurl, propagate, disperse, overlay, scatter, disseminate. *(furl, fold, shut, suppress, restrict, hush, recall, stagnate, localize, close, condense, contract, gather, secrete, confine, repress, conceal, collect, concentrate.)*

spring—*v.* bound, start, issue, originate, emanate, burst, hurdle, flow, leap, jump, emerge, proceed, rise, germinate. *(alight, drop, issue, end, debouch, wither, disembogue, settle, land, arrive, eventuate, terminate.)*

squalid—*adj.* wretched, unkempt, dilapidated, shabby, dingy, filthy, untidy, poor, grimy, vulgar, disheveled, decayed. *(tidy, decent, neat, presentable, noble, well-kept, clean, respectable.)*

staid—*adj.* demure, sober, subdued, sedate, grave, steady, prudent, conservative. *(flighty, wanton, erratic, agitated, ruffled, capricious, unsteady, indiscreet, in-sedate, eccentric, discomposed.)*

stammer—*v.* hesitate, falter, mumble, stutter. *(speak unhesitantly, speak clearly.)*

stamp—*n.* kind, make, impression, print, cast, character, signature, type, genus, description, mark, imprint, brand, mould. *(non-description, heterogeneity, formlessness, unevenness.)*

stand—*v.* remain, be, suffer, rest, depend, consist, continue, pause, tolerate, halt, stop, exist, insist, await, hold, endure. *(move, advance, fail, succumb, lie, fade, depart, oppose, progress, proceed, fall, yield, drop, vanish, run.)*

standard—*n.* gauge, test, exemplar, flag, model, plummet, pennant, measure, criterion, rule, banner, type, scale, emblem. *(misrule, non-criterion, miscomparison, misfit, confusion, incommensurateness, inconformity, mismeasurement, misadjustment.)*

state—*n.* condition, circumstance, predicament, province, position, situation, plight, case, emotion.

state—*v.* declare, aver, narrate, particularize, recite, utter, say, propound, set forth, specify, avow. *(repress, imply,* retract, contradict, repudiate, suppress, suppose, deny.)

stately—adj. imposing, elevated, proud, pompous, grand, lofty, awesome, dignified, lordly, majestic, magnificent. (unimposing, mean, commonplace, squalid, undignified, unstately.)

staunch—adj. resolute, firm, faithful, trustworthy, loyal, devoted, stalwart, reliable, true. (questionable, unreliable, faithless, vacillating, ambivalent.)

stay—v. stop, withhold, hinder, obstruct, rest, remain, dwell, halt, wait, confide, lean, hold, restrain, arrest, delay, support, repose, continue, await, abide, tarry, trust, linger. (liberate, expedite, free, hasten, depress, fail, proceed, depart, mistrust, facilitate, loose, send, speed, accelerate, oppress, burden, fall, move, overthrow.)

steady—adj. fixed, uniform, equable, undeviating, permanent, well-regulated, firm, constant, consistent, regular. (variable, inconstant, wavering, sporadic, ill-regulated, infirm, unsteady, changeable.)

step—n. pace, grade, degree, walk, progression, trace, proceeding, measure, stride, advance, space, gradation, track, vestige, gait, ac-

tion. (recession, station, nongraduation, stand-still, tracklessness, non-impression, desistance, withdrawal, inaction, retreat, stop, halting, standing, non-progression, untraceableness, desinence.)

stern—adj. austere, harsh, rigorous, unyielding, stringent, forbidding, severe, rigid, strict, unrelenting. (genial, easy, lenient, encouraging, compassionate, kindly, flexible.)

stiff—adj. inflexible, unyielding, strong, obstinate, constrained, starched, ceremonious, firm, difficult, unbending, rigid, forceful, stubborn, pertinacious, affected, formal. (flexible, yielding, easy, unaffected, affable, pliable, unceremonious, pliant, flaccid, genial.)

still—adj. calm, hushed, pacific, motionless, peaceful, tranquil, inert, stationary, quiet, noiseless, silent, serene, stagnant, quiescent. (disturbed, moved, resonant, moving, dynamic, transitional, unquiet, agitated, noisy, turbulent.)

stingy—adj. avaricious, niggardly, hide-bound, sparing, penurious, miserly, close, mean, frugal, parsimonious, sordid. (generous, handsome, bountiful, munificent, unsparing, liberal, large, lavish.)

stop—v. obstruct, cork, seal, suspend, rest, hinder, delay, terminate, end, thwart, close, plug, bar, arrest, halt, suppress, cease. (expedite, broach, promote, farther, proceed, hasten, initiate, open, clear, unseal, advance, continue, speed.)

stout—adj. lusty, robust, brawny, resolute, valiant, pudgy, durable, strong, vigorous, sturdy, corpulent, brave. (debile, thin, lean, feeble, timid, fragile, weak, frail, attenuated, slender, irresolute, cowardly.)

straight—adj. rectilinear, linear, unswerving, nearest, direct, undeviating, right, horizontal. (winding, tortuous, serpentine, waving, devious, crooked, indirect, incurved, sinuous, circuitous.)

strange—adj. alien, unfamiliar, odd, abnormal, surprising, marvelous, uncommon, anomalous, peculiar, foreign, exotic, unusual, irregular, exceptional, wonderful, astonishing. (domestic, usual, common, customary, unsurprising, general, indigenous, familiar, ordinary, regular, commonplace, universal.)

strength—n. vigor, security, sinew, vehemence, hardness, nerve, vitality, force, power, validity, intensity, soundness, fibre. (imbecility, insolidity, invalidity, delicacy, flimsiness, vulnerability, hollowness, weakness, feebleness, insecurity, frailty, softness.)

strenuous—adj. resolute, earnest, ardent, energetic, arduous, strong, determined, vigorous, bold, vehement. (irresolute, feeble, unearnest, effortless, emasculate, weak, undetermined, debile.)

strict—adj. exact, rigorous, close, stringent, precise, meticulous, accurate, severe, nice. (inexact, lenient, lax, indulgent, negligent, loose, inaccurate, mild.)

striking—adj. affecting, wonderful, notable, surprising, impressive, admirable. (indifferent, minor, mediocre, ineffectual, commonplace.)

stringent—adj. exacting, hard, severe, stern, rigorous, relentless, firm, compelling, obedient, harsh. (relaxed, equivocal, flexible, moderate, lenient, easy.)

strong—adj. vigorous, secure, forcible, hale, brawny, sound, cogent, dynamic, zealous, pungent, hardy, tenacious, powerful, solid, fortified, hearty, impetuous, sinewy, robust, patent, influential, muscular, staunch. *(weak, insecure, feeble, calm, delicate, inefficacious, frail, unconvincing, vapid, unavailing, debile, nerveless, moderate, powerless, defenseless, mild, gentle, sickly, unsatisfactory, unimpressive, impotent, lukewarm, flaccid, tender, indifferent, fragile.)*

stubborn—*adj.* unbending, hard, intractable, stiff, inflexible, harsh, refractory, contumacious, dogmatic, tough, unyielding, obstinate, heady, obdurate, pig-headed, headstrong. *(tractable, pliant, malleable, indecisive, flexible, docile, manageable pliable.)*

studious—*adj.* diligent, attentive, thoughtful, reflective, erudite, literary, desirous, careful, assiduous. *(illiterate, indulgent, regardless, thoughtless, idle, uneducated, unliterary, careless, inattentive, indifferent, negligent.)*

stupid—*adj.* senseless, doltish, dull, insensate, prosy, dull-witted, vacuous, stolid, besotted, obtuse, asinine. *(sharp, sensible, quick, penetrating, brilliant, bright, clever, sagacious.)*

subdue—*v.* reduce, break, quell, overwhelm, subjugate, conquer, overpower, tame, vanquish, master, suppress. *(exalt, strengthen, liberate, capitulate, enfranchise, aggrandize, fortify, empower.)*

subject—*adj.* subservient, liable, disposed, amenable, dependent, subordinate, exposed, prone, obnoxious. *(independent, dominant, indisposed, unamenable, exempt, superior, unliable.)*

submissive—*adj.* compliant, docile, obsequious, passive, subservient, humble, obedient, yielding, modest, acquiescent. *(incompliant, recusant, inobsequious, refractory, resistant, domineering, disobedient, unyielding, recalcitrant, proud, renitent.)*

substantial—*adj.* real, true, stout, material, bulky, durable, solid, existing, corporeal, strong, massive, tangible, stable. *(unreal, fictitious, incorporeal, visionary, weak, airy, spiritual, fragile, ghostly, frail, imaginary, insubstantial, chimerical, suppositious, immaterial, disembodied.)*

subtle—*adj.* artful, insinuating, astute, discriminating, fine, sophistical, elusive, jesuitical, sly, cunning, wily, nice, crafty, shrewd. *(frank,* *artless, open, rough, undiscerning, simple, obtuse, honest, undiscriminating, blunt, unsophisticated.)*

success—*n.* luck, prosperity, good-fortune, attainment, victory, achievement, consummation. *(defeat, ruin, disgrace, failure, disaster.)*

succession—*n.* supervention, progression, sequence, series, continuity, suite, following, order, rotation, supply. *(anticipation, antecedence, disorder, solution, intermission, gap, inconsecutiveness, interim, precedence, prevention, irregularity, non-sequence, failure, break.)*

succinct—*adj.* short, concise, crisp, laconic, condensed, compressed, compact, pithy, curt, clipped, abbreviated, terse. *(verbose, rambling, circuitous, wordy, loquacious, garrulous.)*

suffer—*v.* endure, undergo, grieve, permit, admit, experience, let, support, bear, sustain, allow, tolerate. *(repel, reject, repudiate, ignore, eliminate, resist, expel, disallow, forbid.)*

sufficient—*adj.* equal, satisfactory, qualified, suited, ample, fit, abundant, adequate, competent, adapted, enough. *(unequal, meagre, unqualified, insufficient, scanty, deficient, incomplete, inadequate, incompetent, short, unadapted, unsuited, bare.)*

suit—*v.* adapt, adjust, apportion, beseem, correspond, comport, serve, become, reconcile, accord, fit, match, harmonize, befit, tally, answer, please, agree. *(misadapt, misapportion, vary, disagree, dissatisfy, differ, miscomport, misfit, mismatch, unbeseem.)*

summary—*n.* tabulation, resume, digest, abstract, recapitulation, analysis, abridgment, compendium, epitome. *(dilution, expansion, dilatation, amplification.)*

superb—*adj.* magnificent, princely, showy, august, gorgeous, grand, exquisite, elegant, splendid, proud, stately. *(common, unimposing, inferior, shabby, mean, worthless.)*

supercilious—*adj.* contemptuous, arrogant, patronizing, insolent, haughty, disdainful. *(courteous, modest, humble, bashful, affable, respectful.)*

superficial—*adj.* slight, showy, flimsy, shallow, skin-deep, peripheral, light, imperfect, external, surface, smattering. *(profound, deep,* *recondite, exact, complex, abstruse, accurate, internal.)*

superior—*adj.* upper, preferable, loftier, remarkable, conspicuous, distinguished, higher, better, surpassing, excellent, eminent. *(lower, subordinate, common, average, mediocre, inferior, imperfect, worse, ordinary, mean, unremarkable.)*

supple—*adj.* bending, flexible, servile, cringing, sycophantic, limber, resilient, compliant, pliant, yielding, elastic, fawning, adulatory, lithe. *(unbending, stiff, inflexible, independent, rigid, supercilious, firm, unyielding, stubborn, inelastic, self-assertive.)*

supply—*v.* afford, accoutre, give, minister, contribute, replenish, furnish, provide, yield. *(use, waste, absorb, withhold, retain, deplete, expend, consume, exhaust, demand, withdraw.)*

support—*n.* stay, buttress, aid, influence, living, subsistence, food, prop, foundation, advocate, help, assistance, maintenance, patronage, livelihood.

support—*v.* uphold, underlie, help, assist, promote, suffer, foster, nourish, endorse, continue, stay, patronize, prop, sustain, bear, befriend, second, buttress, further, defend, nurture, cherish, maintain, countenance, subsidize, back, favor. *(betray, abandon, oppose, weaken, thwart, drop, disfavor, suppress, squelch, surrender, discontinue, discourage, exhaust, subvert.)*

suppose—*v.* presume, deem, fancy, regard, imagine, deduce, presuppose, guess, judge, consider, assume, believe, think, conceive, imply, conjecture, conclude. *(demonstrate, realize, conclude, deny, prove, substantiate, disbelieve.)*

sure—*adj.* secure, assured, stable, knowing, confident, unquestioning, unfailing, permanent, enduring, indisputable, absolute, fast, safe, certain, unmistakable, firm, strong, believing, trusting, positive, abiding, infallible. *(ignorant, doubtful, dubious, distrustful, vacillating, untrustworthy, insecure, transient, fallible, weak, loose, vulnerable, uncertain, hesitating, questioning, precarious, impermanent, evanescent, disputable.)*

surreptitious—*adj.* clandestine, covert, veiled, furtive, secret, stealthy, undercover, sneaky, concealed. *(exposed, candid, overt, public, open, straightforward.)*

susceptible—*adj.* impressible, sensitive, vulnerable, capable, tender. *(unimpressible, insusceptible, resistent, impassible, incapable, insensitive.)*

suspense—*n.* uncertainty, pause, solicitude, intermission, indecision, abeyance, indetermination, doubt, apprehension, protraction, cessation, waiting, discontinuance, stoppage. *(settlement, revival, continuance, finality, resolution, determination, execution, decision, uninterruption.)*

sway—*n.* influence, authority, supremacy, superiority, dominion, preponderance, ascendancy, force, jurisdiction, power, wield, rule, government, bias, control, domination, mastery, weight. *(inferiority, irresistance, subservience, weakness, debility, subjection, subordination, obedience.)*

sway—*v.* govern, bias, swing, teeter, wield, influence, rule, wave.

sweet—*adj.* luscious, dulcet, pure, harmonious, beautiful, wholesome, winning, fresh, amiable, genial, saccharine, fragrant, melodious, musical, lovely, pleasing, mild, agreeable, gentle. *(bitter, fetid, nauseous, stinking, inharmonious, unlovely, unwholesome, tainted, unamiable, repulsive, sour, unsweet, offensive, olid, nasty, discordant, repulsive, putrid, ungentle.)*

swell—*v.* extend, heighten, enhance, expand, augment, aggravate, dilate, distend, multiply, enlarge, heave, rise, increase, protuberate, amplify. *(curtail, diminish, shrivel, retrench, collapse, narrow, contract, concentrate, decrease, lessen, fold, reduce, condense.)*

sympathy—*n.* compassion, understanding, pity, tenderness, kindness, humanity, unselfishness. *(antagonism, animosity, pitilessness, compassionlessness, harshness, unkindliness, antipathy, incongeniality, mercilessness, unkindness.)*

system—*n.* scheme, regularity, arrangement, plan, organization, method, order, classification, rule. *(derangement, fortuity, medley, incongruity, non-classification, chaos, disorder, confusion, chance, haphazard, complication.)*

T

tact—*n.* delicacy, savoir faire, diplomacy, sensitivity, politeness, prudence, polish, subtlety, finesse. *(bluntness, grossness, crudeness, indiscretion, gaucherie, insensitivity, tactlessness.)*

take—*v.* grasp, capture, use, seize, pursue, follow, procure, catch, charm, engage, select, accept, admit, conduct, receive, apprehend, transfer, seige, obtain, employ, assume, captivate, interest, choose. *(reject, surrender, miss, release, repel, drop, abandon, lose.)*

tall—*adj.* lofty, elevated, high, towering, elongated. *(short, low, abbreviated.)*

tame—*adj.* reclaimed, subjugated, gentle, docile, spiritless, dull, subdued, domesticated, tamed, flat, broken, mild, meek, tedious. *(unreclaimed, wild, unbroken, spirited, ferine, exciting, lively, disobedient, savage, undomesticated, untamed, fierce, animated, interesting, stirring.)*

tangible—*adj.* real, solid, actual, concrete, palpable, manifest, veritable, specific, factual, substantial. *(imaginary, flimsy, elusive, vague, ethereal.)*

task—*n.* function, job, business, drudgery, lesson, assignment, work, labor, operation, undertaking, toil.

(leisure, hobby, rest, relaxation, amusement.)

taste—*n.* savor, sapidity, choice, perception, discernment, critique, predilection, elegancy, aroma, refinement, gustation, flavor, relish, judgment, nicety, sensibility, zest, delicacy. *(ill-savor, disrelish, indiscrimination, indelicacy, inelegancy, abhorrence, nongustation, insipidity, nonperception, indiscernment, coarseness.)*

tasteful—*adj.* relishing, agreeable, toothsome, elegant, artistic, refined, sapid, savory, tasty, palatable. *(unrelishing, unpalatable, inelegant, vapid, unrefined, vulgar, insipid, unsavory, nauseous, tasteless.)*

teach—*v.* tell, instruct, counsel, educate, enlighten, indoctrinate, edify, train, impart, direct, inform, admonish, inculcate, advise. *(misteach, misinstruct, misguide, learn, mislead, withhold, misdirect, misinform.)*

teacher—*n.* school-master, tutor, pedagogue, educator, school-mistress, scholar, instructor, preceptor, professor, educationist. *(scholar, learner, student, pupil, disciple.)*

tedious—*adj.* tiresome, dilatory, sluggish, dull, prolix, prosaic, monotonous, wearisome, dreary, irksome. *(exciting, charming, delightful, challenging, stirring, amusing, interesting, fascinating.)*

tell—*v.* number, count, utter, state, disclose, betray, explain, promulgate, teach, report, discern, discriminate, decide, narrate, describe, mention, enumerate, recount, recite, verbalize, publish, divulge, acquaint, inform, communicate, rehearse, judge, ascertain. *(suppress, misnarrate, misdeclare, misjudge, conceal, misdescribe, repress, misrecount, miscommunicate, misrecite.)*

temporary—*adj.* immediate, limited, impermanent, momentary, present, partial, transient. *(lasting, complete, perfect, entire, settled, perpetual, confirmed, final, permanent.)*

tenacious—*adj.* firm, cohesive, obstinate, resolute, persistent, iron, mulish, perseverant, willful, obdurate, adamant, stalwart. *(flexible, loose, yielding, wavering, irresolute, lax, tractable.)*

tendency—*n.* proneness, gravitation, scope, disposition, proclivity, bias, inclination, conduciveness, penchant, course, vergency, drift, aim, predisposition, leaning, attraction. *(aversion, contravention, divergency, divarication, renitency, prevention, termination, hesitancy, disinclination, repulsive, deviation, tangency, opposition, reluctance, neutralization.)*

tender—*v.* proffer, bid, present, submit. *(withdraw, appropriate, withhold, retain, retract.)*

tender—*adj.* frail, susceptible, soft, weak, compassionate, careful, gentle, meek, merciful, sympathetic, pathetic, delicate, impressible, yielding, effeminate, feeble, jealous, affectionate, mild, pitiful. *(sturdy, robust, iron, unmerciful, hard-hearted, liberal, unchary, rough, coarse, unmoving, unimpressive, unimpressed, strong, insensitive, hardy, tough, pitiless, cruel, careless, lavish, ungentle, rude, unsentimental, unfeeling, unimpassioned.)*

tension—*n.* stretch, extension, rigidity, strain, tautness, worry, traction, anxiety, apprehension, stress. *(sag, calm, flexibility, serenity, tranquillity, looseness.)*

terminate—*v.* finish, stop, end, culminate, conclude, complete, expire, lapse, discontinue, cease. *(commence, initiate, pursue, begin, inaugurate, open, start.)*

terrible—*adj.* fearful, formidable, frightful, horrible, intimidating, shocking, awful, dreadful, terrific, tremendous. *(unastounding, unexcruciating, informidable, unstartling, unsevere.)*

terror—*n.* dread, fright, horror, panic, dismay, fear, alarm, consternation. *(fearlessness, confidence, reassurance, security, boldness.)*

test—*n.* trial, proof, standard, touchstone, ordeal, probe, cupel, examination, criterion, experiment, experience. *(misproof, misindication, misjudgment, miscomputation.)*

testimony—*n.* evidence, affirmation, confirmation, affidavit, proof, witness, attestation, corroboration. *(contradiction, confutation, invalidation, denial, refutation, disproof, contravention.)*

theatrical—*adj.* scenic, showy, gesticulatory, meretricious, thespian, dramatic, melodramatic, ceremonious, pompous. *(genuine, unaffected, subdued, plain, retiring, chaste, simple, quiet, mannerless.)*

thick—*adj.* close, turbid, coagulated, dull, foggy, crowded, solid, deep, inarticulate, voluminous, dense, massive, compact, luteous, muddy, misty, vaporous, numerous, bulky, confused. *(fine, sparse, pure, limpid, scanty, slight, laminated, articulate, narrow, distinct, race, thin, strained, percolated, clear, crystalline, incompact, shallow.)*

thicken—*v.* befoul, bemire, increase, amalgamate, intermix, multiply, expand, broaden, intensify, solidify, obscure, becloud, coagulate, commingle, crowd, enlarge, extend, deepen, confuse, obstruct. *(dissipate, attenuate, purify, percolate, defecate, free, brighten, open, diminish, reduce, contract, unravel, loosen, dilute, rarify, refine, clear, strain, clarify, depurate, lighten, filtrate, separate, narrow, liberate, extricate, disentangle.)*

thin—*adj.* slender, attenuated, watery, unsubstantial, translucent, lean, slim, flimsy, diluted, meagre. *(opaque, corpulent, thick, obese, solid, wide, dense.)*

think—*v.* meditate, reflect, conceive, hold, believe, judge, opine, cogitate, reckon, ponder, consider, contemplate, imagine, fancy, regard, deem. *(act rashly, forget, be thoughtless, act unreasonably.)*

thought—*n.* reasoning, supposition, sentiment, conception, opinion, view, conceit, design, intention, care, calculation, provision, reflection, cogitation, meditation, idea, fancy, judgment, purpose, deliberation. *(incogitation, dream, aberration, incogitancy, vacuity, improvidence, inattention, thoughtlessness, hallucination, misconception, carelessness, unreflectiveness, distraction.)*

threatening—*adj.* intimidating, foreboding, imminent, ominous, impending, menacing, unpromising. *(promising, enticing, overpast, auspicious, withdrawn, encouraging, reassuring, passed.)*

thwart—*v.* balk, frustrate, baffle, prevent, circumvent, prevent, outwit, defeat, fail, obstruct, hinder. *(support, abet, help, facilitate, cooperate, aid, magnify, encourage, assist.)*

tide—*n.* course, rush, influx, movement, avalanche, flow, flood, current, inundation, stream. *(arrestation, cessation, subsidence, discontinuance, stagnation, stoppage, motionlessness.)*

tight—*adj.* compact, close, neat, natty, secure, firm, fast, tidy, smart, tense. *(incompact, flowing, large, lax, flexible, loose, open, loosefitting, untidy, relaxed, insecure.)*

time—*n.* duration, interval, era, opportunity, term, span, cycle, spell, period, season, date, age, occasion, space. *(eternity, indetermination, neverness, indeterminableness, perpetuity, non- duration.)*

timid—*adj.* pusillanimous, shy, diffident, timorous, cowardly, inadventurous, apprehensive, coy, fearful, afraid, faint-hearted. *(confident, courageous, rash, spirited, bold, venturesome, overventuresome, audacious, aggressive.)*

tinsel—*adj.* tawdry, garish, cheap, superficial, trashy, gaudy, meretricious, glittering. *(genuine, conservative, previous, understated, lowkey, tasteful.)*

tint—*n.* hue, dye, shade, color, complexion, tinge, stain, tincture. *(decoloration, achromatism, pallor, etiolation, sallowness, cadaverousness, paleness, exsanguineousness, ashenness, bleaching, colorlessness, wanness.)*

tiresome—*adj.* wearisome, dull, monotonous, tedious, fatiguing, arduous, difficult, troublesome, exhausting, laborious. *(stimulating, restful, restorative, refreshing, exciting, delightful, fascinating.)*

title—*n.* heading, style, name, appellation, address, caption, inscription, denomination, designation, distinction, epithet. *(indistinction, namelessness, non-designation, nondescript, indenomination.)*

together—*adv.* conjointly, concertedly, coincidently, concurrently, unitedly, unanimously, contemporaneously, simultaneously, concomitantly. *(disconnectedly, variously, individually, separately, independently, incoincidently.)*

tolerable—*adj.* bearable, sufferable, permissible, passable, defensible, endurable, supportable, allowable, sufficient. (unbearable, insufferable, impermissible, intolerable, admissible, unendurable, insupportable, unallowable, insufficient.)

tolerate—*v.* permit, warrant, admit, indulge, authorize, sanction, concede, license, sustain, accord. *(forbid, ban, veto, prohibit, disapprove, repel, protest, refuse.)*

tongue—*n.* speech, dialect, articulation, idiom, discourse, language.

tool—*n.* implement, instrument, cat's-paw, appliance, hireling, utensil, machine, dupe.

topic—*n.* theme, subject-matter, thesis, question, subject.

torrid—*adj.* hot, fiery, suffocating, parched, scorching, tropical, fervent, amorous, erotic. *(cool, frigid, temperate, cold, arctic, indifferent.)*

tough—*adj.* stubborn, fibrous, refractory, unmanageable, firm, cohesive, strong, resistant, difficult, hard, tenacious. *(tender, soft, crumby, friable, yielding, fragile.)*

traditional—*adj.* usual, familiar, conventional, ritual, routine, prescriptive, normal, customary. *(unusual, rare, uncommon, unconventional, unfamiliar.)*

tragedy—*n.* calamity, adversity, grief, catastrophe, disaster, affliction, misfortune. *(delight, prosperity, fortune, joy, boon, comedy, merriment.)*

train—*n.* procession, cortege, series, appendage, suite, retinue, course.

train—v. rear, habituate, drill, practice, instruct, educate, familiarize with, lead, inure, accustom, exercise, discipline, bend. *(break, disaccustom, miseducate, misguide, disqualify, force, trail, dishabituate.)*

transfer—v. transport, sell, transplant, alienate, transmit, exchange, dispatch, convey, remove, assign, make over, give, translate, forward. *(withhold, retain, appropriate, keep, fix, retain.)*

transient—*adj.* fugitive, temporary, evanescent, momentary, brief, migratory, fleeting, transitory, passing, ephemeral. *(permanent, persistent, enduring, resident, abiding, perpetual, lasting.)*

t r a n s p a r e n t—*a d j.* crystalline, limpid, obvious, indisputable, porous, self-evident, pellucid, translucent, diaphanous, clear. *(turbid, filmy, intransparent, dubious, thick, opaque, mysterious, questionable, complex.)*

travel—*n.* commuting, journey, progress, transportation, passage, expedition, cruising, tour, voyage. *(halt, cessation, pause, stay, rest.)*

treatise—*n.* essay, pamphlet, brochure, tractate, article, thesis, tract, paper, dissertation, monograph. *(notes, memoranda, ephemera, shedding, jottings, adversaria, effusion.)*

treaty—*n.* agreement, covenant, entente, negotiation, contract, convention, league, alliance. *(non-interference, non-agreement, indecision, non-convention, neutrality, non-alliance.)*

tremble—*v.* quake, tatter, shake, shudder, jar, pulsate, quiver, shiver, vibrate. *(steady, still, stand, compose, calm, settle.)*

tremendous—*adj.* dreadful, fearful, enormous, appalling, terrible, awful. *(unappalling, small, inconsiderable, little, unimposing.)*

tremulous—*adj.* quivery, spasmodic, throbbing, hesitant, palpitating, trembling, fearful, uncertain, flinching. *(motionless, brave, fixed, immobile, heroic, still, phlegmatic.)*

trial—*n.* gauge, temptation, proof, affliction, burden, attempt, criterion, tribulation, scrutiny, verification, test, experiment, trouble, grief, suffering, endeavor, essay, ordeal. *(non-probation, miscalculation, trifle, alleviation, disburdenment, comfort, oversight, delight, non-trial,*

*mismeasurement, misesti-
mate, triviality, relief, refreshment, attempt.)*

trick—*n.* contrivance, guile,
wile, cheat, antic, finesse,
deception, delusion, subterfuge, legerdemain, artifice,
machination, stratagem,
fraud, juggle, vagary, slight,
imposition. *(exposure,
mishap, botch, fumbling,
maladroitness, blunder,
openhandedness, betrayal,
artlessness, bungling, inex-
pertness, genuineness.)*

tribulation—*n.* ordeal, oppression, adversity, depression, suffering, curse, misery,
affliction, pain. *(pleasure, joy,
happiness, ease, blessing.)*

trifle—*n.* bagatelle, straw,
triviality, joke, bubble, toy,
kickshaw, plaything, bauble,
trinket, nothing, levity, cipher,
gewgaw. *(portent, crisis,
weight, importance, seriousness, muddle, treasure, phenomenon, conjuncture, ur-
gency, necessity.)*

triumph—*n.* success,
achievement, exultation, conquest, trophy, victory, ovation, coup. *(discomfiture, unsuccess, baffling, fiasco, disappointment, defeat, failure,
abortion.)*

trivial—*adj.* trite, unimportant, nugatory, inconsiderable, paltry, frivolous, trifling,
common, useless. *(weighty,
original, trifle, novel, important, critical.)*

trouble—*n.* disturbance,
perplexity, vexation, calamity,
uneasiness, disaster, misfortune, anxiety, sorrow, grief,
difficulty, toil, agony, effort,
affliction, annoyance, moles-
tation, inconvenience, distress, tribulation, torment, adversity, embarrassment,
misery, depression, labor.
*(composure, appeasement,
assuagement, gratification,
blessing, joy, ease, luck,
amusement, indifference, inertia, treat, pleasure, in-
diligence, alleviation, delight,
happiness, boon, exultation,
gladness, facility, recreation,
carelessness, indolence.)*

trouble—*v.* vex, confuse,
distress, harass, molest, mortify, irritate, oppress, disturb,
agitate, perplex, annoy, tease,
grieve. *(calm, appease,
soothe, gratify, entertain,
refresh, elate, compose, allay,
please, delight, recreate,
relieve.)*

troublesome—*adj.* irksome, tedious, laborious, importunate, agitated, vexa-
tious, tiresome, difficult, arduous, grievous. *(pleasant,
facile, unlaborious, agree-*

able, untroublesome, easy, amusing, light.)

true—*adj.* veracious, precise, faithful, loyal, pure, literal, real, veritable, exact, accurate, actual, genuine. *(unreliable, untrustworthy, false, unfaithful, fickle, erroneous, perfidious, adulterated, inaccurate, fictitious, unhistorical, inveracious, faithless, treacherous, spurious, counterfeit.)*

trust—*n.* confidence, belief, faith, expectation, duty, charge, reliance, dependency, hope, credit, commission. *(suspicion, doubt, distrust, uncertainty.)*

trust—*v.* rely, believe, deposit, repose, depend, hope, confide, credit, charge, entrust. *(suspect, doubt, resume, despair, be wary of, distrust, discredit, disbelieve, withdraw.)*

try—*v.* endeavor, aim, test, gauge, fathom, venture, attempt, strive, examine, sound, probe. *(abandon, ignore, misexamine, neglect, misinvestigate, reject, discard.)*

turbid—*adj.* opaque, thick, dark, foul, smudgy, murky, vague, disoriented, incoherent, rattled, disturbed. *(clear, fresh, crystal, lucid, coherent, placid, limpid.)*

turn—*n.* winding, deflection, deed, alternation, occasion, act, purpose, convenience, gift, character, crisis, cast, manner, fashion, rotation, change, bend, vicissitude, curve, opportunity, time, office, treatment, requirement, talent, tendency, exigence, form, shape, mold, cut, pirouette, revolution, recurrence, alteration. *(fixity, stationariness, uniformity, indeflection, oversight, untimeliness, non-requirement, shapelessness, sameness, stability, immobility, unchangeableness, rectilinearity, continuity, incognizance, independence, malformation.)*

turn—*v.* shape, adapt, reverse, alter, convert, revolve, hinge, deviate, mold, diverge, change, swivel, round, spin, deflect, transform, rotate, metamorphose, depend, incline, decline. *(misadapt, stabilitate, fix, continue, maintain, proceed, misshape, perpetuate, stereotype, arrest.)*

turncoat—*n.* deserter, renegade, trimmer, defector, apostate.

tutor—*n.* governor, teacher, professor, savant, coach, guardian, instructor, preceptor, master. *(pupil, stu-*

dent, learner, ward, tyro, scholar, disciple, neophyte.)

twine—*v.* wind, entwine, wreath, unite, bend, coil, meander, twist, embrace. *(unwind, disunite, separate, unwreath, disentwine, straighten, untangle, untwist, detach, unravel, continue.)*

twist—*v.* convolve, pervert, wrest, wind, form, unite, braid, contort, complicate, distort, wreath, encircle, weave, insinuate, interpenetrate. *(untwist, verify, reflect, preserve, substantiate, unwind, disengage, disunite, disincorporate, attest, unravel, straighten, rectify, represent, render, express, unwreath, detach, separate, disentangle.)*

type—*n.* stamp, kind, sign, form, pattern, idea, likeness, cast, mark, fashion, species, emblem, model, character, symbol, archetype, image, expression, mold. *(nonclassification, misrepresentation, falsification, deviation, monstrosity, aberration, nondescription, inexpression, misindication, abnormity, caricature.)*

tyranny—*n.* autocracy, czarism, despotism, severity, sterness, coercion, terrorism, savagery, authoritarianism, oppression. *(relaxation, understanding, ease, mercy, humanity, benevolence, democracy.)*

tyro—*n.* amateur, neophyte, beginner, student, novice, appretice, freshman, novitiate, greenhorn. *(master, pro, veteran, professional, expert.)*

U

ugly—*adj.* hideous, frightful, ill-favored, ill—looking, hateful, homely, repulsive, loathsome, uncouth, unsightly, plain, ungainly, deformed, monstrous. *(fair, shapely, handsome, comely, attractive, seemly, beautiful.)*

ultimate—*adj.* final, conclusive, farthest, maximum, last, extreme, remotest. *(intermediate, preliminary, prior, proximate, initial.)*

umbrage—*n.* displeasure, antipathy, indignation, offense, pique, resentment, animosity, rancor, anger. *(good will, sympathy, amity, cordiality, harmony.)*

unanimous—*adj.* unified, solid, of one mind, agreeing, undivided, harmonious. *(disagreeing, split, discordant, differing.)*

unappetizing—*adj.* uninviting, stale, unpalatable, vapid, insipid, unpleasant, unappealing, unsavory. *(agreeable, pleasant, attractive, interesting, appealing.)*

unbelievable—*adj.* inconceivable, improbable, preposterous, incredible, untenable, irrational, suspicious, absurd. *(credible, persuasive, convincing, believable, obvious.)*

uncertain—*adj.* dubious, fitful, ambiguous, variable, problematic, fluctuating, doubtful, questionable, equivocal, indistinct. *(fixed, decided, definite, steady, reliable.)*

unconscious—*adj.* comatose, senseless, lethargic, asleep, numb, unaware, incognizant, narcotized, insensible. *(awake, aware, sensible, conscious, alert, cognizant, knowing.)*

undeniable—*adj.* indisputable, incontrovertible, irrefutable, incontestable, unquestionable. *(doubtful, debatable, deniable, untenable, controversial.)*

undergo—*v.* suffer, sustain, bear, tolerate, experience, endure. *(avoid, reject, miss, forego, refuse.)*

underhand—*adj.* furtive, unfair, surreptitious, deceitful, clandestine, dishonest, fraudulent. *(straightforward, honest, candid, undisguised, openhanded, fair.)*

understand—*v.* comprehend, perceive, conceive, recognize, imply, appreciate, apprehend, know, discern, learn, interpret. *(miscomprehend, misinterpret, state, express, misapprehend, ignore, declare, enunciate, neglect.)*

understanding—*n.* discernment, construction, intellect, mind, conception, brains, cognizance, knowledge, interpretation, agreement, intelligence, sense, reason. *(misapprehension, misinterpretation, mindlessness, ignorance, misunderstanding, misconstruction, irrationality, antipathy.)*

unethical—*adj.* dishonorable, shady, improper, corrupt, unscrupulous, immoral, conniving, unfair, unworthy, suspect. *(moral, ethical, upright, scrupulous, worthy, honorable.)*

unfit—*adj.* unsuitable, untimely, ineffective, incompetent, improper, inconsistent. *(suitable, competent, eligible, adequate, equipped, hale, sound.)*

unfortunate—*adj.* ill-fated, wretched, miserable, catastrophic, calamitous, unlucky, unhappy. *(lucky, successful, fortunate, affluent, happy, auspicious.)*

uniform—*adj.* invariable, regular, homogeneous, equal, alike, equable, undiversified, unvarying, even, conformable, consistent, unvaried, symmetrical. *(variable, irregular, incongruous, heterogeneous, diverse, multifarious, polymorphic, varying, eccentric, different, inconformable, inconsistent, unsymmetrical, erratic, multigenous, bizarre.)*

union—*n.* coalition, agreement, conjunction, league, alliance, concord, consolidation, fusion, junction, combination, harmony, concert, connection, confederacy, confederation. *(separation, divorce, discord, secession, multiplication, division, rupture, disjunction, severance, disagreement, disharmony, disruption, diversification.)*

unit—*n.* item, individual, part, piece, ace. *(aggregate, sum, total, mass, collection, composite.)*

unite—*v.* combine, attach, associate, embody, fuse, connect, add, cohere, integrate, converge, join, link, amalgamate, coalesce, merge, conjoin, couple, incorporate with, concatenate, reconcile. *(sever, separate, resolve, disintegrate, disrupt, multiply, sunder, segregate, diverge, disjoin, dissociate, disamalgamate, disunite, disconnect, divide, part.)*

unity—*n.* singleness, concord, agreement, indivisibility, identity, oneness, individuality, conjunction, uniformity. *(multitude, multiplicity, disjunction, severance, heterogeneity, incongruity, disharmony, divisibility, plurality, complexity, discord, separation, variety, diversity.)*

universal—*adj.* unlimited, total, entire, ecumenical, prevalent, pandemic, worldwide, common, comprehensive. *(unique, rare, limited, particular, exclusive.)*

universal—*adj.* embracing, all, unlimited, comprehensive, general, exhaustive, ecumenical, complete, total, boundless, entire, whole. *(local, incomplete, particular, unique, exceptional, partial, limited, exclusive, inexhaustive.)*

unlawful—*adj.* illegal, unlicensed, illicit, unconstitutional, forbidden, lawless. *(licit, authorized, permitted, legal, legitimate.)*

unreasonable—*adj.* silly, exorbitant, preposterous, ridiculous, foolish, extravagant, absurd, immoderate. *(sane, rational, sensible, logical, wise, equitable.)*

upright—*adj.* erect, honest, pure, conscientious, fair, ethical, just, equitable, vertical, perpendicular, honorable, principled. *(inclined, dishonest, dishonorable, unprincipled, unethical, unconscientious, inverted, corrupt.)*

urge—*v.* push, impel, force, press, solicit, incite, stimulate, good, expedite, dispatch, drive, propel, importune, animate, instigate, hasten, accelerate. *(hold, inhibit, restrain, hinder, discourage, obstruct, caution, repress, retain, coerce, cohibit, retard, damp.)*

urgent—*adj.* imperative, grave, importunate, strenuous, serious, indeferrible, pressing, immediate, forcible, momentous, demanding. *(insignificant, trivial, frivolous, deferrible, unimportant, trifling.)*

use—*n.* custom, practice, habit, utility, exercise, advantage, service.

use—*v.* exercise, practice, utilize, habituate, employ, inure, treat, accustom. *(suspend, avoid, dishabituate, save, disinure, discard, ignore, disaccustom.)*

useful—*adj.* profitable, serviceable, available, suited, utilitarian, conducive, advantageous, helpful, beneficial, adapted. *(unprofitable, obstructive, retardative, antagonistic, ineffectual, combersome, unbeneficial, hostile, inconducive, fruitless, applicable, disadvantageous, preventative, useless, burdensome, unavailable.)*

usual—*adj.* customary, normal, habitual, accustomed, prevalent, common, ordinary, regular, wonted, general, frequent. *(rare, uncustomary, abnormal, unusual, sparse, uncommon, exceptional, extraordinary, irregular.)*

utmost—*adj.* maximum, greatest, sovereign, remotest, terminal, uppermost, maximal, extreme, major, cardinal, foremost. *(minimal, adjacent, nearest, smallest, minimum, next, neighboring.)*

utter—*v.* issue, express, speak, pronounce, emit, circulate, promulgate, articulate. *(suppress, hush, check, conceal, swallow, recall, repress, stifle.)*

utter—*adj.* perfect, unqualified, thorough, entire, pure, sheer, unmitigated, extreme, complete, absolute, consummate. *(impure, limited, incomplete, imperfect, reasonable.)*

utterly—*adv.* completely, quite, entirely, extremely, totally, wholly, altogether. *(somewhat, rather, tolerably, partly, moderately, passably.)*

V

vacancy—*n.* void, hollowness, gap, blankness, vacuousness, hole, emptiness, depletion. *(plenitude, profusion, fullness, occupancy, completeness.)*

vacant—*adj.* leisure, unencumbered, void, mindless, depleted, empty, exhausted, unemployed, unoccupied, unfilled. *(replenished, employed, occupied, thoughtful, intelligent, full, business, engaged, filled.)*

vague—*adj.* lax, undetermined, intangible, unsettled, pointless, casual, general, indefinite, popular, equivocal, uncertain, ill-defined. *(definite, limited, pointed, specified, strict, specific, determined, scientific, mysterious.)*

vain—*adj.* worthless, unsatisfying, idle, egotistic,

unreal, arrogant, conceited, complacent, empty, fruitless, unavailing, ineffectual, showy. *(substantial, worthy, effectual, potent, modest, humble, real, solid, sound, efficient, cogent, unconceited.)*

valid—*adj.* powerful, weighty, substantial, efficient, operative, logical, conclusive, strong, cogent, sound, available, sufficient. *(invalid, unsound, unavailable, insufficient, obsolete, superseded, vague, illogical, weak, powerless, unsubstantial, inefficient, inoperative, effete.)*

value—*v.* compute, estimate, treasure, prize, evaluate, appreciate, rate, esteem, appraise. *(misestimate, disregard, underrate, underestimate, scorn, despise, condemn, vilify, miscompute, disesteem, vilipend, undervalue, cheapen.)*

vanity—*n.* unsubstantiality, conceit, falsity, self-sufficiency, pride, triviality, narcissism, emptiness, unreality, ostentation, worthlessness. *(solidity, reality, modesty, simplicity, humility, diffidence, substance, substantiality, truth, self-distrust, unostentatiousness.)*

vaporize—*v.* mist, fume, spray, atomize, humidify,

steam, evaporate, volatilize. *(dry, dehydrate, dehumidify, desiccate.)*

variable—*adj.* mutable, capricious, unsteady, shifting, elastic, changeable, fickle, wavering, inconstant. *(unchangeable, constant, true, staunch, steady, invariable, predictable, firm, unchanging, immutable, fast, unwavering, unalterable.)*

variation—*n.* alteration, diversity, change, exception, transformation, discrepancy, deviation, mutation, departure, abnormity. *(fixity, exemplification, rule, harmony, regularity, law, agreement, continuance, indivergency, uniformity.)*

variety—*n.* diversity, miscellany, multiformity, heterogeneity, abnormity, difference, medley, multiplicity. *(species, specimen, sameness, uniformity, type.)*

various—*adj.* diverse, sundry, multitudinous, manifold, miscellaneous, diversified, different, multiform, several, uncertain. *(same, uniform, similar, equivalent, one, few, identical.)*

vast—*adj.* wild, extensive, huge, spacious, gigantic, boundless, enormous, colossal, far-reaching, substantial, desolate, widespread, wide, measureless, mighty, immense, prodigious. *(close, frequented, cultivated, tilled, bounded, moderate, paltry, narrow, confined, populated, tended, limited, circumscribed.)*

vassal—*n.* serf, underling, slave, hireling, subordinate, puppet, dependent, minion, yes-man. *(overlord, master, boss, ruler.)*

vegetate—*v.* deteriorate, stagnate, languish, waste away, idle, loaf, laze. *(develop, bloom, grow, participate, react, accomplish, bustle, respond.)*

vehement—*adj.* impetuous, urgent, burning, raging, passionate, eager, zealous, violent, ardent, fervent, furious, fervid, forcible. *(feeble, subdued, unimpassioned, cold, gentle, mitigated, timid, mild, inanimate, controlled, passionless, stoical, weak.)*

vengeance—*n.* retaliation, revenge, vindictiveness, retribution, fury. *(pardon, amnesty, remission, oblivion, reprieve, tolerance, forgiveness, condonation, grace, absolution, indulgence.)*

venom—*n.* spite, hate, rancor, malice, hostility, rage, truculence, animosity, resentment, enmity. *(charity, pity, mercy, benevolence, humanitarianism, kindness.)*

venture—*n.* risk, hazard, undertaking, experiment, wager, speculation, chance, stake, luck, gamble. *(caution, calculation, law, surveillance, method, non-speculation, reservation, certainty.)*

veracity—*n.* truthfulness, truth, exactness, integrity, accuracy, credibility. *(dishonesty, lying, mendacity, deceitfulness, guile, error.)*

verdict—*n.* judgment, opinion, sentence, evaluation, finding, answer, decision. *(indecision, bias, misconception, indetermination, nondeclaration.)*

verge—*v.* bend, incline, tend, approximate, bear, gravitate, slope, approach. *(deviate, depart, return, retrocede, deflect, decline, revert, recede, back.)*

verify—*v.* confirm, authenticate, identify, test, demonstrate, corroborate, establish, fulfill, substantiate, realize, warrant. *(subvert, falsify, fail, misrepresent, disappoint, refute, disestablish, mistake, misstate, invalidate.)*

versed—*adj.* practiced, acquainted, indoctrinated, familiar, proficient, qualified, skilled, conversant, initiated, clever, accomplished. *(illversed, untaught, inconversant, uninitiated, awkward, unversed, incompetent, unskilled, unpracticed, unfamiliar, ignorant, strange.)*

vested—*adj.* absolute, independent, statutory, guaranteed, inalienable, established, sanctioned, fixed. *(contingent, occasional, provisional, variable.)*

vex—*v.* irritate, plague, worry, tantalize, trouble, afflict, annoy, tease, provoke, torment, bother, pester, disquiet, harass. *(appease, quiet, mollify, please, soothe, gratify.)*

vibrant—*adj.* pulsing, resonant, ringing, vibrating, throbbing, sonorous, energetic, animated, forceful. *(sluggish, weak, inactive, thin, feeble, dull, phlegmatic.)*

vice—*n.* fault, evil, immorality, badness, imperfection, defect, corruption, crime, sin. *(faultlessness, virtue, goodness, attainment, soundness, purity, perfection, immaculateness.)*

vicious—*adj.* faulty, bad, morbid, peccant, profligate, impure, immoral, depraved, corrupt, defective, debased, unruly. *(sound, virtuous, friendly, healthy, pure, perfect.)*

victory—*n.* triumph, success, domination, conquest, ovation. *(defeat, disappointment, miscarriage, downfall, non-success, failure, frustration, abortion.)*

view—*v.* examine, explore, consider, reconnoitre, regard, judge, glimpse, behold, inspect, survey, contemplate, observe, estimate. *(overlook, misconsider, misobserve, misjudge, ignore, disregard, misinspect, misestimate.)*

view—*n.* vision, examination, light, judgment, scene, apprehension, aim, conception, object, intention, sight, design, scrutiny, survey, estimate, inspection, representation, sentiment, opinion, purpose, end. *(occultation, darkness, deception, delusion, misrepresentation, aimlessness, error, non-intention, blindness, obscuration, misexamination, misjudgment, misconception.)*

vile—*adj.* worthless, low, mean, hateful, impure, abandoned, cheap, sinful, ignoble, villainous, base, wretched, profligate, valueless, despicable, bad, vicious, abject, sordid, wicked, degraded. *(rare, valuable, exalted,*

honorable, venerable, virtuous, costly, precious, high, noble, lofty.)*

villain—*n.* wretch, scoundrel, reprobate, ruffian. *(prince, idol, hero.)*

villainous—*adj.* knavish, infamous, detestable, base, depraved. *(heroic, moral, humane, virtuous, saintly, righteous.)*

vindicate—*v.* maintain, clear, defend, substantiate, establish, exonerate, assert, uphold, support, claim, justify. *(abandon, forego, disestablish, nullify, subvert, vitiate, pardon, waive, surrender, disprove, neutralize, destroy, annul.)*

violate—*v.* injure, disturb, rape, debauch, infringe, transgress, desecrate, disobey, ravish, abuse, hurt, outrage, break, profane. *(foster, regard, cherish, obey, esteem, respect, observe, preserve, protect.)*

violence—*n.* impetuosity, rape, rage, injustice, infringement, oppression, truculence, force, destructiveness, outrage, profanation, fury, fierceness. *(mildness, feebleness, respect, self-control, obedience, conservation, humaneness, lenity, protection, self-restraint,* gentleness, forbearance, observance, preservation.)

virtue—*n.* capacity, force, excellence, morality, uprightness, chastity, rectitude, power, strength, efficacy, value, goodness, purity, salubrity, honor. *(incapacity, inefficacy, corruption, immorality, dishonor, unchastity, malignancy, weakness, inability, badness, vice, impurity, virulence.)*

visible—*adj.* apparent, plain, conspicuous, discernible, clear, manifest, evident, detectable, perceptible, obvious, observable, palpable, distinguishable. *(nonapparent, hidden, impalpable, invisible, concealed, withdrawn, indistinguishable, imperceptible, inconspicuous, microscopic, unobservable, eclipsed, indiscernible.)*

visionary—*adj.* dreamy, baseless, imaginary, fabulous, idealized, romantic, fanciful, chimerical, shadowy, unreal. *(real, sound, veritable, palpable, sober, actual, truthful, substantial, unromantic.)*

vital—*adj.* palpable, animate, viable, functioning, essential, crucial, critical, decisive, fundamental, mortal. *(dead, weak, inanimate, irrelevant, phlegmatic, superficial.)*

vivid—*adj.* brilliant, resplendent, radiant, clear, animated, lively, striking, sunny, scintillant, dynamic, bright, luminous, lustrous, graphic, stirring, glowing. *(opaque, obscure, dim, lurid, non-reflecting, dusky, nebulous, wan, colorless, dull, non-luminous, rayless, somber, cloudy, pale, nondescript.)*

volume—*n.* body, dimensions, work, capacity, compass, magnitude, quantity, aggregate, size, bulk, book, extent. *(tenuity, diminutiveness, minuteness, smallness.)*

voluntary—*adj.* spontaneous, intentional, discretional, willing, deliberate, free, optional, unconstrained, chosen. *(coercive, forced, involuntary, compelled, compulsory, necessitated.)*

volunteer—*v.* proffer, originate, provide, offer, tend. *(suppress, withhold, withdraw, refuse.)*

voluptuous—*adj.* luxurious, licentious, highly pleasant, sensuous, hedonistic, sensual, self-indulgent. *(abstinent, sober, ascetic, monkish, unsensual, self-denying.)*

vulgar—*adj.* general, ordinary, vernacular, uncultivated, low, coarse, uncouth, underbred, popular, loose, public, plebian, unrefined, mean. *(scientific, restricted, accurate, select, cultivated, polite, stylish, elegant, aristocratic, strict, philosophical, technical, patrician, choice, refined, high-bred.)*

vulnerable—*adj.* unguarded, insecure, unprotected, weak, destructible, delicate, defenseless, easily wounded. *(protected, impervious, invincible, guarded.)*

W

wages—*n.* compensation, salary, payment, allowance, remuneration, stipend, hire. *(douceur, bonus, gift, premium, grace, gratuity.)*

wakeful—*adj.* vigilant, restless, alert, cautious, wary, awake. *(dozing, heedless, drowsy, somnolent, asleep.)*

wander—*v.* range, rove, roam, stray, err, straggle, navigate, travel, cruise, ramble, stroll, expatitate, deviate, depart, swerve, saunter, circumnavigate. *(stop, bivouac, lie, alight, moor, repose, remain, pause, settle, rest, perch, halt, anchor.)*

want—*n.* lack, insufficiency, shortage, neglect, absence, hunger, non-production, omission, deficiency, failure, shortness, scantiness. *(sufficiency, abundance, allowance, adequacy, affluence, supply, provision, production, supplement.)*

wanton—*adj.* roving, playful, loose, uncurbed, unrestrained, licentious, inconsiderate, heedless, gratuitous, malicious, wandering, sportive, frolicsome, unbridled, reckless, irregular, dissolute. *(unroving, unplayful, joyless, demure, discreet, self-controlled, formal, purposed, staid, cold-blooded, puritanical, determined, stationary, unsportive, unfrolicsome, thoughtful, sedate, well-regulated, austere, deliberate.)*

warlike—*n.* aggressive, militant, hostile, bellicose, belligerent, pugnacious, strategic. *(nonviolent, friendly, conciliatory, pacifistic, accommodating, peaceful.)*

warm—*adj.* thermal, irascible, ardent, fervid, glowing, zealous, excited, animated, tepid, genial, blood-warm. *(cold, starved, cool, passionless, chilly, frigid, unexcited, indifferent.)*

warmth—*n.* glow, zeal, excitement, earnestness, animation, vehemence, sincerity, irascibility, life, ardor, affability, emotion, fervor, heat, intensity, cordiality, eagerness, passion, geniality. *(frost, iciness, chill, calmness, indifference, insensitiveness, slowness, insincerity, good-temper, frigidity, congelation, coldness, coolness, torpidity, apathy, ungeniality, death, passionlessness.)*

waste—*v.* destroy, impair, pine, squander, throw away, lavish, attenuate, shrivel, wane, trifle, ruin, devastate, consume, decay, dissipate, diminish, desolate, dwindle, wither. *(repair, preserve, stint, protect, economize, hoard, augment, accumulate, flourish, multiply, develop, restore, conserve, perpetuate, husband, utilize, treasure, enrich, luxuriate.)*

watchful—*adj.* expectant, heedful, observant, circumspect, cautious, alert, vigilant, wakeful, careful, attentive, wary. *(invigilant, slumbrous, heedless, inobservant, uncircumspect, incautious, reckless, distracted, unwatchful, unwakeful, drowsy, careless, inattentive, unwary.)*

weak—*adj.* infirm, powerless, fragile, inadhesive, frail, tender, flabby, wishy-washy, watery, spiritless, injudicious, undecided, impressible, ductile, malleable, inconclusive, pointless, enervated, feeble, limp, debile, incompact, pliant, soft, vulnerable, flimsy, foolish, destructible, diluted, inefficient, unsound, unconfirmed, wavering, easy, unconvincing, vapid. *(vigorous, muscular, powerful, stout, sturdy, adhesive, fibrous, indestructible, intoxicating, spirited, wise, judicious, valid, determined, stubborn, inexorable, irresistible, telling, robust, strong, energetic, nervous, tough, lusty, compact, resistant, hard, potent, efficient, animated, sound, cogent, decided, unwavering, unyielding, conclusive, forcible.)*

weaken—*v.* enfeeble, dilute, paralyze, sap, emasculate, debilitate, enervate, impair, attenuate. *(invigorate, corroborate, develop, confirm, strengthen, empower.)*

wealth—*n.* riches, lucre, affluence, opulence, assets, influence, mammon, plenty, abundance. *(poverty, impecuniosity, destitution, indigence, scarcity.)*

wear—*v.* bear, sport, don, impair, channel, excavate,

rub, diminish, manifest, carry, groove, exhibit, consume, waste, hollow. *(abandon, renovate, increase, augment, expand, doff, repair, renew, swell.)*

weary—*adj.* tired, worn, faint, debilitated, toil-worn, fatigued, dispirited, exhausted, jaded, spent. *(vigorous, renovated, bouncy, hearty, fresh, recruited.)*

weather—*v.* withstand, surmount, survive, resist, bear, endure, suffer. *(collapse, fail, succumb, fall.)*

weave—*v.* braid, intermix, complicate, spin, intersect, loop, interlace, intertwine, plait. *(untwist, disentangle, simplify, dissect, segregate, unravel, disunite, extricate, enucleate.)*

weight—*n.* ponderosity, pressure, importance, influence, tonnage, consequence, impressiveness, gravity, heaviness, burden, power, efficacy, moment. *(levity, alleviation, insignificance, inefficacy, triviality, unimportance, worthlessness, lightness, portableness, weakness, unimpressiveness.)*

weird—*adj.* mysterious, mystic, strange, odd, uncanny, bizarre, queer. *(normal, common, orthodox, familiar, mundane, natural.)*

well—*adj.* hale, vigorous, sound, hearty, robust, healthy, strong, chipper. *(sick, ill, weak.)*

white—*adj.* pure, unblemished, stainless, clear, snowy, colorless, alabaster, unspotted, innocent. *(impure, ebony, black, inky.)*

whole—*adj.* entire, well, sound, perfect, undiminished, undivided, gross, total, complete, healthy, unimpaired, integral. *(imperfect, unsound, impaired, fractional, sectional, lacking, partial, incomplete, sick, diminished, divided.)*

wholesome—*adj.* salubrious, salutiferous, nutritious, healthful, invigorating, healing, salutary, beneficial. *(unhealthful, insalutary, unwholesome, detrimental, harmful, morbific, unhealthy, insalubrious, prejudicial, deleterious.)*

whore—*n.* prostitute, cyprian, trollop, night walker, wench, woman of ill-fame, bawd, hussy, fille de joie, harlot, courtesan, streetwalker, strumpet, Magdalen, punk, woman of the town, hustler. *(pure woman, lady, virgin, respectable woman.)*

wicked—*adj.* bad, sinful, iniquitous, unjust, irreligious, ungodly, sinful, atrocious, dark, unhallowed, evil, naughty, flagitious, corrupt, black, godless, immoral, criminal, unrighteous, profane, vicious, foul, nefarious, heinous, abandoned. *(virtuous, godly, religious, honest, honorable, good, sinless, immaculate, ethical, stainless, just, moral, upright, pure, incorrupt, spotless.)*

wide—*adj.* ample, spacious, remote, extended, broad, vast, immense, widespread. *(restricted, scant, small, narrow, limited.)*

wild—*adj.* undomesticated, uninhabited, savage, unrefined, ferocious, violent, loose, turbulent, inordinate, chimerical, incoherent, distracted, barbaric, haggard, untamed, uncultivated, uncivilized, rude, untrained, ferine, disorderly, ungoverned, disorderly, visionary, raving. *(domesticated, inhabited, populous, polite, reclaimed, tame, mild, regulated, rational, trim, coherent, sober, calm, tranquil, cultivated, frequented, civilized, refined, gentle, subdued, orderly, collected, sane, sensible.)*

willful—*adj.* deliberate, intentional, premeditated, way-ward, stubborn, headstrong, contemplated, purposed, designed, preconcerted, refractory, self-willed. *(accidental, unpremeditated, obedient, manageable, considerate, amenable, thoughtful, undersigned, unintentional, docile, obdurate, deferential.)*

wisdom—*n.* erudition, enlightenment, information, judgment, prudence, intelligence, light, knowledge, learning, attainment, discernment, sagacity. *(illiterateness, indiscernment, folly, darkness, smattering, nonsense, ignorance, injudiciousness, imprudence, empiricism, inacquaintance, absurdity.)*

wit—*n.* intellect, reason, humor, imagination, levity, mind, sense, understanding, ingenuity. *(senselessness, dullness, stupidity, doltishness, vapidity, folly, mindlessness, irrationality, stolidity, inanity, platitude.)*

withdraw—*v.* go, retire, leave, retreat, depart, disappear, abdicate. *(arrive, appear, propose, reiterate, come, repeat.)*

withhold—*v.* keep, stay, restrain, detain, suppress, retain, inhibit, refuse, forbear. *(afford, provide, permit, incite, lavish, promote, grant, fur-*

nish, allow, encourage, concede.)

withstand—*v.* resist, thwart, endure, face, oppose, confront. *(surrender, falter, acquiesce, support, aid, back, yield, submit, encourage, abet.)*

witness—*n.* testimony, corroboration, corroborator, spectator, testifier, beholder, attestation, evidence, cognizance, eye-witness, auditor, voucher. *(incognizance, ignorance, ignoramus, alien, illiterate, stranger, invalidation, refutation.)*

woeful—*adj.* unfortunate, grievous, distressing, disastrous, tragic, mournful, doleful, anguished, miserable, pitiful, inadequate, worthless. *(fortunate, auspicious, beneficial, carefree, contented, generous, prosperous, enviable, glad.)*

wolfish—*adj.* savage, fierce, predatory, greedy, ravenous, merciless, pitiless. *(gentle, mild, harmless, generous, benevolent, compassionate.)*

wonder—*n.* miracle, surprise, awe, puzzlement, fascination, phenomenon, admiration, marvel, sign, surprise, prodigy. *(calm, apathy, anticipation, triviality, com-*

posure, expectation, indifference.)

wonderful—*adj.* miraculous, astonishing, wondrous, fabulous, spectacular, awe-inspiring, unusual, startling, portentous, prodigious, strange, admirable, amazing. *(banal, normal, wonted, nondescript, every-day, regular, customary, expected, anticipated, current, natural, usual, expected.)*

wooly—*adj.* fuzzy, blurred, vague, hazy, foggy, clouded, murky, unfocused. *(clear, definite, well-defined, sharp.)*

word—*n.* message, report, news, promise, engagement, signal, warrant, declaration, term. *(idea, conception).*

wordy—*adj.* verbose, prolix, longwinded, talkative, garrulous, inflated, redundant, periphrastic, rambling. *(concise, succinct, brief, terse, trenchant, pithy.)*

work—*n.* travail, labor, toil, drudgery, product, result, issue, composition, operation, profession, business, chore, undertaking, project, feat, achievement. *(play, leisure, rest, non-performance, idleness, sloth, stall, collapse, non-production, fruitlessness.)*

worldly—*adj.* earthly, secular, profane, materialistic, mundane, temporal, carnal, shrewd, practical, urbane, experienced. *(unearthly, spiritual, metaphysical, heavenly, simple, naive, artless.)*

worn—*adj.* frayed, damaged, tattered, used, dingy, exhausted, threadbare. *(undamaged, fresh, unused, new.)*

worry—*v.* fret, brood, pester, harass, molest, annoy, tease, torment, importune, harry, plague, disquiet, vex. *(comfort, pacify, calm, soothe, gratify, please, quiet, amuse, reassure.)*

worsen—*v.* deteriorate, spoil, aggravate, decay, degenerate, contaminate. *(better, brighten, recover, improve, mend.)*

worship—*v.* revere, glorify, honor, respect, idolize, cherish, treasure, admire, venerate. *(dishonor, mock, blaspheme, scoff at, dislike, despise, hate.)*

worth—*n.* estimation, holdings, rate, value, merit, price, expense, importance, significance, estate, property. *(insignificance, worthlessness, inappreciableness,*

paltriness, triviality, demerit, uselessness.)

worthless—*adj.* purposeless, unproductive, useless, valueless, meaningless, empty, trivial, reprobate, vile, trashy. *(important, worthy, essential, precious, virtuous, noble, advantageous, honorable, rare, costly, excellent, useful, lucrative.)*

wrap—*v.* envelop, enfold, cover, package, wind, conceal, roll up, bundle. *(unfurl, open, unwrap, unfold.)*

wrath—*n.* rage, anger, fury, indignation, resentment, choler, exasperation, irritation, vexation. *(pleasure, forbearance, delight, gratification, equanimity.)*

wreak—*v.* inflict, visit, exact, bring about, work, cause, exercise, effect. *(forbear, hold back, abstain from, desist from.)*

wreck—*v.* destroy, ruin, spoil, shatter, devastate, ravage, demolish, blast, smash. *(preserve, guard, secure, conserve, protect.)*

wrench—*v.* contort, jerk, twist, strain, blow, wring, sprain.

wretched—*adj.* dejected, depressed, mournful, forlorn, woeful, unfortunate, worthless, inferior, hopeless, pitiful. *(happy, glad, euphoric, affluent, noble, virtuous, comfortable, worthy, admirable.)*

wrinkle—v. crease, crumple, purse, furrow, fold, crinkle. *(flatten, smooth, straighten, iron, level.)*

wrong—adj. mistaken, faulty, untrue, inaccurate, inequitable, improper, inethical, unjust, unsuitable, erroneous, awkward, imperfect. *(perfect, correct, suitable, good, standard, ethical, fitting, right, fair, moral, beneficial, straight, appropriate.)*

wry—adj. distorted, askew, crooked, twisted, contorted, deformed, awry. *(straight, unbent, normal, supple, limber.)*

Y

yearn—v. crave, want, desire, wish, hunger for, long, covet, thirst for. *(revolt, shudder, recoil, loathe.)*

yet—adv. still, besides, hitherto, ultimately, at last, now, thus far, however, eventually, at last.

yield—v. supply, furnish, render, pay, submit, consent, acquiesce, grant, accede, assent, comply, bear, afford, succumb, give in, engender, resign, relinquish, produce. *(oppose, refute, resist, dissent, protest, retain, disallow, withhold, deny, claim, assert, vindicate, recalcitrate, strive, struggle.)*

yielding—adj. conceding, producing, submissive, unresisting, soft, surrendering, acquiescent, timid, crouching, spongy. *(nonproductive, waste, fallow, stiff, defiant, firm, unyielding, resisting, fierce, unbending.)*

yoke—v. connect, link, hitch, splice, mate, enslave, couple, subjugate, unite. *(release, dissever, divorce, liberate, enfranchise, manumit.)*

yonder—adj. yon, distant, faraway, thither, remote, faroff. *(near, close, nearby.)*

youth—n. minor, adolescence, juvenility, childhood, beginnings, start, youngster, kid, stripling.

youthful—adj. childlike, adolescent, juvenile, fresh, puerile, immature, maiden, early, unripe, virginal. *(elderly, aged, mature, antiquated, olden, time-worn, patriarchal, decrepit, ancient, decayed.)*

Z

zeal—n. zest, drive, enthusiasm, ardor, interest, ambition, earnestness, passion, heartiness, energy. *(detachment, indifference, apathy, coolness, carelessness, aimlessness, sluggishness, incordiality.)*

zenith—*n.* acme, crest, culmination, pinnacle, top, summit, maximum, climax, peak, height. *(bottom, nadir, depths, minimum, lowest point.)*

zest—*n.* enjoyment, relish, gusto, eagerness, delight, exhilaration, life, appetizer, flavor, sharpener, satisfaction. *(apathy, boredom, distaste, detriment, ennui.)*

zip—*n.* energy, vitality, animation, dash, zing, sparkle, punch, drive. *(sloth, lethargy, apathy, laziness, debility.)*

zoom—*v.* climb, soar, rise, ascend, escalate, mount, spiral, grow, increase. *(drop, descend, plummet, decrease, fall.)*

HOMONYMS

A

able, strong, skillful. **Abel,** a name.

accidence, rudiments. **accidents,** mishaps.

acclamation, applause. **acclimation,** used to climate.

acts, deeds. **ax or axe,** a tool.

ad, advertisement. **add,** to increase.

adds, increases. **adze or adz,** a tool.

adherence, constancy. **adherents,** followers.

ail, pain, trouble. **ale,** a liquor.

air, atmosphere. **ere,** before. **heir,** inheritor.

aisle, passage. **isle,** island. **I'll,** I will.

ait, an island. **ate,** devoured. **eight,** a number.

ale, liquor. **ail,** pain, trouble.

all, everyone. **awl,** a tool.

allegation, affirmation. **allegation,** uniting.

aloud, with noise. **allowed,** permitted.

altar, for worship. **alter,** to change.

amend, to make better. **amende,** retraction.

anker, a measure. **anchor,** of a vessel.

Ann, a name. **an,** one.

annalist, historian. **analyst,** analyzer.

annalize, to record. **analyze,** to investigate.

ant, insect. **aunt,** relative.

ante, before. **anti,** opposed to.

arc, part of a circle. **ark,** chest, boat.

arrant, bad. **errant,** wandering.

ascent, act of rising. **assent,** consent.

asperate, make rough. **aspirate,** give sound of "h".

assistance, help, aid. **assistants,** helpers.

ate, consumed or devoured. **ait,** an island. **eight,** a number.

Ate, a goddess. **eighty,** a number.

attendance, waiting on. **attendants,** those who attend, are in attendance.

aught, anything. **ought,** should.

augur, to predict. **auger,** a tool.

aune, a cloth measure. **own,** belonging to oneself.

aunt, relative. **ant,** insect.

auricle, external ear. **oracle,** prophet.

awl, a tool. **all,** everyone.

axe, a tool. **acts,** deeds.

axes, tools. **axis,** turning line.

aye, yes. **eye,** organ of sight. **I,** myself.

B

bacon, pork, **baken,** baked.

bad, wicked. **bade,** past tense of the verb TO BID.

bail, security. **bale,** a bundle.

bait, food to allure. **bate,** to lessen.

baize, cloth. **bays,** water, garland, horses.

bald, hairless. **bawled,** cried aloud.

ball, round body, dance. **bawl,** to cry aloud.

bare, naked. **bear,** animal, to carry.

bard, poet. **barred,** fastened with a bar.

bark, cry of dog, rind of tree. **barque,** vessel.

baron. nobleman. **barren,** unfruitful.

baroness, baron's wife. **barrenness,** sterility.

base, mean. **bass,** musical term.

bask, to lie in warmth. **Basque,** race of people in France or Spain.

bass, musical term. **base,** mean.

bay, water, color, tree. **bey,** governor.

beach, seashore. **beech,** a tree.

bear, an animal, to carry. **bare,** naked.

beat, to strike. **beet,** vegetable.

beau, boyfriend. **bow,** archery term.

bee, insect. **be,** to exist.

been, past participle of the verb TO BE. **bin,** container for grain.

beer, malt liquor. **bier,** carriage for the dead.

berry, fruit. **bury,** to inter.

berth, sleeping place. **birth,** act of being born.

better, superior. **bettor,** one who bets.

bey, governor. **bay,** sea, color, tree.

bier, carriage for the dead. **beer,** malt liquor.

bight, of a rope. **bite,** chew.

billed, furnished with a bill. **build,** to erect.

bin, container. **been,** of the verb TO BE.

binocle, telescope. **binnacle,** compass box.

birth, being born. **berth,** sleeping place.

blew, did blow. **blue,** a color.

bloat, to swell. **blote,** to dry by smoke.

boar, swine. **bore,** to make a hole.

board, timber. **bored,** pierced, tired.

bold, courageous. **bowled,** rolled balls.

boll, a pod, a ball. **bowl,** basin. **bole,** earth, trunk of tree.

border, outer edge. **boarder,** lodger.

bourne, a limit, stream. **borne,** carried. **born,** brought into life.

borough, a town. **burrow,** hole for rabbits, donkey.

bow, used in archery. **beau,** a boyfriend.

bow, to salute, part of ship. **bough,** branch of tree.

bowl, basin. **bole,** earth, trunk of tree. **boll,** a pod, a ball.

boy, male child. **buoy,** floating signal.

braid, to plait. **brayed,** did bray.

brake, device for retarding motion, a thicket. **break,** opening, to part.

bray, harsh sound. **brae,** hillside.

breach, a gap, a break. **breech,** part of a gun.

bread, food. **bred,** brought up.

brewed, fermented. **brood,** offspring.

brews, makes malt liquor. **bruise,** blemish.

bridal, of a wedding. **bridle,** a curb.

Briton, native of Britain. **Britain,** England, Scotland, Wales, Northern Ireland.

broach, to utter. **brooch,** a pin.

brows, foreheads. **browse,** to feed.

bruit, noise, report. **brute,** a beast.

build, to erect. **billed,** furnished with a bill.

buoy, floating signal. **boy,** male child.

burrow, hole for rabbit, donkey. **borough,** a town.

bury, to cover with earth. **berry,** a fruit.

but, except, yet. **butt,** a cask, to push with head.

by, at, near. **buy,** to purchase.

C

cache, hole for hiding goods. **cash,** money.

caddy, a box. **cadi,** a Turkish judge.

Cain, man's name. **cane,** walking stick.

calendar, almanac. **calender,** to polish.

caulk, to stop leaks. **cauk or cawk,** mineral.

call, to name. **caul,** a membrane.

can, could, tin vessel. **Cannes,** French city.

cannon, large gun. **canon,** a law, a rule.

canvas, cloth. **canvass,** to solicit, to examine.

capital, upper part, principal. **capitol,** statehouse.

carat, weight. **caret,** mark. **carrot,** vegetable.

carol, song of joy. **Carroll,** a name.

carrot, vegetable. **carat,** weight. **caret,** mark.

cash, money. **cache,** hole for hiding goods.

cask, wooden vessel. **casque,** a helmet.

cast, to throw, to mold. **caste,** rank.

castor, a beaver. **caster,** frame for bottles, roller.

caudal, tail. **caudle,** drink.

cause, that which produces. **caws,** cries of crows.

cede, to give up. **seed,** germ of plants.

ceiling, overhead of a room. **sealing,** fastening.

cell, small room. **sell,** to part for price.

cellar, a room under house. **seller,** one who sells.

censor, critic. **censer,** vessel.

cent, coin. **sent,** caused to go. **scent,** odor.

cerate, a salve. **serrate,** shaped like a saw.

cere, to cover with wax. **sear,** burn. **seer,** a prophet.

cession, yielding. **session,** a sitting.

cetaceous, whale species. **setaceous,** bristly.

chagrin, ill-humor. **shagreen,** fish skin.

chance, accident. **chants,** melodies.

champaign, open country. **champagne,** a wine.

chaste, pure. **chased,** pursued.

cheap, inexpensive. **cheep,** a bird's chirp.

chews, masticates. **choose,** to select.

choir, singers. **quire,** measure of paper.

choler, anger. **collar,** neckwear.

chord, musical sound. **cord,** string. **cored,** removed center.

chronical, a long duration. **chronicle,** history.

chuff, a clown. **chough,** a sea bird.

cilicious, made of hair. **silicious,** flinty.

cingle, a girth. **single,** alone, only one.

cion or **scion,** a sprout. **sion** or **zion,** mountain.

circle, round figure. **sercle,** a twig.

cit, a citizen. **sit,** to rest.

cite, to summon, to quote, to enumerate. **site,** location. **sight,** view.

clause, part of a sentence. **claws,** talons.

climb, to ascend. **clime,** climate.

coal, fuel. **cole,** cabbage.

coaled, supplied with coal. **cold,** frigid, not hot.

coarse, rough. **course,** route, **corse** or **corpse,** dead body.

coat, garment. **cote,** sheepfold.

coddle, to fondle. see **caudal.**

codling, apple. **coddling,** parboiling.

coffer, money chest. **cougher,** one who coughs.

coin, money. **quoin,** wedge.

colation, straining. **collation,** a repast.

collar, neckwear. see **choler.**

241

colonel, officer. **kernel,** seed in a nut.

color, tint. **culler,** a chooser.

complacence, satisfaction. **complaisance,** affability, compliance.

complacent, civil. **complaisant,** seeking to please.

compliment, flattery. **complement,** the full number.

confidant, one trusted with secrets. **confident,** having full belief.

consonance, concord. **consonants,** letters which are not vowels.

consequence, that which follows. **consequents,** deduction.

consession, a sitting together. **concession,** a yielding.

coolly, without heat, calmly. **coolie,** East Indian laborer.

coom, soot. **coomb,** a measure.

coquet, to deceive in love. **coquette,** vain girl.

coral, from the ocean. **corol,** a corolla.

cord, string. **chord,** musical sound. **cored,** taken from center.

core, inner part. **corps,** soldiers.

correspondence, interchange of letters. **correspondents,** those who correspond.

council, assembly. **counsel,** advice.

cousin, relative. **cozen,** to cheat.

coward, one without courage. **cowered,** frightened.

creak, harsh noise. **creek,** stream.

crewel, yarn. **cruel,** savage.

crews, seamen. **cruise,** voyage. **cruse,** a cruet.

cue, hint, rod, tail. **queue,** pigtail, waiting line.

culler, a selecter. **color,** a tint.

currant, fruit. **current,** flowing stream, present.

cygnet, a swan. **signet,** a seal.

cymbal, musical instrument. **symbol,** sign.

cypress, a tree. **Cyprus,** an island.

D

dam, wall for stream. **damn,** to doom or curse.

dammed, confined by banks. **damned,** doomed.

Dane, a native of Denmark. **deign,** condescend.

day, time. **dey,** a governor.

days, plural of day. **daze,** to dazzle.

dear, beloved, costly. **deer,** an animal.

deformity, defect. **difformity,** diversity of form.

deign, to condescend. **Dane,** native of Denmark.

demean, debase. **demesne,** land.

dents, marks. **dense,** close, compact.

dependents, subordinates. **dependence,** reliance.

depravation, corruption. **deprivation,** loss.

descent, drop downward. **dissent,** disagreement.

descendent, falling. **descendant,** offspring.

desert, to abandon. **dessert,** last course of a meal.

deviser, contriver. **divisor,** a term in arithmetic.

dew, moisture. **do,** to perform. **due,** owed.

die, to expire, a stamp. **dye,** to color.

dire, dreadful. **dyer,** one who dyes.

discous, flat. **discus,** quoit.

discreet, prudent. **discrete,** separate.

doe, female deer. **dough,** unbaked bread.

does, female deer. **doze,** to slumber.

done, performed. **dun,** a color.

dost, from verb TO BE. **dust,** powdered earth.

drachm, monetary unit of Greece. **dram,** small quantity.

draft, bill. **draught,** a drink, a potion.

dual, two. **duel,** combat.

due, owed, **dew,** moisture. **do,** to perform.

dun, color, ask for debt. **done,** finished.

dust, powdered earth. **dost,** from verb TO BE.

dye, to color. **die,** to expire, a stamp.

dyeing, staining. **dying,** expiring.

dyer, one who dyes. **dire,** dreadful.

E

earn, to gain by labor. **urn,** a vase.

eight, a number. **ate,** consumed or devoured.

eighty, a number. **Ate,** a goddess.

ere, before. **air,** atmosphere. **heir,** inheritor.

errant, wandering. **arrant,** bad.

ewe, female sheep. **yew,** tree. **you,** *pronoun*.

ewes, sheep. **yews,** trees. **use,** employ.

eye, organ of sight. **I,** myself. **aye,** yes.

F

fain, pleased. **fane,** temple. **feign,** pretend.

faint, languid. **feint,** pretense.

fair, beautiful, just. **fare,** price, food.

falter, to hesitate. **faulter,** one who commits a fault.

fane, temple. **fain,** pleased. **feign,** to pretend.

fare, price, food. **fair,** beautiful, just.

fate, destiny. **fete,** a festival.

faulter, one who commits a fault. **falter,** to hesitate.

fawn, young deer. **faun,** woodland deity.

feat, deed. **feet,** plural of foot.

feign, pretend. **fain,** pleased. **fane,** temple.

feint, pretense. **faint,** languid.

felloe, rim of wheel. **fellow,** companion.

feod, tenure. **feud,** quarrel.

ferrule, metallic band. **ferule,** wooden pallet.

feted, honored. **fated,** destined.

feud, quarrel. **feod,** tenure.

fillip, jerk of finger. **Philip,** man's name.

filter, to strain. **philter,** love charm.

find, to discover. **fined,** punished.

fir, tree. **fur,** animal hair.

fissure, a crack. **fisher,** fisherman.

fizz, hissing noise. **phiz,** the face.

flea, insect. **flee,** to run away.

flew, did fly. **flue,** chimney. **flu,** influenza.

flour, ground grain. **flower,** a blossom.

flue, chimney. **flu,** influenza. **flew,** did fly.

for, because of. **fore,** preceding. **four,** cardinal number.

fort, fortified place. **forte,** peculiar talent.

forth, forward. **fourth,** ordinal number.

foul, unclean. **fowl,** a bird.

four, cardinal number. **for,** because of. **fore,** preceding.

fourth, ordinal number. **forth,** forward.

franc, French coin. **Frank,** a name, candid.

frays, quarrels. **phrase,** parts of a sentence.

freeze, to congeal with cold. **frieze,** cloth. **frees,** sets at liberty.

fungus, spongy excrescence. **fungous,** as fungus.

fur, hairy coat of animals. **fir,** a tree.

furs, skins of beasts. **furze,** a shrub.

G

gage, a pledge, a fruit. **gauge,** a measure.

gait, manner of walking. **gate,** a door.

gall, bile. **Gaul,** a Frenchman.

gamble, to wager. **gambol,** to skip.

gate, a door. **gait,** manner of walking.

gauge, a measure. **gage,** a pledge, a fruit.

Gaul, a Frenchman. **gall,** bile.

gild, to overflow with gold. **guild,** a corporation.

gilt, gold on surface. **guilt,** crime.

glare, splendor. **glair,** white of an egg.

gneiss, rock similar to granite. **nice,** fine.

gnu, animal. **new,** not old. **knew,** understood.

gourd, a plant. **gored,** pierced.

grate, iron frame. **great,** large.

grater, a rough instrument. **greater,** larger.

great, large. **grate,** iron frame.

greater, larger. **grater,** a rough instrument.

Greece, country in Europe. **grease,** fat.

grisly, frightful. **grizzly,** an animal, gray.

groan, deep sigh. **grown,** increased.

grocer, merchant. **grosser,** coarser.

grown, increased. **groan,** deep sigh.

guessed, conjectured. **guest,** visitor.

guild, a corporation. **gild,** to overflow with gold.

guilt, crime. **gilt,** gold on surface.

guise, appearance. **guys,** ropes, men.

H

hail, ice, to salute. **hale,** healthy.

hair, tresses. **hare,** a rabbit.

hale, healthy. **hail,** ice, to salute.

hall, large room, a passage. **haul,** to pull.

hare, a rabbit. **hair,** tresses.

hart, an animal. **heart,** seat of life.

haul, to pull. **hall,** a large room, a passage.

hay, dried grass. **hey,** an expression.

heal, to cure. **heel,** part of foot or shoe, the end of a loaf of bread, a scoundrel.

hear, to hearken. **here,** in this place.

heard, did hear. **herd,** a drove.

heart, seat of life. **hart,** an animal.

heel, part of foot or shoe, the end of a loaf of bread, a scoundrel. **heal,** to cure.

heir, inheritor. **air,** atmosphere. **ere,** before.

herd, a drove. **heard,** did hear.

here, in this place. **hear,** to hearken.

hew, to cut down. see **hue.**

hey, an expression. **hay,** dried grass.

hide, skin, to conceal. **hied,** hastened.

hie, to hasten. **high,** lofty, tall.

hied, hastened. **hide,** skin, to conceal.

higher, more lofty. **hire,** to employ.

him, that man. **hymn,** sacred song.

hire, to employ. **higher,** more lofty.

hoa, exclamation. **ho,** cry, stop. **hoe,** tool.

hoard, accumulate. **horde,** crowd.

hoarse, husky. **horse,** animal.

hoe, tool. **ho,** cry, stop. **hoa,** exclamation.

hoes, tools. **hose,** stockings, tubing.

hole, cavity. **whole,** all, entire.

holm, evergreen oak. **home,** dwelling.

holy, pure sacred. **wholly,** completely.

home, dwelling. **holm,** evergreen oak.

horde, crowd. **hoard,** accumulate.

horse, animal. **hoarse,** husky.

hose, stockings, tubing. **hoes,** tools.

hour, sixty minutes. **our,** belonging to us.

hue, color. **hew,** to cut down. **Hugh,** man's name.

hymn, sacred song. **him,** that man.

I

idol, graven image. **idle,** unemployed. **idyl,** poem.

I'll, I will. **isle,** island. **aisle,** passage.

in, within. **inn,** a tavern.

indict, to accuse. **indite,** write, compose.

indiscreet, imprudent. **indiscrete,** not separated.

indite, to write. **indict,** to accuse.

inn, a tavern. **in,** within.

innocence, purity. **innocents,** harmless things.

instants, moments. **instance,** example.

intense, extreme. **intents,** purposes.

intention, purpose. **intension,** determination.

intents, purposes. **intense,** extreme.

invade, to infringe. **inveighed,** censured.

irruption, invasion. **eruption,** upheaval.

isle, island. **I'll,** I will. **aisle,** passage.

J

jail, prison. **gaol,** British prison.

jam, preserves. **jamb,** side of door.

K

kernel, seed in nut. **colonel,** officer.

key, for a lock. **quay,** wharf.

knag, prong of deer's horns. **nag,** small horse, torment.

knap, elevation. **nap,** short sleep.

knave, rogue. **nave,** center, hub.

knead, work dough. **need,** want. **kneed,** having knees.

kneel, to rest on knee. **neal,** to temper by heat.

knew, understood. **gnu,** animal. **new,** not old.

knight, title of honor. **night,** darkness.

knit, unite, weave. **nit,** insect's egg.

knot, tie. **not,** word of refusal.

know, understand. **no,** not yes.

knows, understands. **nose,** organ of smell.

L

lack, to want. **lac,** gum.

lacks, wants, needs. **lax,** loose, slack.

lade, to load. **laid,** placed, produced eggs.

lane, a road. **lain,** rested.

Latin, language. **latten,** brass.

lax, loose, slack. **lacks,** wants, needs.

lea, meadow. **lee,** shelter, place.

leach, to filtrate. **leech,** a worm.

lead, metal. **led,** guided.

leaf, part of a plant. **lief,** willingly.

leak, ooze. **leek,** onion-like vegetable.

lean, not fat, to rest, to slant. **lien,** mortgage.

leased, rented. **least,** smallest.

led, guided. **lead,** metal.

lee, shelter, place. **lea,** meadow.

leech, a worm. **leach,** to filtrate.

leek, onion-like vegetable. **leak,** ooze.

lesson, task. **lessen,** to diminish.

levee, bank, visit. **levy,** to collect.

liar, falsifier. **lyre,** musical instrument. **lier,** one who lies down.

lie, falsehood. **lye,** strong alkaline solution.

lief, willingly. **leaf,** part of a plant.

lien, legal claim. **lean,** not fat, to rest, to slant.

lightning, flash in the sky. **lightening,** unloading.

limb, branch. **limn,** to draw.

links, connecting rings. **lynx,** an animal.

lo, look, see. **low,** not high, mean.

loan, to lend. **lone,** solitary.

lock, hair, fastening. **loch** or **lough,** lake.

lone, solitary. **loan,** to lend.

low, not high, mean. **lo,** look, see.

lusern, a lynx. **lucerne,** clover.

lye, strong alkaline solution. **lie,** falsehood.

lynx, animal. **links,** connecting rings.

lyre, musical instrument. **liar,** falsifier. **lier,** one who lies down.

M

made, created. **maid,** unmarried woman, female servant.

mail, armor, postal service. **male,** masculine.

main, principal. **mane,** hair. **Maine,** a state.

maize, corn. **maze,** winding course.

male, masculine. **mail,** armor, postal service.

mall, walk. **maul,** to beat.

manner, method. **manor,** landed estate.

mantel, chimney piece. **mantle,** a cloak.

mark, visible line. **marque,** a pledge.

marshall, officer. **martial,** warlike.

marten, an animal. **martin,** a bird.

martial, warlike. **marshall,** officer.

maul, to beat. **mall,** walk.

mead, drink. **meed,** reward. **Mede,** native of Media.

mean, low. **mien,** aspect.

meat, food. **meet,** to encounter, a match. **mete,** apportion.

Mede, native of Media. **mead,** drink. **meed,** reward.

meddle, interfere. **medal,** a reward.

meddler, one who meddles. **medlar,** a tree.

meed, reward. **mead,** drink. **Mede,** native of Media.

meet, to encounter, a match. **meat,** food. **mete,** apportion.

mettle, spirit, courage. **metal,** ore.

mew or **mue,** to melt. **mew,** fowl enclosure.

mewl, to cry. **mule,** an animal.

mews, cat cries. **muse,** deep thought.

mien, look aspect. **mean,** low.

might, power. **mite,** insect.

mighty, powerful. **mity,** having mites.

mince, to cut. **mints,** coining places, candies.

miner, worker in mines. **minor,** one underage.

mints, coining places, candies. **mince,** to cut.

missal, prayer book. **missel,** bird. **missile,** weapon.

mite, insect, small. **might,** power.

mity, having mites. **mighty,** powerful.

moan, lament. **mown,** cut down.

moat, ditch. **mote,** small particle.

mode, manner. **mowed,** cut down.

morning, before noon. **mourning,** grief.

mote, small particle. **moat,** ditch.

mowed, cut down. **mode,** manner.

mucous, slimy. **mucus,** secretion of mucous membranes.

mue, to molt. **mew,** fowl enclosure.

mule, an animal. **mewl,** to cry.

muscat, grape. **musket,** gun.

muse, deep thought. **mews,** cat cries.

mustard, plant. **mustered,** assembled.

N

nag, small horse. **knag,** prong of deer's horns.

nap, short sleep. **knap,** elevation.

naval, nautical. **navel,** center of abdomen.

nave, center, hub. **knave,** rogue.

navel, center of abdomen. **naval,** nautical.

nay, no. **neigh,** whinny of a horse.

neal, to temper. **kneel,** to rest on knee.

need, necessity, want. **knead,** work dough. *kneed,* having knees.

neigh, whinny of a horse. **nay,** no.

new, not old. **gnu,** animal. **knew,** understood.

nice, fine. **kneiss,** rock similar to granite.

night, darkness. **knight,** title of honor.

nit, insect's egg. **knit,** to unite, to form.

no, not so. **know,** to understand.

none, no one. **nun,** female devotee.

nose, organ of smell. **knows,** understands.

not, word of refusal. **knot,** a tie.

nun, female devotee. **none,** no one.

O

oar, rowing blade. **o'er,** over. **ore,** mineral.

ode, poem. **owed,** under obligation.

o'er, over. **oar,** paddle. **ore,** mineral.

oh, expression of surprise or pain. **owe,** be indebted.

one, single unit. **won,** gained.

onerary, fit for burdens. **honorary,** conferring honor.

oracle, seer. **auricle,** external ear, chamber of heart.

ordinance, a law. **ordnance,** military supplies.

ore, mineral. **o'er,** over. **oar,** paddle.

ought, should. **aught,** anything.

our, belonging to us. **hour,** sixty minutes.

owe, to be indebted. **oh,** expression of surprise or pain.

owed, under obligation. **ode,** poem.

P

paced, strode. **paste,** flour and water mixed.

packed, bound in a bundle. **pact,** contract.

pail, bucket. **pale,** whitish.

pain, agony. **pane,** a square of glass.

pair, a couple, two. **pare,** to peel. **pear,** a fruit.

palace, princely home. **Pallas,** heathen deity.

palate, roof of the mouth. **pallette,** artist's board. **pallet,** a bed.

pale, whitish. **pail,** bucket.

pall, covering for the dead. **Paul,** man's name.

pare, to peel. **pair,** a couple, two. **pear,** a fruit.

passable, tolerable. **passible,** with feeling.

paste, flour and water mixed. **paced,** strode.

patience, calmness. **patients,** sick persons.

paw, foot of a beast. **pa,** papa.

paws, beasts' feet. **pause,** stop.

peace, quiet. **piece,** a part.

peak, the top. **pique,** grudge. **peek,** to peep.

peal, ring. **peel,** to pare.

pealing, tolling. **peeling,** shredding.

pear, a fruit. **pair,** a couple, two. **pare,** to peel.

pearl, a precious substance. **purl,** a knitting stitch.

pedal, lever worked by foot. **peddle,** to sell.

peek, to peep. **peak,** the top. **pique,** grudge.

peer, nobleman. **pier,** column, wharf.

pencil, writing instrument. **pensile,** suspended.

pendant, an ornament. **pendent,** hanging.

philter, love charm. **filter,** to strain.

phiz, the face. **phizz,** hissing noise.

phrase, expression. **frays,** quarrels.

piece, a part. **peace,** quiet.

pier, a column, wharf. **peer,** nobleman.

pique, grudge. **peak,** the top. **peek,** to peep.

pistil, part of a flower. **pistol,** firearm.

place, position. **plaice,** a fish.

plain, clear, simple, meadow. **plane,** aircraft, tool.

pleas, arguments. **please,** to delight.

plum, a fruit. **plumb,** perpendicular, leaden weight.

pole, stick. **poll,** vote.

pool, water. **poule** or **pool,** stakes played for.

pore, opening. **pour,** cause to flow.

poring, looking intently. **pouring,** raining, flowing.

port, harbor, wine. **porte,** Turkish court.

praise, commendation. **prays,** entreats, petitions. **preys,** feeds by violence, plunders.

pray, to supplicate. **prey,** plunder.

presence, being present. **presents,** gifts.

pride, self-esteem. **pried,** moved by a lever, snooped.

prier, inquirer. **prior,** previous.

pries, looks into. **prize,** reward.

prints, impressions. **prince,** king's son.

principal, chief. **principle,** doctrine.

prior, previous. **prier,** inquirer.

prize, reward. **pries,** looks into.

profit, gain. **prophet,** a fore-teller.

purl, a knitting stitch. **pearl,** precious substance.

Q

quarts, measures, **quartz,** rock crystal.

quay, wharf. **key,** lock fastener.

queen, king's wife. **quean,** worthless woman.

queue, pigtail, waiting line. **cue,** hint, rod.

quire, package of paper. **choir,** church singers.

quoin, wedge. **coin,** money.

R

rabbet, a joint. **rabbit,** small animal.

radical, of first principles. **radicle,** a root.

rain, shower. **reign,** rule. **rein,** bridle.

raise, to lift. **rays,** sunbeams. **raze,** to demolish.

raised, lifted. **razed,** demolished.

raiser, one who raises. **razor,** shaving blade.

rancor, spite. **ranker,** stronger, more immoderate.

rap, knock. **wrap,** enclose.

rapped, knocked. **wrapped,** enclosed.

rapping, striking. **wrapping,** a cover.

rays, sunbeams. **raise,** to lift. **raze,** to demolish.

raze, to demolish. **raise,** to lift. **rays,** sunbeams.

razed, demolished. **raised,** lifted.

razor, shaving blade. **raiser,** one who raises.

read, to peruse. **reed,** a plant.

real, true. **reel,** winding machine, to stagger.

receipt, acknowledgment. **reseat,** to sit again.

reck, to heed. **wreck,** destruction.

red, color. **read,** perused.

reek, to emit vapor. **wreak,** to inflict.

reel, winding machine, to stagger. **real,** true.

reign, rule. **rein,** bridle. **rain,** shower.

reseat, to seat again. **receipt,** acknowledgment.

residence, place of abode. **residents,** citizens.

rest, quiet. **wrest,** to twist.

retch, to vomit. **wretch,** miserable person.

rheum, thin, watery matter. **room,** space.

Rhodes, name of an island. **roads,** highways.

rhumb, point of a compass. **rum,** liquor.

rhyme, poetry. **rime,** hoar frost.

rigger, rope fixer. **rigor,** severity.

right, correct. **rite,** ceremony. **write,** to form letters.

rime, hoar frost. **rhyme,** poetry.

ring, circle, sound of bells. **wring,** to twist.

road, highway. **rode,** did ride. **rowed,** did row.

roads, highways. **Rhodes,** name of an island.

roan, color. **rown,** impelled by oars. **Rhone,** river.

roe, deer, fish eggs. **row,** to impel with oars, a line.

roes, eggs, deer. **rows,** uses oars. **rose,** a flower.

Rome, city in Italy. **roam,** to wander.

rood, a measure. **rude,** rough.

rote, memory of words. **wrote,** did write.

rough, not smooth. **ruff,** plaited collar.

rouse, stir up, provoke. **rows,** disturbances, tiers.

rout, rabble, disperse. **route,** road.

row, to impel with oars, a line. **roe,** a deer, fish eggs.

rowed, did row. **road,** highway. **rode,** did ride.

rows, uses oars. **roes,** deer, fish eggs. **rose,** a flower.

rude, rough. **rood,** measure.

ruff, collar. **rough,** not smooth.

rum, liquor. **rhumb,** point of a compass.

rung, sounded, a step on a ladder. **wrung,** twisted.

rye, grain. **wry,** crooked.

S

sail, canvas of a boat. **sale,** act of selling.

sailer, vessel. **sailor,** seaman.

sale, act of selling. **sail,** canvas of a boat.

sane, sound in mind. **seine,** fish net.

saver, one who saves. **savor,** taste.

scene, a view. **seen,** viewed.

scent, odor. **sent,** caused to go. **cent,** coin.

scion or **cion.** sprout. **sion** or **zion,** a mountain.

scull, oar, boat. **skull,** bony framework of the head.

sea, ocean. **see,** to perceive.

seal, stamp, an animal. **seel,** to close the eyes.

sealing, fastening. **ceiling,** overhead of a room.

seam, a juncture. **seem,** to appear.

seamed, joined together. **seemed,** appeared.

sear, to burn. **cere,** wax.

seas, water. **sees,** looks. **seize,** take hold of.

seed, germ of a plant. **cede,** to give up.

seen, viewed. **scene,** a view.

seine, a net. **sane,** sound in mind.

sell, to part for price. **cell,** small room.

seller, one who sells. **cellar,** basement.

sense, feeling. **scents,** odors. **cents,** coins.

sent, caused to go. **scent,** odor. **cent,** coin.

serf, a slave. **surf,** breaking waves.

serge, a cloth. **surge,** a billow.

serrate, notched, like a saw. **cerate,** salve.

session, a sitting. **cession,** a yielding.

setaceous, bristly. **cetaceous,** whale species.

sew, to stitch. **sow,** to scatter seed. **so,** in this manner.

sewer, one who uses a needle. **sower,** one who scatters seed.

sewer, a drain. **suer,** one who sues.

shear, to clip. **sheer,** to deviate, pure, see-through.

shoe, covering for foot. **shoo,** begone.

shone, did shine. **shown,** exhibited.

shoo, begone. **shoe,** covering for foot.

shoot, to kill. **chute,** a fall.

shown, exhibited. **shone,** did shine.

side, edge, margin. **sighed,** did sigh.

sigher, one who sighs. **sire,** father.

sighs, deep breathings. **size,** bulk.

sight, view. **site,** position. **cite,** to summon.

signet, a seal. **cygnet,** a swan.

silicious, flinty. **cilicious,** made of hair.

silly, foolish. **Scilly,** name of islands.

single, alone. **cingle,** a girth.

sit, to rest. **cit,** a citizen.

skull, bony framework of the head. **scull,** oar, boat.

slay, to kill. **sley,** weaver's reed. **sleigh,** vehicle.

sleeve, cover for arm. **sleave,** untwisted silk.

slight, neglect, small. **sleight,** artful trick.

sloe, fruit, animal. **slow,** not swift.

soar, to rise high. **sore,** painful.

soared, ascended. **sword,** a weapon.

sold, did sell. **soled,** furnished with soles. **souled,** having a soul or feeling.

sole, part of foot, only. **soul,** spirit of man.

some, a part. **sum,** the whole

son, a male child. **sun,** luminous orb.

sow, to scatter seed. **sew,** to stitch.

sower, one who scatters seed. **sewer,** one who uses a needle.

staid, sober, **stayed,** supported, remained.

stair, step. **stare,** to gaze.

stake, a post, a wager. **steak,** meat.

stare, to gaze. **stair,** step.

stationary, motionless. **stationery,** paper, etc.

steel, metal. **steal,** to thieve.

sticks, pieces of wood. **Styx,** a fabulous river.

stile, stairway. **style,** manner.

straight, not crooked. **strait,** narrow pass.

style, manner. **stile,** stairway.

Styx, a fabulous river, **sticks,** pieces of wood.

subtle, cunning. **suttle,** to carry on business of a sutler.

subtler, more cunning. **sutler,** trader.

succor, aid. **sucker,** a shoot of a plant, slang for a victim.

suer, one who sues. **sewer,** a drain.

suite, train of followers. **sweet,** having a pleasant taste, dear.

sum, the whole. **some,** a part.

sun, luminous orb. **son,** a male child.

surcle, a twig. **circle,** a round figure.

surf, dashing waves. **serf,** a slave.

surge, a billow. **serge,** cloth.

sutler, trader. **subtler,** more cunning.

suttle, to carry on business of a sutler. **subtle,** cunning.

swap, to barter. **swop,** a blow.

symbol, emblem. **cymbal,** musical instrument.

T

tacked, nailed. **tact,** skill.

tacks, small nails. **tax,** a tariff.

tale, story. **tail,** the hinder part.

taper, a wax candle, lessen. **tapir,** an animal.

tare, a weed, allowance. **tear,** to pull to pieces.

taught, instructed. **taut,** tight.

teal, a water fowl, grayish-blue. **teil,** a tree.

team, two or more horses, squad. **teem,** to be full.

tear, moisture from eyes. **tier,** a rank, a row.

tear, to pull to pieces. **tare,** weed, allowance.

teas, different kinds of tea. **tease,** to torment.

tense, rigid, form of a verb. **tents,** canvas houses.

the, adjective. **thee,** thyself.

their, belonging to them. **there,** in that place. **they're,** they are.

threw, did throw. **through,** from end to end.

throne, seat of a king. **thrown,** hurled.

throw, to hurl. **throe,** extreme pain.

thrown, hurled. **throne,** seat of a king.

thyme, a plant. **time,** duration.

tide, stream, current. **tied,** fastened.

tier, a rank, a row. **tear,** moisture from eyes.

timber, wood. **timbre,** crest, quality.

time, duration. **thyme,** a plant.

tire, part of a wheel, weary. **Tyre,** city. **tier,** one who ties.

toad, reptile. **toed,** having toes. **towed,** drawn.

toe, part of foot. **tow,** to drag.

told, related. **tolled,** rang.

tole, to allure. **toll,** a tax.

ton, a weight. **tun,** a large cask.

too, also. **to,** toward. **two,** couple.

tracked, followed. **tract,** region.

tray, shallow vessel. **trey,** three of cards.

tun, a large cask. **ton,** a weight.

two, a couple. **to,** toward. **too,** also.

U

urn, a vase. **earn,** to gain by labor.

use, to employ. **yews,** trees. **ewes,** sheep.

V

vain, proud. **vane,** weathercock. **vein,** blood vessel.

vale, valley. **veil,** to cover, netting.

vane, weathercock. **vein,** blood vessel. **vain,** proud.

Venus, planet. **venous,** relating to the veins.

vial, a bottle. **viol,** violin. **vile,** wicked.

vice, sin. **vise,** a press.

W

wade, to ford. **weighed,** balanced.

wail, to moan. **wale,** a mark. **whale,** a sea animal.

waist, part of the body. **waste,** destruction.

wait, to stay for. **weight,** heaviness.

waive, to relinquish. **wave,** a billow.

wall, a fence. **wawl,** wail, bowl.

wane, to decrease. **wain,** a wagon.

want, desire. **wont,** custom, habit.

ware, merchandise. see **wear.**

wart, hard excrescence. **wort,** beer.

way, road, manner. **whey,** curdled milk. **weigh,** to balance.

weak, not strong. **week,** seven days.

weal, happiness. **wheal,** a pustule. **wheel,** circular body.

wear, to impair by use. **ware,** merchandise.

weasel, an animal. **weazel,** thin, weasen.

ween, to think. **wean,** to alienate.

weigh, to balance. **way,** road. **whey,** of milk.

weighed, balanced. **wade,** to ford.

weight, heaviness. **wait,** to stay for.

wen, a tumor. **when,** at what time.

wether, a ram. **weather,** state of air.

what, that which. **wot,** to know.

wheel, circular body. **wheal,** a pustule.

whey, thin part of milk. **way,** road, manner. **weigh,** to balance.

Whig, name of a party. **wig,** false hair.

whist, a game of cards. **wist,** thought, knew.

whole, all, entire. **hole,** a cavity.

wholly, completely. **holy,** sacred, pure.

wig, false hair. **Whig,** name of a party.

wight, a person. **wite,** blame.

wist, thought, knew. **whist,** a game of cards.

won, gained. **one,** single, unit.

wont, custom, habit. **want,** desire.

wood, substance of trees. **would,** was willing.

wort, beer, herb. **wart,** hard excrescence.

wot, to know. **what,** that which.

wrap, to enclose. **rap,** knock.

wrapped, covered. **rapped,** knocked.

wrapping, a cover. **rapping,** knocking.

wreak, to inflict. **reek,** to emit vapor.

wrest, to twist. **rest,** quiet.

wretch, miserable person. **retch,** to vomit.

wring, to twist. **ring,** a circle, a sound.

write, to form letters. **wright,** workman. **right,** correct.

wrote, did write. **rote,** a memory of words.

wrung, twisted. **rung,** sounded.

wry, crooked. **rye,** a grain.

Y

yew, a tree. **you,** person spoken to. **ewe,** a sheep.

yews, trees. **use,** employ. **ewes,** sheep.

yolk, yellow of egg. **yoke,** collar for oxen.

your, belonging to you. **you're,** you are.

EDDIE'S
VALUABLE PROPERTY

Published by Harcourt Brace Jovanovich, Inc.

PENNY AND PETER.   1946
BETSY AND THE BOYS.   1945
HERE'S A PENNY.   1944
BACK TO SCHOOL WITH BETSY.   1943
PRIMROSE DAY.   1942
BETSY AND BILLY.   1941
TWO AND TWO ARE FOUR.   1940
"B" IS FOR BETSY.   1939

By the Same Author

Published by William Morrow & Company

EDDIE'S
VALUABLE
PROPERTY

written and illustrated by

Carolyn Haywood

71176
William Morrow and Company

New York 1975

Copyright © 1975 by Carolyn Haywood

Printed in the United States of America.

2   3   4   5

Library of Congress Cataloging in Publication Data

Haywood, Carolyn (date)
   Eddie's valuable property.

   SUMMARY: Eddie's dismay at the family's move is relieved by his pleasure in a new friend, a valuable property they share, and a happy school situation.
   [1. Family life—Fiction]   I.   Title.
PZ7.H31496Ek   [Fic]   74-17499
ISBN 0-688-22014-2
ISBN 0-688-32014-7 (lib. bdg.)

Dedicated
to
Constance Carstens Epstein
with love

CONTENTS

Chapter 1

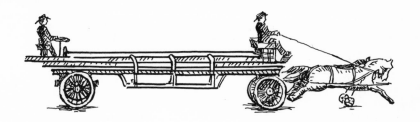

EDDIE'S
VALUABLE PROPERTY

T HE DAY had been just like any other until
Eddie Wilson arrived at the dinner table.
Then, while he was eating his pecan pie—Ed-
die's favorite dessert—Mr. Wilson dropped the
bomb. The news was that Mr. and Mrs. George
Wilson and their four sons were going to move.

II

The move was not to another house in the neighborhood but to another town, a hundred and fifty miles away. Mr. Wilson explained that the company he worked for was transferring him to the headquarters of the firm.

For the first time in Eddie's life he lost interest in pecan pie. No announcement could have shaken him more.

Rudy was the first of the boys to speak. "I guess it's good for you, Dad, but I wonder what it will be like to go into a strange school where I don't know anybody."

Eddie toyed with what was left of his pie and said, "Sure will seem funny without Boodles and the rest of my crowd. I'll miss Tookey, Dumpty, and Annie Pat, and having Sidney right next door."

"Well, remember," said his father, "Mother will have to make new friends, too. We'll all be in the same boat."

The twins, Joe and Frank, looked glum. "Just

as Joe and I made the Little League," said Frank.

"That's too bad," said Mr. Wilson, "but there are Little Leagues all over the country. If you're good enough to be on the Little League here, you should be good enough to get on the Little League anywhere."

"That's what you think, Dad," said Joe.

"Yes," said Frank, "fathers always think their kids can do anything."

"Well," said Eddie, "guess I better start packing up my valuable property." Eddie got up from his chair.

"Just a minute, Eddie," said his father. "I want to make one thing clear right now. We are not taking that pile of junk in the basement with us when we move."

Eddie looked pained. It always hurt him to have what he called his "valuable property" referred to as junk. "You can't really mean it," Dad!" he exclaimed. "All that valuable property! Think how long it's taken me to find all that valuable property. Just the other day I brought home two boxes. I haven't had time to see what's in them, but they look good on the top."

"Well, you needn't empty them, because none of it is going with us. That is settled. You can start thinking about how you are going to get rid of it."

Eddie went to bed that night feeling very depressed. Leaving all of his friends was hard enough, but giving up his collection of valuable property, which filled a large area of the Wilsons' basement, was almost more than he could bear.

The following morning Eddie went to school with a heavy heart. Usually he arrived with shining eyes and a wide grin on his face. In fact, Eddie always blew into the room. His greeting was, "Hi, everybody! What's cookin'?" It was hard to depress Eddie, but today he was depressed and everybody knew it.

"Great snakes, Eddie! What's the matter with you?" Boodles asked.

"What happened?" said Anna Patricia.

"Something awful," Eddie replied. "Just awful. We're going to move."

"Oh, that's nothing at all," said Anna Patricia. "We moved once, and the new house was much nicer."

"You don't understand," said Eddie. "We're going to move away. To another town. One hundred and fifty miles away."

"You mean, you mean," Boodles stammered, "we won't see you anymore?"

"That's it," Eddie replied.

"Sure is bad news," said Tookey, who had arrived in time to hear Eddie's announcement.

"Won't be the same without Eddie," said Dumpty Peterson.

"How do you think I feel?" said Sidney. "I live right next door to Eddie. Probably some sissy girl who doesn't know a good piece of stuff from bad will move in now."

This remark made Eddie feel worse. Although Sidney was a girl, she too collected valuable property. Sidney, however, always called it her "stuff."

Eddie sat down and held his head between his hands. "It's awful!" he said.

"Never mind, Eddie," said Sidney, "I'll come over and help you pack up all your swell stuff."

Eddie groaned. "My father says I can't take my valuable property with me. He says I have to get rid of it."

"Oh," cried Anna Patricia, "you can have a garage sale! I just love garage sales!"

"That's a swell idea," said Boodles. "We'll all help, and you can make some money, Eddie."

Eddie began to feel somewhat better. After all he liked to make money, and he had never had a garage sale. It was just like Annie Pat to think of something he had never done before. He would miss Annie Pat. She always sparked new ideas. Although the future did not look bright, Eddie decided to have as good a time as possible. A garage sale was the answer!

Several days later Mr. Wilson said to Eddie, "You haven't forgotten about that junk in the basement, have you?"

"Oh, no, Dad!" Eddie replied. "I'm going to have a garage sale. Now you'll see that it really is valuable property."

"Great!" said his father. "Have the sale soon, and get the garage cleared out."

At school Eddie's friends kept asking him, "When's the garage sale?"

"Don't push me," said Eddie. "I haven't had time to carry everything out of the basement into the garage yet."

Two days later Eddie announced that the day had come for moving the valuable property. By

four o'clock in the afternoon, Sidney and Anna
Patricia, Boodles and Tookey, Dumpty and
Rodney were all in the Wilsons' basement to
help Eddie.

"Now everything over on this side of the basement is mine," said Eddie, waving his arm
toward a large pile of things of all sizes and
shapes. There were many boxes without lids. "Be
careful," said Eddie, "that nothing falls out."

"Hey, Eddie! What's this?" said Boodles,
opening up a large carton. Boodles looked inside. "Eddie," he cried out, "it's a circus! Look
at these wooden animals!" Boodles lifted an elephant out of the box. He placed it on the floor
and said, "Look! You can make 'em stand up.
Their legs are jointed."

Eddie started to rummage in the box. "I just
got this box," he said. "Look at these clowns!
Oh, they're great!"

"I'll say!" said Anna Patricia. "I'll bet you
could get five dollars for that circus."

Boodles and Dumpty sat down on an old piece of carpet and began to play with the circus.

Tookey, who had been picking things up and putting things down, called out, "Hey, Eddie! What's in the bottom of this box? It's heavy."

"Let's see!" Eddie replied. "I just found that box last week. It was outside of a house around the corner, waiting for the rubbish collection. This old Teddy bear was sticking out of the top, so I brought the whole box along."

"What a cute Teddy bear!" exclaimed Anna Patricia. "It's a big one."

"It's lost an eye!" said Sidney. "If we could just find an eye, we could make it look nice."

Eddie looked over at the girls and said, "Sid, there's a box of buttons on the windowsill. Maybe you'll find something for an eye in it."

By now Tookey had reached the bottom of the box that had contained the Teddy bear. He pulled up an old iron fire engine. It was covered with rust. "Look at this!" he exclaimed.

Eddie took it in his hands. His face was shining. "Isn't that the greatest!" he said. "I could take all that rust off and paint it, and it would look like new."

"And here's another one!" Tookey shouted. "Here's the hook and ladder! Ladders and everything! Even the firemen are here. Awful rusty, but they'd be okay with a coat of paint."

Just then Sidney called out, "I've found a button that will make a perfect eye for that Teddy bear! I'll run home and get a needle and thread. Then I can sew his eye on. I'll be right back."

As Sidney went through the Wilsons' kitchen, she said to Mrs. Wilson, who was putting the kettle on the stove, "I'm just going to get a needle and thread." Sidney ran out the door.

Mrs. Wilson went to the head of the stairs. "Eddie," she called, "why does Sidney need a needle and thread to help you move that pile of junk into the garage?"

"She has to sew an eye onto the Teddy bear," he called back.

Mrs. Wilson shook her head. Eddie's replies were hardly ever what one expected.

Boodles and Dumpty were still playing with the circus. Eddie had found some sandpaper, and he and Rodney and Tookey were busily removing rust from the fire engines. "I have some red paint down here," said Eddie, "and some brushes. When we get this rust off, we can paint these trucks."

"Man, have you got valuable property," said Tookey. "I'll bet you'll get a couple of dollars for each of these fire engines."

Soon Sidney was back with her needle and thread. When she saw what the boys were doing, she said, "I can help with that."

"So can I," said Anna Patricia.

The children worked over the iron toys until their fingers were red with rust. It was beginning to get dark. Soon Mrs. Wilson called down, "It's time for all of you to go home now."

"It won't take me a minute to sew the Teddy bear's eye on," said Sidney.

Boodles looked at the circus animals and clowns and at the iron fire engines. "Eddie," he said, "I can't wait for your garage sale. I'm going to bring plenty of money with me."

"I am too," said Tookey, surveying the fire engines.

"I'm going to buy this Teddy bear," said Sidney.

"I sure hate to sell all this valuable property," said Eddie, "but my father says I can't take it with me."

At last Sidney had the Teddy bear's eye in place, and the children clumped up the stairs. "Thanks for helping me," said Eddie, as he opened the front door for his friends.

"We'll be back," said Boodles.

"Sure!" said Anna Patricia. "We want to help you move everything into the garage."

"It's fun!" said Sidney.

"Really exciting," said Tookey.

"I guess you'll make a lot of money," said Rodney. "So long!"

When Eddie closed the door, he went back to the basement. He opened his can of quick-drying red paint and started to paint the fire engines. He had one finished when his mother called him to dinner.

The family was seated at the table, when Mr. Wilson said, "How are you getting along in the basement, Eddie?"

"Okay!" Eddie replied. "My friends came over this afternoon to help me. We're making progress."

"I'm glad to hear it," said his father. "Be sure you get everything out."

"Yes, sir!" said Eddie.

After dinner Eddie went back to his painting job. By bedtime the fire engines, shining in their new coat of red paint, stood on a table. Eddie had painted the firemen's clothes blue and their buttons gold. He was delighted with every piece but sorrier than ever to part with them. At least, he could look forward to making some money at the garage sale. He might even make a lot.

Eddie's friends came the next two days. At the end of each day the basement had less in it and the garage had more. By Friday Eddie was ready to make the sign. He made a big one. It said, *Garage Sale! The Valuable Property of E. Wilson to Be Sold Saturday at 10 A.M.* He fastened it to the garage door.

Friday evening his father said to Eddie, "You've done a good job, Son, moving all that junk from the basement to the garage."

"I had a lot of help," Eddie replied. "I sure will miss my pals when we move away."

"Let's go into the garage," said his father, "and see how you have set things up."

"Okay!" Eddie agreed.

Eddie followed his father to the garage. He waited while Mr. Wilson unlocked the door. Then he switched on the light. The light fell on the shiny red fire engines. "Eddie!" Mr. Wilson shouted. "Where did you get these fire engines?"

"Oh, I just found them last week. They were in the bottom of a box that somebody put out with the rubbish. This Teddy bear was sticking out of the top of the box, so I lugged it home. You never know what might be in the bottom of a box. When we unpacked it, we found the fire engines. They were all rusty, but we sandpapered 'em and painted 'em."

Mr. Wilson was holding the hook and ladder in his hand. "Why, Eddie," he said, "these are valuable. Your grandfather played with iron toys like these. We'll have to take them into the house."

Next his father's eyes fell upon the circus animals. "Where did you get these circus animals?"

"Picked 'em up someplace," said Eddie. "They were in a box down under some other boxes. Boodles pulled them out the other day. They're nice, aren't they? Maybe I can get a couple of dollars for them."

"A couple of dollars!" his father exclaimed. "They are valuable! Better not leave them here. We'll take them inside."

As Eddie and his father turned to leave the garage, his father picked up the Teddy bear. "Your Aunt Betty had a Teddy bear like this one," he said. "It belonged to our mother. They don't make them like this today. Better take it in the house."

Once inside the house, Mr. Wilson placed the fire engines on a table in the living room. He placed the circus figures on the windowsill and the Teddy bear on a chair. "Eddie," he said, "you don't seem to know the value of things. I have no idea what you have out there in the garage. Those boxes may contain some real antiques. I think we shall have to take them along to the new house. Someday, when I have time, I'll go over everything."

Eddie's mouth fell open in surprise. When he finally found his tongue, he said, "But what about the garage sale, Daddy?"

"Oh, I'll take care of that," his father replied.

"No problem! We'll just bring down all the stuff that your mother has been keeping up in the attic."

Early the following morning Eddie went outside with a brush and some black ink. In a few minutes he had changed the sign. Now it said, *Sale Postponed Until Next Saturday*. He also changed the *E* for Eddie to *G* for George.

Then he rushed to the telephone to tell his friends that his father had changed his mind and that none of his valuable property would be sold. Eddie spent most of the morning explaining to them. They were glad for Eddie but a bit sorry for themselves.

The rest of the day Eddie helped the Wilson family carry things from the attic to the garage. Over and over he heard his mother say to his father, "I really don't want to get rid of this," and Eddie knew how his mother felt.

That evening the real-estate man came to call

on Mr. Wilson to make some final arrangements for the sale of the house. Mr. Wilson brought the man into the living room, where Eddie was reading a book. When the man saw the fire engines, he said, "My, I haven't seen toys like those for many a year."

"Neither have I," said Mr. Wilson.

"They're worth at least a hundred dollars," said the caller. "Antique toys get more valuable every year."

"Yes, I'm sure of that," Eddie's father agreed. "This is my son, Edward," said Mr. Wilson. "He's quite a collector."

"So I see!" said the man, as he shook Eddie's hand.

The man picked up the elephant from the circus. "Really remarkable to have such a collection," he said.

"Show Mr. Brown the Teddy bear," Mr. Wilson said to Eddie. As Eddie handed it to Mr.

Brown, his father said, "It's a very fine old one. Just look at the eyes!"

Mr. Brown looked at the eyes and so did Eddie. The man said, "Remarkable!"

Out loud Eddie said, "Jeepers!" To himself he said, "I sure have a very remarkable father!"

Chapter 2

EDDIE GETS A DOG

A T THE GARAGE SALE, where Eddie's valuable property was not sold and the stuff from the attic was, Eddie received his next piece of news. There he learned that he could have a dog. Life, Eddie realized, was full of surprises. You got up in the morning without a dog, and you went to bed with a dog. Actually the dog had not arrived yet, but it was on its way.

Eddie had not had a dog for a long time. In fact, Eddie had never had a dog very long. He had found a great many of them, because Eddie attracted lost dogs as a magnet draws pins and needles. But they always had dog tags, and their rightful owners soon were located.

From time to time Eddie had asked his father if he could have a dog of his own, but his father was not enthusiastic. "There are always strange dogs around here," his father would say. "If you had a dog, there would be another one."

"Dad, I promise!" said Eddie. "If I could have a dog of my own, I would never bring any other dog into the house."

"Well, we'll see!" his father had said. "Perhaps someday you can have a dog."

Now Eddie was to have a dog. Mr. Brown, the real-estate man, was the one who brought up the subject of the dog. He had just bought Big

Bertha, Mrs. Wilson's old dressmaking form, which had been in the attic ever since the sewing room had been made into a bedroom for Eddie.

Mr. Brown had looked down at Eddie and said, "I say, Eddie!"

Eddie looked up, expecting Mr. Brown to say something about Big Bertha.

Instead he said, "Would you like to have a dog?"

"You bet!" Eddie replied.

"Well, I know a nice dog that needs a good home," said Mr. Brown. "It belongs to a friend of mine who is going to live in a rest home. He can't take the dog with him. It's a young dog, about three years old, and it has a pedigree, too."

"That would be great!" said Eddie. "What kind of dog is it?"

"It's an old English sheepdog," Mr. Brown answered.

"Oh!" said Eddie. Then, although he had never seen an old English sheepdog, he added,

"They're wonderful dogs! I'll go ask my father if I can have it."

Eddie ran off, but before he found his father he met Anna Patricia. "Hi, Annie Pat!" Eddie called out. "You'll never guess! I'm going to get a dog! Isn't that great?"

"Oh, Eddie!" Anna Patricia exclaimed. "What kind is it?"

"It's an old English sheepdog," Eddie replied.

"Why do you want to get an old dog?" Anna Patricia asked.

"It's not an old dog," Eddie replied. "It's a young dog."

"You just said it's an old English sheepdog," said Anna Patricia. "How can it be young if it's old?"

"Don't you understand, Annie Pat? It's a young old English sheepdog," said Eddie. "Its first name is old, its second name is English, and its third name is sheepdog."

"Oh!" said Anna Patricia. "What's its other name?"

"I don't know yet, but I know it has a pedigree," Eddie replied. "I have to find my father now. I have to ask him if I can have the dog."

"I'll come with you," said Anna Patricia. "I think your father is talking to my mother."

Eddie found his father showing a lamp to Anna Patricia's mother. Eddie didn't want to interrupt his father, so he went on talking to Anna Patricia. "Just think, Annie Pat!" he said. "Me with a dog of my own!" Then he added, "Maybe!"

Mr. Wilson overheard Eddie's remark to Anna Patricia. He looked down at Eddie and said, "What's this about a dog?"

"Oh, Dad!" Eddie replied. "Mr. Brown says he can get me a nice dog. It's an old English sheepdog. Not an old one. A young one. It even has a pedigree. Please can I have it, Dad?"

"It's a bad time to get a dog, Eddie," said his father. "We're just about to move. We have to take all your stuff with us, and now you want to take a dog along."

"But this dog is just part of my valuable property," said Eddie. "And I'm getting him for nothing."

"Very well!" said his father. "You can have the dog."

Eddie dashed off to find Mr. Brown. He saw him examining an old rocking chair. "I can have the dog, Mr. Brown," Eddie shouted. "My father says I can have it."

"Good!" said Mr. Brown. "I'll bring him over to you tomorrow night."

Just then Boodles arrived. "Hi, Eddie!" he said. "Thought I'd come over to see how things are going."

"Boodles!" Eddie cried. "I've got a dog!"

"Where is it?" Boodles asked, looking around the garage.

"I'm getting it tomorrow night," Eddie answered. "A man Mr. Brown knows is giving the dog to me."

"That's nifty!" Boodles exclaimed.

Anna Patricia joined Eddie and Boodles. "Eddie's getting an old English sheepdog," she said, "and it has a pedigree!"

"It has a what?" said Boodles.

"A pedigree," said Anna Patricia, as Eddie turned to greet Sidney, who had just appeared.

"What's up?" she asked.

"Eddie's getting an old dog with a pedigree," said Boodles. "It must have something the matter with its feet."

"It is not an old dog, and it does not have anything the matter with its feet. It's a young old English sheepdog with a pedigree," said Eddie.

"That's it!" said Boodles. "Any word that begins with *ped* has something to do with feet. You know, like pedals on a bike. You put your feet on 'em, don't you?"

"You're right!" said Anna Patricia. "My mother always gets a pedicure."

"What's that?" Sidney asked.

"A pedicure is when you get your toenails cut," Anna Patricia answered. "That's a pedicure."

"You mean your mother can't cut her own toenails?" Boodles exclaimed.

"Oh, she could cut her toenails if she wanted to," Anna Patricia replied. "But she likes to have them cut for her. Then she has red polish put on them."

"Can you imagine that?" said Boodles to Sidney. Then he said to Eddie, "Take my advice, Eddie. Don't get a dog with a pedigree. What good is a dog with foot trouble? It's probably the reason why the man wants to get rid of the dog."

Eddie looked troubled, but he said, "Now, Bood! This is an old English sheepdog. Sheepdogs have to run, you know. They run after the sheep."

"Sure!" Boodles agreed. "He's probably run after the sheep so long his feet have given out. You said he was old."

"I did not!" Eddie shouted. "I said he was young."

Anna Patricia chimed in. "He's a young old English sheepdog."

"Oh!" said Boodles. "Well, if he's young, he must have been born with this pedicure thing."

"Pedicure is toenails, Boodles," said Anna Patricia. "You're all mixed up."

"It's pedigree," said Eddie.

"Foot trouble!" Boodles replied, as the group of children broke up. "Too bad, Eddie!" Boodles called back.

Eddie was concerned, but he decided not to say anything to his father. Instead, he would call up Mr. Brown, who had left the sale by now, and ask him about the pedigree. However, when he tried to reach Mr. Brown, there was no answer.

When Eddie went to bed, he could not get to sleep. He kept thinking about the dog. He could see the dog limping around the house. Probably he would have to bandage its feet. Maybe it wouldn't be able to walk to its supper dish or get a drink of water. Eddie pictured himself carrying the supper dish to the dog, who would be lying in front of the open fire, keeping its poor feet warm.

Finally Eddie went to sleep. He dreamed that he was putting red polish on his dog's toenails. The dog turned into a lion and roared, but the noise was just Eddie's father calling to him to get up.

The first thing Eddie thought of was the dog. He decided that he would have to speak to his father about this foot business. By now he couldn't remember whether the old English sheepdog had a pedigree or a pedicure.

Eddie got out of bed and padded over to his father's bathroom. He knew his father was shaving, because he could hear the electric razor. "Dad," Eddie called outside the door, "can I come in?"

"Come in!" his father answered.

Eddie went into the bathroom and sat down on the edge of the tub.

"Why this early-morning call?" his father asked.

"Dad, what kind of foot trouble is pedicure?"

"It isn't any kind of foot trouble," his father replied. "It's just getting your toenails trimmed. Ladies sometimes have pedicures."

"Anna Patricia's mother has them," said Eddie.

Mr. Wilson looked into the mirror over the sink. "Did you come all the way over here to tell me that Anna Patricia's mother has pedicures?" he asked.

"No," Eddie replied. "It's about the pedigree of the dog that Mr. Brown said I could have. What kind of foot trouble is pedigree?"

Mr. Wilson put down his razor. He threw back his head and laughed. He laughed and laughed. He laughed so hard that Eddie began laughing too.

At last Mr. Wilson was able to speak. "Eddie," he said, "when a dog has a pedigree, it means that all of his ancestors are known and that they come from the same breed."

Eddie laughed again. "Wait till I tell Boodles," he said. "He said it was some kind of foot trouble."

"Boodles was a bit mixed up," said his father, as Eddie left the bathroom.

When Eddie reached his own room, he could hear his father laughing. Eddie laughed too. "Wait until Monday when I tell Boodles. Annie

Pat used to be the mixed-up one. Now it's Boo-dles," he said to himself. He would miss Boodles and all his misinformation when they moved away.

That evening Mr. Brown brought the dog to Eddie. Eddie had never seen an old English sheepdog, and he was somewhat surprised when he arrived. The dog was so covered with long hair that it was hard to see what he looked like. Eddie had never seen such a hairy dog. He couldn't see the dog's face at all, because hair hung over his eyes like a thick curtain. Still, Eddie loved him at once. Just as all dogs made friends with Eddie, so this dog showed at once that Eddie seemed to be exactly what he wanted in a master.

"He's a swell dog," said Eddie, "but he sure looks like a hippie with all that hair hanging over his face. He needs a haircut."

"Oh, no!" said Mr. Brown. "You mustn't cut

his hair! It's one of the marks of a pedigreed old English sheepdog."

"What's his name?" Eddie asked, fondling the dog's head.

Mr. Brown laughed. "Well, you said it! It's Hippie!"

"Couldn't be better!" Eddie agreed.

As soon as Mr. Brown left, Eddie read everything in the encyclopedia about old English sheepdogs. When Eddie finally got into bed,

Hippie jumped up and lay down at his feet, and they both went to sleep.

Eddie could hardly wait for school on Monday. First of all he had to tell Boodles that he was wrong about the word *pedigree,* and secondly he wanted to invite his pals over to see Hippie.

When Boodles heard the dog's name, he said, "Why Hippie?"

"You'll see!" Eddie replied. "And he doesn't have foot trouble. He just has a pedigree, which means he has good ancestors."

By four o'clock Sidney, Anna Patricia, Boodles, and Dumpty arrived at Eddie's house. A few minutes later Tookey and Rodney came in. Eddie brought his dog into the sun porch, where the children had gathered. "Here's Hippie!" he said, as the dog flew in.

"Some dog!" said Boodles. "You can hardly tell which is the front of him and which is the back."

"Can he see?" Anna Patricia asked. "I don't

understand how he can see with all that hair over his eyes."

"I'll bet he doesn't know what a dog looks like," said Tookey, " 'cause he's never seen one."

"I guess he just smells 'em," said Dumpty.

"Anyway I know why his name is Hippie," said Rodney. "It's all that hair over his face."

"I read in a book the other night about these old English sheepdogs, and do you know what?" said Eddie.

The children regarded Eddie with great interest. Eddie was always good for a surprise. "These dogs have to be combed and brushed every day, and you'll never guess what you can do with their combings!"

Anna Patricia's mouth was open, waiting to hear.

Eddie continued. "You can have the combings woven into cloth to make a coat," he said.

"You're kidding!" said Sidney.

"It's the truth!" Eddie replied.

"Man! I can't wait to see you in your dog coat, Eddie!" exclaimed Boodles.

"He'll be in college before he gets enough hair out of that dog to make a coat," said Tookey.

"They say they're very warm," said Eddie.

"Well, if you have any left over, could I have some for a skating cap?" Anna Patricia asked.

"Oh, sure!" said Eddie, being generous with Hippie's hair.

At dinner that evening Mr. Wilson said, "What did your friends think of your dog, Eddie?"

"Oh, they thought Hippie was great," Eddie replied, "and I'm going to get a coat made out of Hippie's combings and maybe a skating cap for Annie Pat."

Everyone at the table put down their forks and looked at Eddie in amazement. Rudy was the first to speak. "Eddie and his pals are all crackers!" he said. "Only Eddie would think of getting a coat from his dog!"

"And don't forget the skating cap for Anna Patricia!" said Joe.

Chapter 3

THE NEW HOUSE

Mr. BROWN sold the Wilsons' house, and Eddie's father had to find another one for the family in the new town. It was not easy. Prices were high and houses were scarce, and moreover Mr. Wilson did not have much time to shop around on the days when he went to his company's headquarters.

Once Mrs. Wilson went with him, but at the end of the day she was discouraged. "I can't go again," she said to Eddie's father, "because I am busy getting ready to move. Whatever you find now will be all right with me. We need a roof over our heads. So as long as the house has a roof that doesn't leak, I'll be happy."

Finally, Mr. Wilson came home one day and announced, "I've found a house at last, and I hope you'll like it. It's very different from this one, but it has a good roof."

"Is it right in town?" Eddie asked his father.

"No," his father replied. "It's outside a short distance. It's not a new house, but it's on a nice bit of ground, and it has a barn."

"Oh, it's out in the country!" exclaimed Joe.

"Can we keep some sheep for Hippie?" Eddie asked. "I'll bet Hippie would like some sheep.

What's the use of being an old English sheepdog if you don't have any sheep?"

Before Mr. Wilson could reply to Eddie, Rudy said, "What about a couple of horses, Dad?"

"Look," said his father, "I'm not a gentleman farmer, and I'm not a millionaire."

"You don't have to be rich, Dad, to have sheep," said Eddie. "I'm always reading stories about poor shepherds. Couldn't I be a shepherd? I'd take the sheep up into the mountains, and Hippie and I would tend the flock. That would be super, Dad."

"There are no mountains," his father replied. "The country is very flat, and you will be going to school, not tending a flock of sheep."

"Well, it was a good idea," said Eddie. "I'll bet it's a real nifty house!"

"I'll bring back a photograph of it the next time I go out on business," said Mr. Wilson.

Two weeks later Mr. Wilson produced a

photograph of the new house. He handed it to Mrs. Wilson, and the boys gathered around her.

Eddie was the first to speak. "That's some house!" he said. "I'll bet it has a ghost. Imagine me living in a house with a ghost! Hot dickity! That's better than having sheep!"

"I'll bet it has plenty of cobwebs!" said Eddie's mother.

"Looks as though it's made of gingerbread," said Frank.

"Good!" cried Joe. "We can eat it. Whenever I get hungry, I'll just go out and eat a piece of that trimming on the front porch."

"Does it have plumbing?" Rudy asked. "Or do you have to go to a little house outside?"

"Of course, it has plumbing!" his father replied. "It's a great house! A perfect house in which to bring up four boys."

Eddie's mother was examining the photograph. "It looks as though we could bring up sixteen. What is this tower on the side of the house?"

"Probably where the ghost lives," said Rudy.

Mr. Wilson spoke with enthusiasm. "There's a nice little room right at the top of that tower."

"That's the room I want," said Eddie. "Can that be my room, Dad?"

"I thought you'd like that room," his father replied.

Joe looked at Frank and said, "Wouldn't you know Eddie would get the ghost!"

"He hasn't gotten it yet," Frank replied. "He's just got the room. Anyway I don't believe there is a ghost."

"That's what you think," said Frank. "If Eddie wants a ghost, he'll get a ghost. No kidding."

The following day, when Eddie was eating his lunch in the cafeteria, he said to his friends at the table, "You should see the swell house we're going to live in when we move! My mother says there's room enough to raise sixteen kids."

"Man!" cried Boodles. "Is your mother going to have sixteen kids?"

"No," replied Eddie, "I'm just telling you how big the house is. It's sort of like a castle."

"Nuts!" said Tookey.

"Well, it has a tower!" said Eddie. "And guess what?"

"What?" said Anna Patricia, as the children waited for Eddie's latest news.

"It has a ghost," Eddie replied.

"What kind of ghost?" Sidney asked.

"What do you mean?" said Eddie.

"Well, what kind? Is it one that drags chains or one that moans or one that just flies around?"

"How do I know?" Eddie answered. "I haven't met him yet."

"It's witches that fly around," said Anna Patricia, "not ghosts. They walk, and what makes you so sure it's a him, Eddie? Maybe it's a lady ghost."

"Nuts!" said Tookey.

"Well, anyway," said Sidney, "when you get acquainted with this ghost, will you invite me to come and meet whatever it is? I've always wanted to meet a ghost personally. I hope it's a friendly ghost."

"Oh, you never know," said Boodles. "Trouble is nobody wants to make friends with them. First you have to catch them."

"Nuts!" said Tookey.

"Let me tell you about ghosts," said Boodles. "Some of them are friendly, and some of them are devilish mean. The important thing is to make friends with them."

"Now, Bood!" exclaimed Eddie. "How do you make friends with a ghost?"

"You put out little goodies for him," Boodles replied.

"Like what?" Eddie asked.

"Oh, candy, cinnamon buns, chocolate cake, cookies," Boodles answered. "All those things make good ghost food."

"Nuts!" said Tookey.

"Yes, I guess they like nuts," said Boodles.

"I didn't mean that," said Tookey. "I just mean, *nuts!* Whoever heard of ghost food!"

"It's in the dictionary," said Boodles. "I read about it there. I read the dictionary a lot. That's how I know so much about words."

"If you don't know any more about ghost food than you did about a pedigree, you don't know what you're talking about," said Eddie.

Boodles ignored this remark and went on. "There's ghostwriting too. The President of the United States uses a ghost to write his speeches. He keeps his ghost in a closet, and when he wants to write a speech, he brings him out, and the ghost writes the President's speech."

"That's pretty neat!" said Sidney. "Maybe you

can get your ghost to do your homework for you, Eddie."

"Nuts!" said Tookey. "Ghosts are just fairies. First cousin to the tooth fairy. Remember the tooth fairy? You left your tooth for the fairy, and the fairy left you a dime."

"I don't think you should sneer at the tooth fairy, Tookey," said Anna Patricia, whose father was a dentist. "Anyway fairies are little and ghosts are big."

"Just overfed fairies," said Tookey. "That's what they are." At that moment the bell rang and the lunch period was over.

Moving day for the Wilson family finally arrived. Eddie and his brothers were sent off to school while the moving trucks were loaded. The boys were told to come home as soon as school was out. Mr. Wilson would have the station wagon ready by that time to set off for their new home.

When the bell rang for dismissal, Eddie shook hands with his teacher, Mrs. Andrews. The children crowded around, saying good-bye to Eddie. Then, to Eddie's surprise, Boodles and Rodney, who had left the room, came back carrying a very large parcel. It was wrapped in brown paper and tied with red and white ribbon. "What's that?" Eddie asked.

"It's a going-away present," said Anna Patricia. "It's from the whole class."

"Jeepers!" Eddie exclaimed, while his ears turned bright red with pleasure. "What is it?"

"Open it!" said Sidney. "See if you like it."

Boodles and Rodney put the big parcel down on the floor, and Eddie ripped off the ribbon and the wrapping paper. When he first looked at his present, he didn't know what it was, but he said, "Oh, this is great!" Eddie felt that any present was great no matter what it was. This one appeared to be a wooden box with a roof on it, and when he found that a piece had been cut out of

one end, he realized that he had been given a doghouse.

"It's for Hippie!" said Boodles, in case Eddie didn't realize it.

"Well, it sure is a swell house for Hippie!" said Eddie. "Thanks a million!"

"Boodles and I will carry it home for you," said Rodney.

"Oh, thanks!" said Eddie.

The boys started off carrying the doghouse. Eddie, Anna Patricia, Tookey, and Dumpty, as well as half a dozen other children, trooped along.

When they reached the Wilsons' station wagon, Mr. Wilson was shoving one last carton into the back of the car. The car was bulging with things left behind by the men on the moving trucks.

Before the children reached Mr. Wilson, Eddie called out, "Look at my present, Dad!

See what my friends gave me for a going-away present! It's a doghouse for Hippie!"

"Isn't that nice!" replied Eddie's father, not meaning a word of what he said, because there wasn't room for one more thing in the station wagon.

Evidently all of Eddie's friends were going to stay to see Eddie and the doghouse off. The only space left in the car was the seat where Eddie and his brothers would have to sit with Hippie. Mr. Wilson would share the front seat with Mrs. Wilson, and it could not be shared with a doghouse.

Eddie saw his father's problem. "Maybe Mom could hold it on her lap," Eddie suggested.

"Your mother can't ride for a hundred and fifty miles with a doghouse on her lap," his father replied.

"Maybe Hippie could ride inside the dog-house," Sidney suggested.

"Hippie has to sit beside Eddie," said Rudy,

who was now looking over the situation. "There isn't room for Hippie to lie down."

"Couldn't he sit up inside the doghouse?" Boodles questioned. He proceeded to demonstrate. "If you sit the back wall of the doghouse on the seat, beside Eddie, Hippie's head can stick out of the door of the doghouse."

"I don't think Hippie would like that," said Eddie. "I don't mean he doesn't like his house. I just mean dogs don't usually sit on any wall of their house. They lie down on the floor."

"But this is an unusual situation," said Boodles, to which Eddie and his father agreed.

"I guess you'll have to tie it on top, Dad," said Rudy.

"I believe so," said his father. "There's some clothesline in this car somewhere. I'll see if I can find it."

When the clothesline was finally located, Mr. Wilson set to work tying the doghouse on the roof of the car. Finally it was secured. Mrs. Wilson and the four boys climbed into the station wagon, and with all of Eddie's friends shouting, "Good-bye, Eddie! Good-bye!" the Wilsons were on their way to their new home.

They hadn't gone far when Eddie's father called back to Eddie, "I wish your friends had given you a box of candy as a going-away present. I could have found a place for that."

"Yes, on my lap!" Eddie called back, laughing.

"That doghouse isn't half big enough for Hippie," said Rudy.

"I know," said Eddie, "but I didn't let on to my friends, 'cause it was nice of them to give me a present. We can always get a cute little dog to fit the doghouse."

Everyone in the car laughed, and his mother called back, "Eddie, you are the limit!"

Since the moving vans were not arriving until early the following morning, the family was spending the night at a motel. Now it was growing dark. Mr. Wilson said, "I lost a lot of time over that doghouse. I had hoped to show you our new house in the daylight."

"I can't wait to see it!" said Eddie.

"Well, there's no use going to the house tonight," his father said. "We'll go right to the motel in town."

"Oh, we want to see the house!" exclaimed the four boys in a chorus.

"It's not only dark, it's beginning to rain," their father replied.

"What's a little rain!" said Eddie. "Can't we just have a peek?"

"Let's see it," said Mrs. Wilson.

"Very well," said Mr. Wilson, as the windshield wipers flew back and forth.

Soon the storm increased. The rain now blew in great gusts, whipping against the side of the car. Passing cars threw great torrents of rainwater onto the windshield. By the time the Wilsons reached the entrance to their new home, the

driveway was a rushing stream of muddy water.
The car stopped, and everyone stepped out into
what seemed to be a lake surrounding the house.

"The place has a moat!" said Rudy.

"Didn't I say it was a castle?" said Eddie.

"Some castle!" said Frank.

As Eddie stepped up to the porch, he said to
his father, "Why do you call this a new house,
Dad? It looks pretty old to me."

Eddie's brother Joe spoke up. "It's an old new

house, Eddie, just the way Hippie is a young old English sheepdog."

Mr. Wilson unlocked the door. An especially strong gust of wind blew in. It was followed by a terrible bang. Then there was a rumble. It sounded like a large ball rolling toward tenpins. Hippie howled.

"Eddie's right!" said Joe. "The place is haunted."

"Don't be ridiculous!" said his father, in the pitch-darkness. "I can't find the light. Where's the light switch?"

"Are you sure there is one?" Mrs. Wilson asked. "Perhaps we should have brought candles. I'm not going in until you find out what made that terrible bang. I might fall over something."

"There's a flashlight in the car," said Mr. Wilson. "Somebody get it."

Eddie ran back to the car for the flashlight. Hippie went on howling. In a moment Eddie was back. He handed the flashlight to his father, and with it Mr. Wilson was able to find the switch.

As soon as the light flooded the hall, the whole family looked on the floor to see what had made the terrible noise. They saw nothing but an empty hall with a marred floor. Mr. Wilson then turned on the light in the room next to the hall. There on the floor lay a large mahogany ball.

"Oh!" said Mr. Wilson, picking it up. "This belongs on the post at the end of the stair railing. I knew it was loose."

Mrs. Wilson looked around. "I bet there are a lot of things loose in this house," she said. "In fact, I don't believe there is much that isn't loose."

Hippie wouldn't come into the room. He stood in the hall, howling. "What's the matter with that dog?" asked Mrs. Wilson.

"Maybe he sees something!" said Eddie. "I'll bet he sees something."

"What could he see?" Rudy asked. "It's just an empty house."

"Oh, dogs see things people can't see," said Eddie.

"Has anyone thought to feed him?" Mrs. Wilson asked.

"He's Eddie's dog," said Frank.

"Eddie, did you feed him?" Joe asked.

"I thought Mom fed him," Eddie replied. "What do you think he sees?"

"I don't think he sees anything," his mother replied. "I think he's just hungry."

"Oh!" said Eddie, coming out of his dream world. "I'll get him something." Eddie ran back to the car to get the dog food and Hippie's bowl. As soon as Hippie saw his bowl he calmed down. Eddie opened the can of food and poured its contents into the bowl. Hippie ate ravenously.

"I guess Hippie didn't see anything after all," said Eddie. "He was just hungry."

"We'll all feel better when we've had something to eat," said Mr. Wilson, putting his arm around Mrs. Wilson. "I think you'll like the house more in the morning."

"I'm sure it will look nicer when the furniture arrives," Eddie's mother replied, "but do get that ball glued onto the post. I don't want it to fall off every time someone opens the front door."

"Sure was spooky!" said Eddie.

When the family was back in the car, Eddie told them, "Boodles says that the President of the United States has a ghost that writes his speeches for him. He says the President keeps his ghost in a closet, and when he wants a speech, he takes the ghost out of the closet and the ghost sits down and writes his speech."

"That's ridiculous!" exclaimed Rudy. "All important persons in politics have people who help them write speeches. They're called 'ghostwriters,' because nobody knows who they are.

They're just people, and ghostwriting is their job. Isn't that right, Dad?"

"Quite right," Mr. Wilson replied.

"Imagine that!" said Eddie. "I'll have to write and tell Boodles. He sure gets mixed up with his dictionary! By the way, Dad, is it too late to stop and buy some ghost food?"

"Ghost food!" exclaimed the twins together. "What's that?"

"It's bait to catch a ghost," Eddie replied.

"Now it's ghost food!" said Rudy. "Eddie, I hope the new friends that you make here won't be as wacky as the ones you've left behind."

"Why, they're great kids! They're full of information," cried Eddie. Then he asked his father again, "Is it too late to stop, Dad?"

"Wilson food is all that I'm stopping for," his father replied. "Just food for the Wilsons!"

Chapter 4

JIMMIE
AND THE INDIAN

EARLY Saturday morning the Wilson family drove back to their new home. The storm had passed in the night, and the sun was shining. On the way to the house Eddie's father showed the boys the school they would be attending.

"That's where you will go on Monday," he said. "I've already registered you."

"I hope they have a hockey team," said Rudy.

"A good cafeteria is what I'm hoping for," said Eddie.

"Some ballplayers for me," said Joe.

"Good teachers is all that I want!" said their mother.

When they reached the house, the driveway was still muddy but the house was no longer surrounded by water. "The moat's gone," said Rudy. "We won't need a drawbridge after all."

As soon as Eddie jumped out of the car, he said, "I want to see what the barn looks like," and, with Hippie at his heels, he took off.

Eddie and Hippie flew to the barn, but Hippie flew farther for he had caught sight of a rabbit. Eddie paid no attention and tried the door of the barn, which was unlocked. He pushed it, and it slid open enough for him to step inside. Com-

ing from the bright sunlight into the gloom of
the barn, Eddie's eyes could see nothing. Rubbing his eyes, he stepped forward, and suddenly
two arms grabbed him. Eddie struggled and
freed himself. Now he could see his attacker. He
was a boy about the same size as Eddie.

"Hey, what's the idea?" said Eddie.

"Get out!" said the boy, and he pushed Eddie
back through the barn door.

"What's the matter with you?" said Eddie. "Don't you know this is our barn?"

"It is?" said the boy. "Well, there's an Indian in there."

"What do you mean?" Eddie asked.

"I mean an Indian," the boy replied. "I come to see him every day. This used to be real Indian country in the old days. You'll let me come and see him, won't you?"

Eddie was startled. "You mean he's a real live Indian!" Eddie exclaimed, his eyes wide.

"He's a dead Indian," the boy answered. "He's lying in a box. Part of the box is covered with boards, but you can see his head and his chest. I've never touched him, but he has his feathers and everything."

"Show me where he is," said Eddie. "I want to see him."

"Okay!" said the boy. "My name's James. James Jarvis. They call me Jimmie."

"I'm Eddie. Where's the Indian?"

"Up in the loft," Jimmie replied. "You have to climb up the ladder. I'm ten," he called back.

"Me too," Eddie replied, as he stuck his head into the loft.

Jimmie led the way to a large wooden box. The box was covered with what appeared to be an old faded curtain, covered with barn dust. "I keep him covered," said Jimmie, "so he doesn't get dirty."

"Is he a mummy?" Eddie asked.

"No!" Jimmie replied. "He must have been a daddy not a mummy."

Eddie decided he would clear up this misunderstanding later. First, he was eager to see the Indian.

There was very little light in the loft. What there was came in through a small window and cast a single shaft over the covering of the box. With a flourish and a cloud of dust, Jimmie pulled back the cover, and Eddie looked into the

box. Sure enough, there was an Indian. Eddie had been holding his breath. Now he let it out in a long whistle. "Wow!" he said.

Eddie put out his hand, and Jimmie cried, "Don't touch him!"

"I'm not afraid to touch him," said Eddie.

"Well, just touch his feathers," said Jimmie.

Eddie put out his finger. He touched one of the feathers. "It's hard!" he said. "That's peculiar. Feathers are always soft. These are hard feathers."

"Maybe they're frozen," said Jimmie.

"How could they be frozen?" said Eddie. "It isn't even cold around here. I bet he's hard all over."

"You think so?" Jimmie asked.

"I'm going to touch his face," said Eddie.

"Oh," cried Jimmie, "I wouldn't if I were you."

"I'm not afraid of this Indian!" said Eddie. "I'm going to touch him."

Jimmie stood by, his eyes big with wonder, as he watched Eddie place his finger on the Indian's cheek. "Hard!" said Eddie.

"I always wanted to see what the rest of him looks like," said Jimmie, "but I could never lift these boards off the box."

"Well, come on!" said Eddie. "We can lift them together."

In another cloud of dust, Jimmie pulled the old curtain onto the floor. As the dust settled, Eddie and his newfound friend lifted the boards and placed them against the wall.

At last the Indian lay completely revealed. He was wrapped in a dark blanket that Eddie thought must be red in the daylight. He soon found that it too was hard.

Jimmie peered down at the Indian. "He's got something in his hand. Look, Eddie! He's holding something in his hand."

Eddie leaned close and looked at the Indian's

right hand. "Well, what do you know!" he said, straightening up.

"What is it?" Jimmie questioned.

"It's a bunch of cigars!" Eddie replied.

"What's he doing with a bunch of cigars?" Jimmie exclaimed.

"You know what?" said Eddie.

"What?" Jimmie asked.

"This Indian's made of wood," Eddie replied.

"Well, what's he doing with the cigars?" Jimmie repeated.

"Sit down, and I'll tell you," Eddie replied. The boys sat down beside the Indian.

"It's like this. I saw one in a museum once," Eddie began. "A long time ago, I guess when my grandfather was a little boy, cigar stores used to have wooden Indians, just like this one, standing outside the store. They stood right beside the door."

"What for?" Jimmie asked.

"To show everybody that it was a cigar store," said Eddie.

"But why an Indian!" said Jimmie.

"It's this way," Eddie replied. "We studied about tobacco in school last year. The people who came to settle in this country didn't know about tobacco, but they found the Indians were growing it and learned how to use it from them. That's why the wooden Indians were put in front of cigar stores."

"Well, what's this Indian doing here?" asked Jimmie. "This isn't a cigar store."

"Maybe, a long time ago, the man who owned this barn had a cigar store in town, and maybe he ordered this Indian and something happened before he got the Indian to the store. Maybe the man died."

"Could be!" Jimmie agreed.

"Look, Jimmie," said Eddie, taking charge of the situation, "does anybody know about this Indian?"

"I never told a single soul," Jimmie replied. "It was my secret."

"Well, now it's our secret," said Eddie. Then Eddie sat, thinking, with his head in his hands.

Finally Jimmie said, "You asleep, Eddie?"

"No, I'm just thinking," Eddie replied. "Now that my father owns this barn and this house and everything, 'course this Indian belongs to us."

"I guess it does," said Jimmie, with a deep sigh.

"Oh, you can come and see him anytime," said Eddie.

"Thanks," said Jimmie. "You gonna leave him here?"

"I've been thinking," said Eddie. "Where do you go to school, Jimmie?"

"I go to that big school over there," Jimmie replied, pointing out the window.

"That big red brick one?" Eddie asked.

"That's it," said Jimmie. "It's the only one around here."

"I'm going to that school," said Eddie. "What grade are you in?"

"Fifth!" said Jimmie. "Mr. Jeffrey's the teacher."

"That's great!" Eddie exclaimed. "My father told me I'm going to be in Mr. Jeffrey's room too."

Jimmie grinned and hugged his legs. "I'm glad," he said.

Eddie was quiet again as he thought some more.

After a while Jimmie said, "You asleep, Eddie?"

"No," Eddie replied, "I was just thinking. In the school I used to go to the kids brought things to school to show the class and talk about."

"We do that, too," said Jimmie.

"Well, I've been thinking," said Eddie. "How about helping me to take this Indian to school on Monday?"

Jimmie looked ready to burst with joy. "Oh,

Eddie!" he said. "Would you really let me?"

"Sure!" Eddie replied. "Just think what a swell story it will be to tell!"

Then it was Jimmie's turn to think. In a minute he said, "If we take it to school, it won't be our secret anymore."

"That's right," said Eddie, "but sometimes you have to decide which you like best, a secret or a surprise. Just think how we'll surprise everybody!"

"Okay," said Jimmie, "but how are we going to get him to school?"

"I don't know yet," said Eddie. "My dad always says, 'First things first.' So first we have to get him out of this box."

"I guess he's pretty heavy," said Jimmie, "but maybe if you take him by his feathers and I take him by his feet, we can lift him out."

"Let's see!" said Eddie, getting on his feet again.

The boys reached into the box, Eddie at the

head and Jimmie at the feet. They both took hold of the figure and heaved. Up came the Indian. "He's not so heavy, Jimmie," said Eddie.

"No," Jimmie agreed. "Where shall we put him?"

"Let's stand him against the wall," said Eddie. "We have to think how we can get him down the ladder. If we had a rope, we could tie it around his neck and drop him down." Eddie started to look for some rope.

Soon he found a long, heavy piece of rope. "This will be good," he said.

Together the boys tied the rope around the Indian's neck and feathers. "Now," said Eddie, "Jimmie, you get on the ladder and support his legs, and I'll play out the rope. We mustn't let him go down too fast."

"You be careful, Eddie, that he doesn't pull you along with him," said Jimmie.

"Don't worry," Eddie replied. "I'll brace myself against this post."

"Okay! I'll start down the ladder," said Jimmie.

"Tell me when to start letting the rope out," Eddie called out, as Jimmie's head disappeared.

In a moment, Jimmie called out, "Okay! Let it come."

Eddie moved the Indian to the edge of the loft. He could see Jimmie's hands take hold of the feet. "Push it out," said Jimmie. Eddie pushed, and suddenly he heard Jimmie call out, "We can't do it, Eddie. He won't bend."

"Well, I can't just drop him over. He might break," said Eddie. "Run and see if one of the moving men at the house will come and help us."

Jimmie ran off and Eddie waited. Jimmie seemed to be gone a long time, but finally Eddie heard his voice. "It's an Indian!" he was saying. "We're trying to get him down out of the loft."

Eddie looked down and saw Jimmie and two big men enter the barn. "It's up here," Eddie called out.

The two men mounted the ladder. When they saw the figure, one of the men said to the other, "Well, this is an old boy!"

"Sure is!" replied the other man. "Must have been here a long time."

The men didn't need long to get the "old boy" down to the floor of the barn. "Where do you want it?" one of them asked.

"I guess we better leave it standing beside the ladder," said Eddie. "I don't think my mother would want it in the house."

"Considering all that we've taken into the house today," said the other man, "I don't believe she would want an Indian."

The men went off to their trucks and drove away. "That was lucky!" said Jimmie. "I just caught those men before they left for lunch."

Eddie looked at Jimmie and said, "I'll call you up as soon as I know how we're going to take this Indian to school."

"Mr. Jeffrey sure will be pleased to see that Indian!" said Jimmie. "He likes to have things brought to school, but nobody ever brought anything so big."

"I'll call you!" said Eddie.

"Okay!" Jimmie replied. "I have to go home and get my lunch now."

"So long!" Eddie called. "Sure am glad you're in my room in school!"

Eddie ran into the house. Everyone was in the kitchen, where Eddie's mother was fixing some lunch. When she saw Eddie, she said, "Where have you been all morning?"

"Oh, have I got news," Eddie said, "and have I got valuable property."

"Come on!" said Rudy. "What is it, and where did you find it?"

"In the barn," said Eddie. "It's an Indian!"

"Don't kid us!" said Joe.

"Well, I found Jimmie first," said Eddie, "and

he showed me where the Indian was. Jimmie's been coming to see him every day."

"First it's ghosts!" said Frank. "Now it's an Indian!"

"Come on out, and I'll show you," said Eddie. The boys followed Eddie to the barn. On the way Eddie said, "Jimmie and I are going to take it to school on Monday. We'll tell all about it."

When Eddie's brothers saw the Indian, they could hardly believe their eyes.

"Jimmie and I haven't figured out yet how we're going to get it to school," said Eddie.

Joe looked at Frank and said, "Wouldn't you guess! Eddie goes to a new school, he doesn't know anybody, and the very first day he walks in with a life-size wooden Indian."

"Everybody will know him after that," said Rudy.

"I do so know somebody," said Eddie. "I know Jimmie. He's my best friend."

Chapter 5

A LOST DOG

EDDIE had been so absorbed with his thoughts about the Indian that he had forgotten all about his dog. When he and his brothers returned to the house from the barn, however, Eddie looked around and said, "Where's Hippie?"

"I haven't seen him all morning," said his

mother. "He went off with you when you went to the barn."

"Well, he didn't go into the barn with me," said Eddie. "I thought he came back to the house."

"He must be outside somewhere," said Rudy.

Eddie went outside and called, "Hippie!" Then he yelled, "Hippie!" He made a mega-phone with his hands. "Hippie!" he called. The dog did not appear.

Mrs. Wilson called Eddie to come into lunch, but he kept right on calling Hippie. Finally his mother said, "Eddie, if you don't come to lunch right now, there won't be any for you."

Eddie came in. His forehead was wrinkled, for Eddie was worried about his dog. "I'm afraid he's lost," he said to the family.

"Don't worry," said Rudy. "He has a collar with his dog tag."

This remark caused Eddie to jump up from his chair. "Oh," he cried, "oh, what shall I do?

His dog tag has our old address on it! A hundred and fifty miles away! Nobody will know that he lives here."

Mrs. Wilson reached out and put her arm around Eddie. "Now don't get upset," she said. "You'll find him. He can't be far away. Come eat your soup and sandwich. The soup is getting cold."

Eddie sat down again and began to eat his lunch. He also went right on talking. "Dad, Dad," he said, "what shall we do about Hippie?"

"As soon as we finish our lunch, we can call up the S.P.C.A.," said his father. "If they don't know anything, we'll call up the dog pound."

"You don't think a car hit him, do you, Dad?" asked Eddie.

"He's quite spry!" his father replied. "He can take care of himself."

As soon as the family had finished their lunch, Eddie rushed for the telephone directory. "Here, Dad!" he said. "Call the S.P.C.A."

"Oh!" his father exclaimed. "I just remembered. The telephone hasn't been connected."

"What am I going to do!" cried Eddie.

"Come," said his father, "I'll look up the address of the S.P.C.A., and we'll drive there and see if they know anything about the dog."

"And to the dog pound, too," said Eddie.

Soon Eddie and his father were off, but they were not successful at either the S.P.C.A. or the dog pound. "Haven't seen an old English sheepdog for a long time," said the woman at the S.P.C.A.

"I'll let you know if one comes in," said the man at the pound. "Just leave your name and address."

When Eddie and his father got back to the car, Eddie said, "Now what, Dad?"

"Let's drive around. Maybe we'll see him," his father replied.

They started off, up one street and down another. They stopped and spoke to several traffic officers, but they had not seen an old English sheepdog. "I wouldn't know one if I saw one," said one of the men. "What do they look like?"

"They have a lot of hair," Eddie replied. "It hangs down over their faces. Sort of a long bang. That means it's a very good dog."

"Okay!" said the officer. "If I see one with hair all over his face, I'll let you know."

Finally Mr. Wilson and Eddie left the streets of the town and headed back to their own neighborhood. When they passed a yard where Jimmie was playing on a swing, Eddie called to him, "Hey, Jimmie! Have you seen my dog?"

Jimmie came running to the car. "Hi, Eddie!" he answered. "Did you lose your dog?"

"Dad," said Eddie, "this is Jimmie Jarvis, my friend."

"Hello, Jimmie!" said Mr. Wilson. "I'm glad to see you."

"I'm sorry your dog's lost," said Jimmie. "That's too bad."

"Do you want to come with us?" Mr. Wilson asked. "Maybe you can help us find him."

"Sure!" Jimmie replied, and he climbed in beside Eddie.

Mr. Wilson drove around for some time, but there was no sign of Hippie. Finally Eddie's father said, "I'll have to give up the search for the time being, because I have to get back and see the painter."

"Oh, Dad!" Eddie exclaimed. "What am I going to do?"

"Why don't you ride around on your bike?" said his father. "Perhaps you'll find him without me."

This suggestion did not cheer Eddie. "I don't know my way around here yet," he said.

"I'll get my bike and come with you, if you like," said Jimmie.

"Oh, thanks!" Eddie replied. "That would be a big help."

"That's good of you, Jimmie," said Mr. Wilson. "I'll drop you off at your place, and you can get your bike. Then I'll take Eddie home to pick up his."

When Jimmie got out of the car, he said, "I'll wait here for you, Eddie. You sure you know how to get back here?"

"Oh, yes!" Eddie replied. "I'll be right back."

Eddie was not long returning to Jimmie's. He found Jimmie riding in circles in the driveway of the house. "Hi!" Jimmie called out, when he saw Eddie. "Let's go in the opposite direction from where we were this morning."

"That's a good idea!" said Eddie.

"It will take us out where there are not so many houses," said Jimmie.

"You mean more like the country?" Eddie asked.

"That's right," Jimmie replied. "Where people raise corn and tomatoes. Hippie may have gone a long way. He may have been walking back to the place where you lived before. Animals do that sometimes."

"I sure hope he doesn't," said Eddie. "We can't ride these bikes for a hundred and fifty miles."

"Oh, we'll find him," said Jimmie. "He couldn't go too far just in one morning."

The boys started off with Jimmie leading the way. Soon they reached open country. Stone walls separated fields that had been planted and were already showing some green. Small farmhouses sat back from the road. Occasionally a car passed the bicyclers, but apart from the low whirr of the wheels under them Eddie heard few sounds. Suddenly he called out, "Jimmie, did you hear that dog?"

Jimmie braked his wheels and listened.

"There he goes again!" said Eddie. "That sounds like Hippie!"

"I bet that dog is at Roland's place," said Jimmie.

"Who's he?" Eddie asked.

"Roland's in our class in school," Jimmie replied. "If we go up this next road, you'll see the house."

The boys turned up the next road. Soon they could see a small farmhouse, set back from the road, behind a wooden fence. Then Eddie spotted the dog. To his horror, the dog was tied to a tree. "That's Hippie!" Eddie cried, as he hopped off his bicycle. "We've found him, Jimmie!"

Eddie leaned his bicycle against the fence. When he opened the gate, the dog began to bark wildly. Eddie ran to him, "Hi, Hippie!" he called, as the dog responded with happy cries. Eddie patted him. "It's all right, Hippie!" he said. "Everything is all right."

Things did not seem all right, however, when

Eddie went to the front door of the house. The door was closed. Eddie pushed the button for the doorbell. He waited. There was no reply. He knocked with his fist on the door. The door remained closed. Then Jimmie called out, "Hey, Roland! Roland!"

In a few moments the door was opened but only a crack. A boy's face appeared. "What do you want?" he asked.

"Hi, Roland!" said Jimmie. "This is Eddie Wilson."

"Well, what do you want?" said Roland.

"I see you found my dog, Hippie," said Eddie. "Why did you tie him up? Dogs don't like to be tied up."

"My father tied him up, so he wouldn't run away," said Roland. "You want him to run away?"

" 'Course not!" Eddie replied.

"Then you have to tie him up," said Roland.

"Well, I can take him now," said Eddie.

"You say he's your dog," said Roland, "but how do I know he's your dog?"

"He has a collar with a dog tag," said Eddie.

The door was still open only a crack. Eddie put his foot in the crack. "You can't come in," said Roland. "My father's gone to work, and I can't let anybody in."

"Is your mother in?" Eddie asked.

"I just have a father," said Roland. "I told you he's not here."

"But I'm just Eddie Wilson," said Eddie, "and all I want is my dog."

"Yes," said Jimmie, "he just wants his dog."

Roland ignored Jimmie. "Where do you live?" he asked Eddie.

"We live in that house over on West Street. You know, that funny-looking house with a tower. It has a lot of gingerbread trimming."

"You're making that up," said Roland. "Who ever heard of a house made of gingerbread."

"I didn't mean it's real gingerbread," said Eddie. "It just has that kind of trimming."

"Where did you say it is?" Roland asked.

"On West Street," Eddie replied.

"Well, that isn't where this dog lives," said Roland. "That's not what it says on his dog tag."

"I know that, Roland," said Eddie, "but, you see, we just moved from the address that's on the dog tag. That's where we used to live."

"Well, I can't let you have the dog, because you don't live where the dog tag says," Roland insisted.

"If you look at that dog tag," said Eddie, "you'll see that it has E. Wilson on it, and that's me. I'm Eddie Wilson. Jimmie just told you."

"You don't live in the right place," said Roland.

Eddie realized that he was not convincing Roland, so he changed the subject. "Did you feed Hippie?" he asked.

"What makes you think I don't know how to feed a dog?" said Roland.

"I didn't say you didn't know how to feed a dog," said Eddie. "I just asked you if you fed him. I thought maybe you didn't have any dog food."

"What makes you think my father can't afford to buy dog food?" said Roland.

Eddie was beginning to get tired of this conversation. It didn't seem to be getting anywhere. In fact, it was getting worse with every word. Eddie took his foot out of the doorway, and Roland closed the door with a bang.

Eddie turned away. He was discouraged. He walked over to Hippie and patted him. Hippie responded with plaintive cries. Eddie's heart was wrung. He felt that he could not walk away and leave Hippie tied to that tree. "Jimmie," said Eddie, "I'm going to untie him and take him."

"Sure," said Jimmie, "he's your dog."

Eddie set to work on the knot that was fastened to the dog's collar. It was as hard as a stone. After several minutes Eddie said, "I can't untie this knot."

"Maybe you can untie the one around the tree," Jimmie suggested.

Eddie turned his attention to the knot on the other end of the rope while Jimmie tried working on the one tied to the dog's collar.

Just then the door of the house opened, and Roland called out, "I see what you're trying to do! You can't untie that dog. What makes you think my father doesn't know how to tie good knots?"

Eddie made no reply, but he said to Jimmie, "It's no use trying to untie these knots. I've tried my best, and my fingers are all sore."

As Eddie and Jimmie were walking back to their bicycles, Eddie said, "That kid's as prickly as a hedgehog! Every time you say something to him he comes back with something you didn't mean at all."

"I know!" said Jimmie. "That's Roland! He's somethin'! He does the same thing in school. Somebody's always stepping on his toes. I don't mean his real toes; I mean the toes in his head."

"I know what you mean, Jimmie," said Eddie.

Just as Eddie was climbing back on his bicycle, the door of the little farmhouse opened again, and Roland yelled out, "I'll ask my father when he comes home."

This parting shout from Roland made Eddie feel just a mite better as he pedaled back home. When he came into the house, he told his mother about his conversation with Roland. "The only good thing he said, Mom, was he'd ask his father when he gets home."

"Well, stop worrying about it," said his mother. "Nothing can be done about it now. Your father is busy with the painter."

Late in the afternoon Jimmie arrived at Eddie's house. The first thing he said to Eddie was, "Hear anything about your dog?"

"Nope!" Eddie replied.

"Well, let's go to the barn and look at the Indian," said Jimmie.

"All right. If you want to," Eddie replied.

The two boys ran to the barn. They opened the barn door and went inside. Just as they reached the Indian, Jimmie heard a car stop. He ran to the barn door. Then he called to Eddie. "Hey, Eddie! Look!"

Eddie came to the door and looked. There, coming toward the barn, was Roland with Hippie on a leash. Hippie was pulling on the leash and making happy noises. Roland could hardly hold the dog in.

"I saw you running to the barn," said Roland. "My father brought us over in his pickup truck."

"Oh, thanks, Roland!" said Eddie. "Thanks for bringing him back."

"Hi, Roland!" said Jimmie. "Come see the Indian that's here in the barn." Jimmie led Roland inside the barn. Eddie followed with Hippie. Roland looked at the Indian with amazement. "Where did you ever get a thing like that?" he said. "It's enough to scare the liver out of you."

There wasn't much light in the barn, but as Eddie petted Hippie he felt that there was something different about his dog. When Roland turned away from examining the Indian, he said to Eddie, "Your poor dog couldn't see with all that hair over his eyes. You should take better care of your dog. I cut his bang for you."

"Oh!" Eddie gasped. "I thought there was something different about him."

"I gotta go now," said Roland. "My father's waiting for me."

Eddie and Jimmie went outside with Roland. They found Eddie's father, by the truck, talking to Roland's father. "This is my son, Eddie," said Mr. Wilson to Roland's father, Mr. Smoot, "and I guess you know Jimmie."

"Don't believe I do," Mr. Smoot replied. "My boy doesn't seem to have very many friends, but we've only been in this town a year."

Eddie thought of all the friends he had left behind and how in one day he had found a new friend in Jimmie. Suddenly Eddie felt sorry for Roland. "Say, Roland," he said impulsively, "how about helping Jimmie and me take the Indian to school on Monday?"

"What makes you think I'd do a thing like that?" said Roland.

"Oh, come on, Roland!" said Eddie. "Jimmie and I want to tell the class about the Indian."

"What makes you think the bus driver will let you take it on the bus?" Roland asked.

"We can try," said Eddie.

"Not me. I'll *be* on the bus," said Roland. "I get on at the first stop."

"Well, can't you get off and help us?" Eddie asked.

"I'll think about it," said Roland. "But I'm not promising."

As soon as Roland and his father drove away, Eddie led Jimmie and Hippie into the house. Eddie fell on his knees in front of Hippie. "My gosh," said Eddie, "look what Roland did to my dog! He's ruined him! My pedigree dog!"

"What's the matter with him?" Jimmie asked.

"He's cut Hippie's hair," said Eddie. "He's cut his bang."

"Well, hair grows," said Jimmie. "It will grow again."

Eddie put his arms around his dog. "Oh, he looks awful! He looks so embarrassed!"

"Maybe he likes to see out," Jimmie suggested.

"It's supposed to be very bad for their eyes," said Eddie. "I read all about it in my dog book."

"Maybe you could get him some dark glasses," said Jimmie. "You know, those great big ones."

"Who ever heard of dog glasses!" Eddie exclaimed.

"Well, *you* think of something," said Jimmie.

Eddie sat observing the strange appearance of his dog. Finally he said, "I'll have to make a bang. Sort of a wig. No, more like a veil."

"What you gonna make it out of, Eddie?" Jimmie asked with great interest.

"Maybe I could use some of my mother's floor

mop," said Eddie. "It's the same color as Hippie's hair."

Eddie ran to the foot of the stairs and called up to his mother, who was taking a nap, "Mom, can I have a little bit of your floor mop?"

"All right!" his mother called back. All she had heard were the words *floor mop*.

Eddie soon located the floor mop. He cut off enough to cover Hippie's face. "Now I'll have to sew these pieces to a bit of tape," he said.

In his mother's sewing table, he found some tape. It was bright red, having been left over from Christmas. He also found scissors and a needle and thread.

Jimmie was fascinated as he watched Eddie at work. After some time and trouble, Eddie held up the finished product. "Now," he said, "we'll try it on."

Hippie was quite cooperative as Eddie tied the red tape across his head and back of his ears. Then Eddie surveyed the results. "It looks good," he said. "That old mop's just right. It looks exactly like Hippie's hair."

Jimmie looked at Eddie with admiration. "Eddie," he said, "I sure am glad you've come to live here. You have great ideas."

Hippie wasn't able to say whether they were great or not. He padded over to the corner and went to sleep. When Eddie's mother saw Hippie's new hairdo, she said, "I hope you have enough money to buy me a new mop, because that is exactly what you must do."

"Okay, Mom," said Eddie, "it's worth it. That old mop was perfect for Hippie, and it doesn't have any fleas."

Chapter 6

WHAT EDDIE TOOK
TO SCHOOL

E ARLY Monday morning Jimmie arrived at
Eddie's house. Eddie and his brothers, Joe
and Frank, were at breakfast in the kitchen. "I
came to help you with the Indian," said Jimmie
to Eddie. "How are we going to get it to the bus
stop?"

"Not with my help," said Joe, who was pouring milk on his cereal.

"Nor with mine," said Frank. "Rudy had the right idea. He went to school on his bike."

Eddie paid no attention to his brothers. He popped his last bite of toast into his mouth and got up from the table. "Come along, Jimmie," he said. "We can get the Indian to the bus stop without any help."

Jimmie followed Eddie to the barn. Eddie opened the barn door, and the boys went inside. The Indian was by the ladder, where the men had left it.

"You think we can carry him, don't you, Eddie?" asked Jimmie.

"Oh, sure, sure!" said Eddie. "Now when I push him over, you take hold of his head. We'll lay him on the floor."

"Okay!" said Jimmie.

"Easy does it," said Eddie. "Don't let him bang."

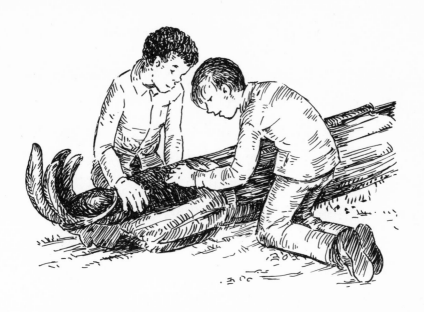

In a moment the Indian was on the floor, face
down. For the first time Eddie looked at the back
of the Indian, and he found that there were holes
up and down him. "This Indian doesn't look as
good from the back as he does from the front,"
said Eddie. "Just look at these holes."

Jimmie examined the holes. "That's too bad,"
he said. "I guess he laid on his back too long."

"When we get him to school, we'll stand him
up with his back to the wall," said Eddie. "The
holes won't show."

"Shall we carry him front up or back up?" Jimmie asked.

"Front up," said Eddie, rolling the Indian over on his back. "Now, Jimmie! You pick up his head, and I'll take his feet."

Jimmie lifted the Indian's head with the feather headdress, and Eddie lifted the opposite end. "He's not heavy," said Eddie.

"No," Jimmie agreed. "He's lighter than I thought."

"Feels sort of empty," said Eddie.

"Funny!" said Jimmie. "He sure looks heavy."

"We won't have any trouble putting him on the bus," said Eddie.

"We won't even need Roland to help us," said Jimmie.

When Jimmie and Eddie arrived at the school-bus stop with the Indian, Joe and Frank were already there. Eddie called to them, "Here we are!"

"You're out of your mind, Eddie," said Joe.

"You and Frank never go to any trouble to take things to school," said Eddie. "I'm the one who shares."

"I hate to think what the kids in school are going to say about that Indian," said Joe to Frank.

"I know what they're going to say," said Frank. "They're going to say, 'Those Wilson twins have a kid brother who's as nutty as a fruitcake. He brought a five-foot Indian to school.'"

At that moment the yellow school bus appeared around a bend in West Street. When it reached the boys, it stopped. The driver opened the door. "Good morning!" he called out. "Who have we got here?"

Joe spoke up. "We're the Wilson boys."

Then the bus driver pointed to the Indian and said, "You don't expect to put that thing on this bus, do you?"

"It isn't heavy," said Eddie.

"It may not be heavy," the bus driver re-marked, "but it's too big. You can't take that thing on the bus."

Joe and Frank stepped into the bus. Joe looked back at Eddie and said, "Didn't I tell you?"

Then the bus driver called out to Jimmie. "Jimmie, are you coming? I'm waiting."

"You better go, Jimmie," said Eddie.

Jimmie hesitated. Then he said, "I gotta stay with Eddie."

"You better go, Jimmie," Eddie urged. "You'll be late for school." Jimmie shook his head.

The door of the bus closed, and soon the bus had disappeared around a corner.

"I wonder where Roland was," said Eddie.

"I didn't see him," said Jimmie. "What are you going to do now, Eddie?"

"I don't know," Eddie replied. "You should have gone on the bus."

"I couldn't leave you here with this Indian,"

said Jimmie, "and we can't go off without it. Somebody might steal it."

"That's right," said Eddie. "I guess it wasn't such a good idea to take him to school."

Just then Eddie saw a green pickup truck coming toward them. As it came near, Eddie saw Roland waving. He was sitting on the front seat beside his father.

"Hi, Roland!" Eddie cried, as the truck stopped. "Did you miss the bus?"

"What makes you think I missed the bus?" said Roland. "I didn't miss it. My dad's come to pick you up with the Indian."

"Oh, that's great!" said Eddie. "The driver on the bus wouldn't let us on."

"I didn't think he would," said Roland's father, as he got out of the truck. "I'll put the Indian in the back. You boys climb in beside Roland."

Eddie settled himself on the seat with a great

sigh of relief. Then laughing, he said, "I hope we pass the school bus. I want to wave to my brothers."

"We'll beat the school bus," said Mr. Smoot. "The bus has to make a lot of stops."

Soon the yellow bus could be seen ahead. It was taking on children at the next corner. In a few moments the pickup truck stopped behind the bus. As soon as the bus started, the truck sped ahead. Eddie waved to the children inside. As the truck passed Eddie was pleased to see the surprise on his brothers' faces.

Before long Roland's father drew up at the front of the school. Then he lifted the Indian out of the back of the truck. As he set it down, he said, "This Indian isn't nearly as heavy as he looks."

"No, he isn't," said Eddie. "We can carry him into the school. No trouble at all." Then he added, "It sure was nice of you to bring us to school, Mr. Smoot. Thanks for everything."

"Have a good day!" Mr. Smoot replied, as he got back into his truck.

"Come on now!" said Eddie to Jimmie and Roland. "Let's get the Indian inside. Jimmie, you take his head and lead the way. Roland, you take the middle, and I'll take the end."

Jimmie led the way through the front door, up some steps, and into a wide hall. The children who had arrived early looked with surprise at the boys carrying the Indian. Of course, they were interested to know where it was going, so they joined the boys.

By the time Jimmie opened the door of his classroom, a parade of children followed the Indian into the room.

Mr. Jeffrey was writing on the blackboard. "Morning, Mr. Jeffrey!" said Jimmie. "Here's Eddie Wilson. He's brought his Indian to show to the class."

Mr. Jeffrey shook hands with Eddie and said,

"I've been expecting you, Eddie, but the Indian is a surprise. I see you've had some help from Roland too."

"We couldn't have gotten here without Roland," said Eddie. "His father brought us in his pickup truck."

"Where shall we put the Indian, Mr. Jeffrey?" Jimmie asked.

"Let's put him right in the corner, where everyone can see him," said Mr. Jeffrey. "We can have a very interesting lesson this afternoon. These tobacco-store Indians are part of our country's folklore."

Mr. Jeffrey helped the boys stand the Indian in the corner. More children were coming in, for the buses had arrived. The children gathered around the Indian and asked questions of Eddie and Jimmie.

Almost the entire class had assembled when a girl pushed her way through the crowd of children. "Oh, here's Gloria!" someone called out.

"Oh, yes!" a girl shouted. "Let Gloria see the Indian."

"Who's this?" said Gloria. "Who's this?"

"Eddie Wilson," said a boy at her elbow.

"Well," said Gloria, "I never heard of an Indian named Eddie Wilson."

"Not the Indian! This kid who owns it is Eddie Wilson," said the boy, pointing to Eddie.

"Oh!" said Gloria. "Well, Eddie! I'm Gloria."

"Hi!" Eddie replied, taking a good look at Gloria. She was taller than Eddie and very thin, and she had a mop of the reddest hair Eddie had ever seen. Resting on her freckled nose was a pair of large, round eyeglasses. She reminded Eddie of a praying mantis that he had kept as a pet in a box one summer. Soon Eddie saw that Gloria was a girl who took charge.

"What's this Indian's name?" Gloria asked.

"He doesn't have a name," Eddie replied.

"Oh, he has to have a name!" said Gloria. "All Indians have names like Hiawatha and Pocahontas and Gitche Gumee. We'll have to name this Indian. It can be our project for today."

Gloria made her way to Mr. Jeffrey. "Mr. Jeffrey," she said, "don't you think we could have a project to name the Indian?"

Just as the bell rang for school to begin, Mr. Jeffrey replied to Gloria, "If Eddie wants you to name his Indian, it's all right with me. But remember he's Eddie's Indian."

Mr. Jeffrey put his class through a very busy morning. There was no chance to discuss the Indian.

At lunchtime Eddie was the center of attention. Everyone wanted to eat with him. He had a hard time holding on to Jimmie and Roland. They were his new friends, and he was not going to be separated from them. Jimmie had never had so much attention paid to him, and Roland kept saying to everyone who asked him a question,

"What makes you think I know anything about this Indian?"

Gloria kept gathering suggestions for the Indian's name. "Imagine not having a name for something so important!" she said. "I would have named him as soon as I found him."

"What would you have named him?" Eddie asked her.

"Well!" Gloria hesitated. "I haven't quite decided, but I have loads of ideas." There was something about Gloria that reminded Eddie of Anna Patricia. He wondered whether Gloria had any removable teeth like his friend Annie Pat.

When the lunch period was over, the children returned to their classroom. Eddie sat down at a table near the Indian. He was surprised to find the table covered with tiny white wings. As he was examining them, Jimmie called out, "Mr. Jeffrey, there're some little bugs flying around."

"Here's one on the back of Gloria's dress," said the boy behind Gloria.

"Oh, oh!" Gloria cried. "Take it off! Take it off! I hate bugs! Where's the insect spray! The spray! The spray!"

"Here's a bug on my sleeve," said another girl. "It looks like an ant with white wings."

Mr. Jeffrey leaned over Eddie's table and examined the wings. When he straightened up, he said, "We have termites with us."

"Do they bite?" Gloria cried, as she shot insect spray around the room.

"What are termites?" Eddie asked.

"They are very small insects, very much like ants," Mr. Jeffrey replied. "They eat wood, especially old wood. They can eat out the inside of a log. Although the log may look large and heavy, it will be very light because the inside will have been eaten by termites."

Eddie's thoughts turned to the Indian. The Indian fitted Mr. Jeffrey's description of a place that attracted termites. "Mr. Jeffrey," said Eddie, "you don't suppose my Indian has termites, do you?"

"Let's take a look," said his teacher.

"There are some funny-looking holes in his back," said Eddie. "I'll show you."

Mr. Jeffrey turned the Indian around, and Eddie pointed to the holes. As soon as Mr. Jeffrey had examined the holes, he said, "That's where the termites came from. I guess the warm air of the room brought them out."

"I'll spray!" said Gloria. "I'll spray the Indian." Gloria sprayed.

"Let's put him down on the floor," said Mr. Jeffrey, "and see what the inside of this Indian looks like."

All the children gathered around. They were interested to see whether the Indian was like a hollow log.

Mr. Jeffrey brought his flashlight. He saw at once that the base of the figure was eaten away.

When he turned the bright light into the interior, the reason why the Indian was so light in weight was plain.

Gloria made a pronouncement. "This Indian hasn't any insides at all."

Eddie looked troubled. "Will he fall into bits and pieces?" he asked Mr. Jeffrey.

"If you have the interior treated, you can get rid of the termites," said Mr. Jeffrey.

"How do I get him treated?" Eddie asked.

"Have to take him to a medicine man, I guess," said Gloria, giving the inside of the Indian a good shot of insect spray.

"A coating of creosote is what he needs," said Mr. Jeffrey.

The rest of the afternoon was devoted to All about Indians and All about Termites.

Just before the bell rang for dismissal, Gloria said, "We haven't named the Indian. We must name him."

Roland, who hadn't said a word all afternoon,

suddenly called out, "Big Chief Termites-in-the-Tummy."

Everyone turned and looked at Roland. If he had suddenly coughed up a live rabbit, they could not have been more surprised. Roland turned bright pink and covered his face with his hands. He had never been so brave before.

"That's what we'll call the Indian," said Eddie. "The name couldn't be better."

After school Mr. Jeffrey drove Eddie and Jimmie and Roland home, and the Indian was put back in the barn.

That evening, when the Wilson family was at dinner, Eddie said to his father, "Dad, I have to have the Indian treated."

"Treated for what?" his father asked.

"He's got termites in the tummy," Eddie replied.

Once again the family laid down their forks and looked at Eddie.

"How's that again?" his father asked.

"That's right, Dad," said Eddie. "I took him to school, and we had termites all over the room."

"I can see," said his father, "that you are going to be very popular at your new school having introduced termites."

"Yes," said Rudy, "it wasn't enough to take the Indian; he had to take termites, too."

Eddie ignored his brother's remark. "He just needs a dose of creosote," he said. "Mr. Jeffrey says that fixes termites."

Chapter 7

ROLAND
THE THINK TANK

THE FOLLOWING MORNING when Eddie went
to school there was less excitement, for
there was no Indian present. Eddie had plenty
of time to observe his fellow-classmates. As Eddie looked them over, he was surprised to see so
many of them wearing eyeglasses. He wondered

whether their need for eyeglasses had anything to do with the climate of the town. Perhaps the trouble was pollution.

Soon Mr. Jeffrey called the class to order, and the morning work began. All went well for Eddie. He liked his new school.

When the bell rang for lunch period, Eddie and Jimmie went together to the cafeteria. At the food counter, Eddie selected soup, a roll, a glass of milk, and chocolate pudding. Jimmie had milk and a sandwich, jello and sponge cake on his tray as he and Eddie emerged from the line.

Eddie was about to set his tray down on a table where Gloria and a bunch of children from Mr. Jeffrey's class were sitting, when Jimmie said, "Not there, Eddie! Over here." Jimmie set his tray down on a nearby table.

As Eddie removed his lunch from his tray, he said, "Why not there? We ate with that crowd yesterday."

"That was because we brought the Indian,"

said Jimmie. "Today is different. It's Tuesday. It's their club meeting day. You have to be a member of the Eyeglass Club to sit there."

"No kidding!" said Eddie, as he looked over at the boys and girls chattering among themselves at the other table. Sure enough! They were all wearing eyeglasses. Eddie noted, too, that they all had something else in common. They all pushed their eyeglasses up on their noses between bites of their lunches.

"The poor kids!" said Eddie. "I guess they

stick together because they feel sorry for each
other. Must be an awful nuisance to wear those
things all the time."

"Oh, no!" said Jimmie. "You have to be asked
to join their club. It's supposed to be something
great."

"Oh!" said Eddie. "Like if your father owns a
Cadillac car?"

"Sort of," Jimmie replied. "Tell you what, Eddie! I don't think all of those kids need glasses.
They just put 'em on to get into the club."

"Did you ever try it?" Eddie asked.

"Once," Jimmie replied. "I brought an old
pair of glasses that belonged to my grandmother
to school. I wore 'em all day. I couldn't see a
thing, and nobody asked me to join the club. I
figured there must be somethin' else to it."

"I guess you're right, Jimmie," said Eddie.

Roland was about to pass the table where Eddie and Jimmie were sitting when Eddie saw

him. "Hey, Roland!" Eddie called to him. "Aren't you eating with Jimmie and me?"

Roland stood with his tray in his hands and said, "What makes you think I want to eat with you?"

"Well, Roland," said Eddie, "maybe you don't want to, but sit down anyway."

"Why wouldn't I want to?" was Roland's next comment.

Eddie ignored this remark and asked instead, "Roland, were you ever invited to join the Eye-glass Club?"

"Never heard of it," said Roland.

"They're over at that table," said Jimmie, nodding his head toward Gloria.

Roland looked at Gloria and her club members and said, "I didn't know they were a club. I just thought they couldn't see without glasses."

Eddie had just finished his chocolate pudding, when Gloria came over to him. "Eddie," she said, "the Eyeglass Club would like you to join. We've talked it over."

Jimmie and Roland looked at Eddie. "I don't wear eyeglasses," Eddie replied.

"Oh, you can get some," said Gloria. "You don't have to see through them."

"If I have glasses on that I can't see through," Eddie asked, "how can I see?"

"Well, what I mean is," Gloria explained, "you can get them with plain glass, and it's just like looking through a windowpane."

"Is that all there is to this club?" Eddie asked.

"On Tuesdays we have club meeting," said Gloria, "and we all eat lunch at the table over there. Then once a month we meet at a member's house."

"Well, I eat with Jimmie and Roland," said Eddie, "and any club that I join is a club that Jimmie and Roland are in."

"Oh!" exclaimed Gloria. "Well, Jimmie and Roland don't wear glasses."

"No," said Eddie, "and neither do I." As Gloria walked back to her table, Eddie thought she looked like a matchstick with a flame on the end.

"Eyeglass Club!" Roland muttered. "Crazy! That's what it is. Crazy!"

When Eddie reached home that afternoon, his mother said, "Well, Eddie! How do you like your new school?"

"It's okay!" Eddie replied. "I was invited to join the Eyeglass Club."

"Eyeglass Club!" his mother exclaimed. "You don't need eyeglasses, do you? Who said you need them?"

"Oh, no!" Eddie answered. "You don't have to need 'em to belong to the club. I guess you could belong if you just wore frames without any glass in 'em."

"Are you thinking of joining?" his mother asked.

"No," Eddie replied. "I'm going to start a club of my own."

After dinner Eddie spent the evening in the cellar, where his father had put Eddie's valuable property. Eddie was looking for something he knew was there. He hadn't seen it for a long time. In fact, he had forgotten about it until the middle of the afternoon while contemplating Gloria's invitation to join the Eyeglass Club.

Eddie went through box after box. He rummaged through cartons. Just as he was beginning to feel discouraged, he found what he had been looking for. He took it in his hands, dusted it off, and examined it. It had been around the house as long as he could remember, and when his mother was about to throw it out, he had said, "Oh, let me have that for my valuable property."

"Very well," his mother had said, "but put it out of sight. I am tired of seeing it around."

"Who did it belong to?" Eddie asked.

"It belonged to my great-grandfather," his mother replied. "I remember him using it when I was a little girl."

Eddie looked at it carefully. He wondered whether he could make something like it, because he would need one for Jimmie and one for Roland. If he was going to have a club, he needed members, and Jimmie and Roland would be the members.

Eddie went up to his room. In a drawer in his desk, he found some sheets of heavy paper. With poster paint, with which he was always well supplied, he changed two sheets from white to black. Then he rolled each one into a horn and glued it fast. That night, when he went to bed, he left three black horns sitting on the top of his desk.

The following morning Eddie left for school with a large paper bag. When he sat down in the bus beside Jimmie, he said, "Jimmie, you're going to be the first member of my club."

"You got a club, Eddie?" Jimmie asked with great interest.

"Yepper!" Eddie answered. "You and Roland are the members, along with me."

"That's pretty swell," said Jimmie.

"We're going to have a clubhouse, too," said Eddie. "We'll meet once a month in our barn and have eats as well."

"That's great!" said Jimmie.

"It's the Ear Trumpet Club," said Eddie. "You see this bag? In this bag, I have three horns. My great-great-grandfather's and one I made for you and one for Roland."

"Does he know?" Jimmie asked.

"Not yet," Eddie replied. "He's in the back of the bus. When we get to school, I'll give you your horn and you must hold it to your ear. When the kids say, 'What's that?' you say, 'How's that? What did you say? Speak into my ear trumpet! I belong to the Ear Trumpet Club.' "

Jimmie laughed so hard that he nearly fell off the seat. "I can't wait to do it," said Jimmie. "Eddie, you're always cookin' up somethin'."

When the boys left the bus, they waited for Roland. As sóon as he appeared, Eddie said, "Roland, Jimmie and I have a club and we want you to join."

"Now you're crazy!" said Roland. "What makes you think I'd be in any old club?"

"Well, we want you, Roland!" said Eddie. "It's the Ear Trumpet Club."

"I tell you, you're crazy!" Roland repeated. "I don't need an ear trumpet. I can hear perfectly well."

"Look, Roland," said Eddie, "don't you ever want to have any fun? Why be so cranky all the time?"

Roland thought for a moment. Finally he said, "Okay! What do you want me to do?"

When Eddie explained the plan to Roland,

Roland said, "What makes you think those kids won't punch me in the face?"

"They won't punch you in the face," said Eddie.

Roland finally agreed, so outside the door of the classroom Eddie handed a black horn to each of the boys. Eddie had the old heavy ear trumpet, and the three boys walked into the room, holding the horns to their ears.

The children in the room screamed with laughter when Eddie and the two members of his Ear Trumpet Club went to them and said, "How's that? Speak into my trumpet. I'm a bit hard of hearing."

Mr. Jeffrey saw Eddie's joke, and he laughed so hard that he could be heard all the way down the hall.

At lunchtime, Eddie and Jimmie and Roland ate their lunch together, and only once did Roland start to say, "What makes you think . . .?"

"Roland," said Eddie, "what makes you think

so much? Roland the Think Tank, that's you."

Jimmie laughed. For a moment Eddie didn't know whether Roland was going to laugh or not. Both Eddie and Jimmie were glad when Roland's face finally cracked into a wide grin.

Before long there were fewer children in the class wearing eyeglasses. More boys and girls were eating at Eddie's table with Eddie and his friends, Jimmie and Roland. Whenever Roland started to say, "What makes you think," everyone laughed, for they all knew that Eddie had nicknamed him Roland the Think Tank.

When Valentine's Day arrived, Eddie's class had a party. Roland was asked to act as the postman, and he didn't say, "What makes you think I want to be postman?" He seemed just as pleased to hand out the valentines as the children were to receive them.

Eddie was eating his cookies with Robert, one of the former Eyeglass Club members. As they watched Roland delivering the valentines, Robert said to Eddie, "We've got a new Roland around here. Remember how grouchy he used to be?"

"He's okay," Eddie replied. "I think he likes himself better than he used to!"

Chapter 8

BOODLES
SPENDS THE NIGHT

SINCE the Wilsons had moved into the old house, many changes had taken place. The cobwebs were gone, woodwork had been painted, and ruffled curtains hung at the windows. The big ball on the post, at the foot of the stairs, had been glued fast.

From the outside the room at the top of the tower did not look big enough to hold all that was in it. There was a double bed, a chest of drawers, Eddie's desk, a bedside table, and two small chairs. Eddie liked many things about his room, but the thing he liked best was the way to get to it. A small circular stairway, made of iron, led from the top floor of the house, where his brothers slept, up to Eddie's room. There were times when Eddie felt as though he were living in a treehouse. He planned to drop a basket on a rope out of the window and haul up sandwiches and cookies. So far he had acquired an old basket and a long rope, but no one had offered to put sandwiches and cookies in the basket.

Sometimes he liked to think of his room as the crow's nest on a sailing ship. Then he was Christopher Columbus on the *Santa María*. He would look out through his spyglass, made of a roll of cardboard, and see if he could sight land. Suddenly he would cry "Ahoy!" and reach for a

large bell that stood on his desk. He would ring
the bell, and anyone in the house at the time
knew that Columbus had sighted land.

On other days he was one of King Arthur's
knights, Sir Gawaine, besieged in his castle. He
was always Sir Gawaine, because he liked the
name. He was beleaguered by warring Vikings
from across the sea! Boiling oil was the way to
handle that vicious enemy! Once he went so far
as to lug a bucket of water up the circular stairway. He carried it across the room. It was so
heavy that Eddie could hardly lift it to the windowsill. Unable to look over the bucket, he
poured the contents out the window. "Take that,
you devils!" he cried.

Mrs. Wilson had been planting zinnias in a
flower bed at the foot of the tower. Fortunately,
for both Eddie and his mother, she had just risen
from her knees. Thus, Mrs. Wilson escaped with
only a few splashes of boiling oil, but the zinnias got the full dose.

"Eddie," cried Mrs. Wilson, looking up at Eddie's window, "just what do you think you're doing?"

Eddie stuck his head out the window. He was surprised when he looked down and saw his mother. "Sorry, Mom!" he called back. "I was just pouring boiling oil on my vicious enemies. I'm under siege! I'm without food and water! If I let down my basket, Mom, would you kindly put a peanut-butter sandwich in it?"

"If you want a sandwich, come down to the kitchen and get it," his mother replied.

"Okay!" said Eddie, and immediately all of Eddie's dreams about Sir Gawaine and the boiling oil followed the water out the window. As he went down to the kitchen, Eddie was again just Eddie Wilson. He forgot the bucket, leaving it at the head of the iron stairs. It sat there for days, although his mother kept saying to him, "Eddie, when are you going to bring down that bucket?"

Eddie was feeling quite settled in his new

home when he received a letter from Boodles. He was always glad to hear from his friends, but when he read that Boodles was coming to visit him, he was elated. Boodles wrote that his father was driving on business to a town not far from where Eddie lived. He could drop Boodles off on Friday and pick him up on Saturday morning.

"Isn't this great news!" said Eddie to his family. "He says he can get here by four o'clock, 'cause he doesn't have school that afternoon. Teachers are having a meeting."

"How nice to have Boodles," said his mother.

"I can hardly wait to see good old Bood!" said Eddie. "I wonder how he's getting along with the dictionary?"

"Better I hope!" said Rudy.

"Just wait till Boodles sees my Indian," said Eddie.

"Wait till he smells him!" said Rudy. "Boy, is that creosote potent!"

When Friday came, Eddie was out in the driveway, impatiently waiting for Boodles. Now and then he ran into the house to see what time it was. He thought four o'clock would never come. When the clock struck four, Eddie was pacing the driveway, but Boodles did not arrive. When he hadn't appeared by five o'clock, Eddie was sure Boodles' father had lost his way. The next hour seemed endless, but a few minutes before six Boodles and his father drove in. "Hi, Boodles! Hi, Mr. Cary!" Eddie cried out. "Am I glad to see you!"

"We took the wrong turn," said Boodles' father.

"You're just in time for dinner," said Eddie's mother, as she welcomed Boodles and his father.

"Thank you," Mr. Cary replied, "but I have to get right along. I have a dinner engagement."

Mr. Cary handed Boodles a small overnight bag and said, "I'll pick you up after breakfast tomorrow. Have fun and behave yourself."

"Okay, Dad!" Boodles replied. "Take care!"

Mrs. Wilson and the boys called "Good-bye" as Mr. Cary drove away.

"Dinner is ready," said Eddie's mother, "so come right in." Then she said to Boodles, "I'm glad to see you, Boodles."

"I thought we were never going to get here," said Boodles.

Eddie led Boodles inside. Boodles looked around. "Man," he said, "this is some house!"

"Wait until you see my room," said Eddie, as they sat down to dinner. "It's super! And have I got something to show you!"

"What is it?" Boodles asked.

"I'll show it to you after dinner," said Eddie.

"You and your surprises, Eddie!" said Boodles. "Just like old times."

At that moment Hippie came rushing up to Boodles. "Here's good old Hippie!" said Boodles. Then he said, "What's hanging over his face?"

"Oh, he's wearing a sort of wig," Eddie replied. "You see, his bang got cut off by mistake, so I made it for him. It protects his eyes while his bang is growing."

"It looks like part of a floor mop," said Boodles.

"That's just what it is," Eddie replied. "Looks great, doesn't it? 'Course, he takes it off when he goes to bed."

Boodles sighed. "Boy, Eddie," he said, "I sure miss you and all your super ideas!"

As soon as dinner was over, Eddie said to Boodles, "Now I'll show you what's in the barn. I have to take a flashlight, because there isn't any light out there."

Eddie led the way to the barn. When he opened the barn door, a bat flew out. "Eddie," cried Boodles, "what was that?"

"I guess it was a bat," Eddie replied. "Some bats were living in the barn when we came here."

"*Bats*!" exclaimed Boodles, but at that moment Eddie beamed the flashlight on the Indian's face. Boodles grabbed hold of Eddie and began to tremble. "It's a ghost!" Boodles cried out.

"It's no ghost," said Eddie. "It's my new valuable property." Eddie played the light over the Indian. "Isn't it the greatest piece of valuable property you ever saw?"

"It sure is!" Boodles agreed, still trembling.

"It has termites," said Eddie, "so it smells bad right now from the creosote."

"I'll say it smells bad!" said Boodles.

"I'd like to have it in my bedroom," said Eddie, "but my mother won't let me because of the smell. 'Course, if I had it in my room, it wouldn't be so easy for Jimmie to come to see it."

"Who's Jimmie?" Boodles asked.

"He's my friend," said Eddie.

"Have you got a lot of friends?" Boodles asked.

"Oh, yes!" said Eddie. "Jimmie and Roland and the kids in my class."

"That's good, Eddie," said Boodles.

"Jimmie's my best friend," said Eddie.

Then he told Boodles about finding Jimmie and the Indian and about taking the Indian to school.

Boodles was fascinated. "You sure do find great stuff!" he said.

Eddie and Boodles spent the rest of the evening playing a game that Boodles had brought to Eddie. Finally it was bedtime, and Eddie carried Boodles' bag up the winding stairs to Eddie's room.

Boodles looked around and said, "This is really neat! The whole house is great. I never slept in a haunted house before! I'll bet it has a great ghost! Have you seen it, Eddie?"

"Oh, the ghost!" said Eddie.

"I'll bet you haven't seen him," said Boodles. "I'll bet you never put out any ghost food."

"I've been pretty busy," Eddie replied.

"Just wait till you see what I brought with

me!" said Boodles, unpacking his bag. Boodles took a small cardboard box out of his bag. He lifted the lid, and Eddie looked inside.

"A chocolate cupcake!" Eddie exclaimed.

"Ghost food!" Boodles replied. "It's to put out tonight."

"Where do you think is a good place to put it?" asked Eddie.

"Right on this table beside the bed," Boodles answered.

Eddie put the cupcake on the table. "Sure was good of you to bring it!" he said. "I've been so busy with the Indian and everything, I forgot all about ghost food."

When the boys were in their pajamas, Boodles said, "Which side of the bed are you going to sleep on, Eddie?"

"You can have the side near the cupcake," said Eddie.

Boodles got into bed, and Eddie followed. Eddie put out the light that was over the bed, and moonlight streamed in the window. It filled the room with dark shadows and made the white curtains at the windows look eerie as they fluttered in the slight breeze.

In a few minutes, Boodles got up.

"What's the matter?" Eddie asked.

"I'm just moving the cupcake to the top of your desk," said Boodles. "The smell of the chocolate makes me hungry." Boodles got back into bed.

A few minutes later, Boodles whispered, "Eddie, do you hear that moaning sound?"

"Yes," Eddie replied. "It's an owl that lives in a tree back of the house."

"Oh!" said Boodles.

Eddie was just about to drop off to sleep, when Boodles said, "Eddie, do you hear that terrible sound, like somebody wailing?"

"It's a beagle hound next door," said Eddie. "Whenever it's full moon, he comes out and wails."

"Oh!" said Boodles.

Five minutes later Boodles slid under the bedcovers. "What's bugging you, Bood?" Eddie asked.

"Somebody's sneaking up your stairs," Boodles said in a barely audible voice.

"It's just Hippie!" Eddie replied. "He's coming to bed. He sleeps on the foot of my bed."

"Oh!" said Boodles, emerging from the covers. "I thought Hippie slept in his doghouse."

"No," said Eddie, "he likes to sleep with me. It's a shame, 'cause it's a swell doghouse."

"Oh!" said Boodles.

Eddie was almost asleep when Boodles sat up. "Eddie!" he whispered. "You asleep?"

"S'matter?" Eddie inquired.

"Are you hungry?" Boodles asked.

"Well, I can always eat," Eddie replied. "Why?"

"I can't go to sleep because of the smell of that chocolate cupcake," said Boodles.

"Now you mention it," said Eddie. "I'm hungry too."

Boodles hopped out of bed and came back with the cupcake. He broke it in half, and Boodles and Eddie sat up in bed and ate the cupcake. "Swell chocolate icing!" said Boodles. "Too good to waste on a ghost."

Hippie moved up to the boys, but all he got was a chance to lick their fingers.

When the boys had lain down again, Eddie said, "You all right now, Bood?"

"Fine!" Boodles replied. "I'm glad we didn't leave that good cupcake for the ghost."

Eddie turned over with his back to Boodles, but just as Eddie was about to doze off Boodles sat up again. "Eddie," he yelled, "there's a bat in the room. I can hear it flying around." Boodles dived under the covers and disappeared.

Eddie turned on the light. Hippie jumped off the bed and began to bark. The bat flew around the room.

Eddie leaped out of bed and ran to the head
of his stairs. In his haste he accidentally kicked
the bucket, and the noise of the tin bucket falling down the iron stairs rang through the whole
house.

"Dad!" Eddie cried, but the cry was not
heard above the noise of the bucket as it rattled
down the stairs. Still, the racket brought his
brothers, his father, and his mother rushing to
the rescue almost immediately.

"There's a bat up here!" Eddie cried. "Dad, bring an umbrella!"

Mr. Wilson rushed up the stairs while Mrs. Wilson picked up the bucket.

"Get an umbrella!" Eddie cried. "An umbrella!"

"Be quiet, Eddie!" said his father, looking for the bat. In the midst of the commotion, the bat had flown out the window.

"I don't see any bat!" said his father.

"Well, there was a bat," said Eddie. "Boodles and I saw it."

"Where is Boodles?" said Mr. Wilson, looking around the room.

"I'm here!" Boodles replied, sticking his head out from under the covers at the foot of the bed. Gazing at Mr. Wilson, he said, "Did you know that the dictionary says that bats are the best flyers of all flying species and some of them suck the blood from mammals?"

"Very interesting," said Mr. Wilson.

"I just wanted you to know why I got under the covers," said Boodles. "I'm a mammal, the highest form of life, and I didn't want my blood sucked."

"Naturally," said Mr. Wilson. "Now go to sleep, both of you."

At the head of the stairs, Mr. Wilson turned back and said to Eddie, "Eddie, why were you screaming for an umbrella?"

"An umbrella is the best weapon for attacking bats," Eddie answered. "In case the bat returns the attack, you can open the umbrella and hide under it."

"I see!" said his father. Mr. Wilson departed, marveling at the information one could pick up from two boys in the middle of the night.

Eddie and Boodles settled down once more. "Now about this ghost!" said Boodles.

"Forget it, Boodles!" said Eddie. "Let's keep all the ghosts for Halloween! I want to go to sleep."

"Okay!" Boodles replied. "But we may be missing a great opportunity!"

The next morning Mr. Cary arrived right after breakfast to take Boodles home. Eddie was sorry to see his friend leave. He wished that Boodles could have stayed longer.

The whole Wilson family gathered around the car to see Boodles off. "Come back soon!" Eddie cried.

"Thanks for the good time," Boodles called back. "I'll tell all your friends back home about your new piece of valuable property!"

"Tell 'em all to come see it," said Eddie.

"Will do!" Boodles called back, as the car began to move.

Chapter 9

EDDIE HAS A PARTY

B Y THE END of the school term Eddie had many new friends. While Jimmie and Roland were the ones he saw most often, there were Gloria and Robert and the whole crowd that used to be in the Eyeglass Club. Eddie liked his new friends, but he often thought of the ones he had left when he moved to his new home: Boodles, Anna Patricia, Tookey, Sidney, Rodney, and Dumpty. They were the friends who had always come to his birthday parties. He was beginning to think about his next birthday, because it was coming soon. As he had been invited to several birthday parties since he had arrived in his new school, he decided to ask his mother if he could have a party too.

"We could have it in the barn," said Eddie, when he spoke to his mother about it.

"I think it would be very nice," his mother replied.

"Can it be a big party, Mom?" Eddie asked. "After all it's a big barn, so it might as well be a big party."

"How big?" his mother asked.

"I thought maybe the whole class from school," Eddie replied.

"All right," his mother agreed. "That should be about twenty-five."

"Great!" exclaimed Eddie. "Of course, I wish Boodles and my old gang could come."

"Maybe they could!" said his mother, to Eddie's great surprise. "Perhaps Sidney's mother would drive them up in the Stewarts' station wagon. I should like to have a visit with Sidney's mother. I have forgotten how many children there are in your old crowd."

"Oh, there's Sidney and Boodles and Annie Pat and Tookey and Rodney and Dumpty. Just six. They could all fit into that big station wagon."

"If they left early, they should be able to get here by lunchtime," said his mother. "I can give them a nice lunch."

"A cookout!" exclaimed Eddie. "With hamburgers and baked potatoes and ice cream and birthday cake. Hot dickity! I'll bet Dad will cook the hamburgers, too."

Eddie lost no time in sending out his invitations to his birthday party, and he was delighted

when most of his friends said they could come.
He was especially pleased when Sidney's mother
said she would bring his old pals to the party.
Eddie was looking forward eagerly to seeing the
old crowd again.

There was one thing, however, that troubled
Eddie. It was the doghouse. He felt that Boodles was disappointed when he found out that the
doghouse was not being used. Eddie didn't want
the rest of his friends who had given it to him to
see that the doghouse was empty.

The following Saturday he decided to speak
to his father about it. "Dad," he said, "what am
I going to do about the doghouse?"

"What about it?" his father asked.

"Well, I can't have my friends think I didn't
appreciate their going-away present. I can't do
that, can I, Daddy?"

"I know exactly what you're leading up to,
Eddie," said his father. "When you call me
Daddy, I know there is something in the wind."

"Oh, Daddy," said Eddie, "you do understand, don't you, that I have to make use of that nice doghouse? We're just wasting that doghouse."

"Just how do you intend to make use of it?" his father asked.

"Oh, you know!" said Eddie. "Get a nice little dog to fit into the doghouse. We can get one from the S.P.C.A. They have loads of little dogs."

Mr. Wilson didn't reply for some time, and Eddie waited. Finally his father said, "Very well! But remember if you get a dog for the doghouse that is where the dog is going to live. It's enough to have Hippie living in the house with us. Another dog will live in the doghouse. That is final."

"Good! Good!" said Eddie. "Can we go now to the S.P.C.A.?"

"Might as well get it over with," said his father.

Eddie stood thinking. "Maybe we should bring several dogs back with us," he said at last.

"Several dogs!" his father exclaimed. "What do you mean, Eddie?"

"Well, we have to get one that fits in the doghouse," said Eddie.

"One dog, Eddie!" said his father. "Just one dog!"

"Okay!" Eddie agreed. "Come on, Joe. Help me put the doghouse in the station wagon."

"Just why do you want to put the doghouse in the station wagon?" his father asked.

"Dad," exclaimed Eddie, "we have to try it on for size!"

"I think I can tell what size dog will fit into that doghouse," his father replied.

"All right, Dad!" said Eddie. "I'm just trying to be helpful."

"Come along," said his father, "and stop trying to be helpful."

Eddie climbed into the station wagon, and they soon reached the S.P.C.A. When Mr. Wilson opened the door, Mrs. Small, who was in charge of the office, said, "Did you find your old English sheepdog?"

"We found him!" Eddie replied, as he stepped into the office.

"I'm glad," said Mrs. Small. "What can I do for you today?"

"My son Eddie wants a small dog," said his father.

"We haven't very many at this time," said Mrs. Small, "but come right out to the kennels. You can see if there is one you would care to take."

Eddie and his father followed Mrs. Small to the kennels. The dogs began to bark. Eddie could hardly believe that five dogs could make so much noise.

Eddie looked them over. There was a big one that had black and white spots and looked more like a Dalmatian than anything else. Clearly he was not a pedigreed dog, and he was much too big. There was a tiny one that was evidently mostly Mexican hairless. Eddie decided that anything that little could not be left out in a doghouse. It would need a pillow in his bedroom. Then there were three other choices: a dachshund, a terrier of sorts, and a small collie.

"Oh," cried Eddie, "I always wanted a collie. Let's take the collie."

"It's too big for it," said Mr. Wilson.

"Too big for what?" Mrs. Small inquired.

"For the doghouse," Mr. Wilson answered.

"Perhaps, Dad, you could enlarge the doghouse," Eddie suggested.

"I am not going to enlarge the doghouse," said his father. "We came here to get a dog to fit the doghouse."

Mrs. Small, standing by, said, "Would it help if I got a tape measure?"

"No, thank you!" said Eddie's father. "It's a

choice now between the dachshund and the terrier."

"I like the dachshund best," said Eddie.

Mr. Wilson looked at the dachshund and said, "He may be too long for the doghouse."

"But, Dad, the terrier is too high when he stands up," Eddie complained, for he had set his heart on the dachshund.

"Dogs don't stand up in their doghouses," said his father. "They lie down."

"But he might want to get up," Eddie argued, "and I wouldn't want him to bump his head."

"All right!" said his father. "It's the dachshund!"

Eddie was delighted, as he picked up his new dog.

Mr. Wilson paid the fee, and Eddie carried it in his arms to the car.

"Oh, Dad," said Eddie, "this is a nice dog. I don't know why anybody got rid of such a swell dog. Just look at his nice coat. I never saw one of these dogs with long hair before. I thought they were always smooth and shiny."

"This one happens to be a long-haired dachshund," his father replied. "That may be the reason why the owners got rid of him. They may have thought that all dachshunds should be smooth."

"I think he's a real prize," said Eddie, "and I think I'll name him after you, Dad, if you would like it."

"No, thanks!" his father replied. "We are not going to have a dog named George around."

"Well then," said Eddie, "I think I'll call him Fritz."

"That's better," said his father.

"I'll bet Hippie will like Fritz," said Eddie.

As soon as Eddie showed Fritz to Hippie, it was evident that Eddie had spoken the truth. The two dogs liked each other so much that Fritz followed Hippie like a shadow. Eddie soon saw that he was facing a problem. Fritz would not

go into the doghouse, because Hippie wouldn't
go in, and Hippie couldn't go in, because he was
too big to get in. Eddie tried everything, including placing Fritz's dish of food in the doghouse.
Nothing worked. If Fritz was separated from
Hippie for a minute, Fritz began to cry like a
baby for its mother.

Before Eddie went to bed he carried Fritz outside to the doghouse. Fritz cried all the way.
Even though Eddie had put a soft blanket in the

doghouse, Fritz would have nothing to do with the place.

"Fritz," said Eddie, "if you don't sleep in this doghouse, I'll have to take you back to the S.P.C.A." Fritz paid no attention. He ran to the kitchen door where Hippie was making a fuss inside. Now both dogs were crying.

Eddie didn't know what to do. He couldn't stay outside all night with Fritz, and Eddie's father had said that Fritz must sleep in the doghouse. Finally Eddie decided he would have to appeal to his father. He ran into the house, followed by the little dog, and called upstairs to his father. "Dad," he cried, "I guess we'll have to take Fritz back to the S.P.C.A., 'cause he won't sleep in the doghouse. I don't know why he doesn't like the doghouse. Maybe it has termites."

Then Eddie heard his father call back, "I can't take him back to the S.P.C.A. tonight, so go to bed with your dogs. I'm tired of all the noise."

Eddie went up to his room followed by the two dogs, and he had a feeling that Fritz had come to stay.

When Eddie's birthday arrived, he was up early. Eddie was excited for he was not only having a birthday, he would soon see Boodles and his old friends again.

Eddie spent the morning running back and forth from the house to the barn, helping his mother prepare for the party. Everyone helped, for his brothers and father were busy getting the grill ready. They all were looking forward to the cookout.

About twelve o'clock Sidney's mother drove into the Wilsons' driveway with the six children. Eddie and the whole family rushed to meet them. There was a great deal of shouting and yelling as they all greeted each other.

As Anna Patricia got out of the car, Eddie

cried, "Here's good old Annie Pat!" Then he looked at what Anna Patricia had in her arms. It was a dog!

"Hi, Eddie," said Anna Patricia, "here's our birthday present for you." Anna Patricia held out a little black poodle. "Boodles said the dog-house was too little for Hippie, so we decided to get you a smaller dog. We hope you'll like her."

Eddie took the dog out of Anna Patricia's arms and said, "That's wonderful! Thank you so much! It's just what I wanted."

When the rest of Eddie's guests arrived, the party soon got under way. Before long Eddie noticed that Anna Patricia and Gloria had their arms around each other's waist. "I thought those two would get on together," Eddie said to himself.

When he heard Jimmie yell, "Hey, Toothpick!" to Tookey, Eddie knew that a friendship had been made.

After the hamburgers, baked potatoes, ice

cream, and birthday cake, the children played games and danced to records. During the dancing Eddie saw Boodles showing Roland how to do the latest step. Eddie knew then that the party for his old friends and his new friends was a great success.

When it came time for Sidney's mother to leave with Eddie's old gang, everyone crowded around the car to say good-bye. Eddie stood holding the poodle and shouting, "Thanks for the nice dog. I'm going to call her Patsy!" For some reason Anna Patricia looked pleased.

Amidst all the shouting, Eddie was surprised to hear Boodles call out to Roland, "What makes you think you don't know how to dance, Roland? You're okay now that I showed you."

As the car drove away, Jimmie said to Eddie, "Golly, Eddie, you sure have a lot of friends!"

"I know!" Eddie replied. "You see, every time you move, you get a new bunch. It's the best thing about moving."

When Eddie showed Patsy to his father, Eddie said, "Isn't she the nicest dog you ever saw? I'm sure she'll sleep in the doghouse. Don't you think so?"

"I think it is unlikely," said his father. "I think we now have three dogs and that they have moved in on us."

"Well," said Eddie, "I guess I'll have to sleep on the floor and give my bed to the three dogs, but it's worth it."